# CHEMISORPTION

| | |
|---|---|
| ENGLAND: | BUTTERWORTH & CO. (PUBLISHERS) LTD<br>LONDON: 88 Kingsway, W.C.2 |
| AUSTRALIA: | BUTTERWORTH & CO. (AUSTRALIA) LTD<br>SYDNEY: 6/8 O'Connell Street<br>MELBOURNE: 473 Bourke Street<br>BRISBANE: 240 Queen Street |
| CANADA: | BUTTERWORTH & CO. (CANADA) LTD<br>TORONTO: 1367 Danforth Avenue, 6 |
| NEW ZEALAND: | BUTTERWORTH & CO. (NEW ZEALAND) LTD<br>WELLINGTON: 49/51 Ballance Street<br>AUCKLAND: 35 High Street |
| SOUTH AFRICA: | BUTTERWORTH & CO. (SOUTH AFRICA) LTD<br>DURBAN: 33/35 Beach Grove |
| U.S.A.: | BUTTERWORTH INC.<br>WASHINGTON, D.C.: 7235 Wisconsin Avenue, 14 |

# CHEMISORPTION

D. O. HAYWARD, M.A., Ph.D.,
*Lecturer in Chemistry,*
*Imperial College of Science and Technology*

and

B. M. W. TRAPNELL, M.A., Ph.D.,
*Headmaster, Denstone College*

SECOND EDITION

LONDON
BUTTERWORTHS
1964

*First edition published* 1955

*Second edition published* 1964

*Suggested U.D.C. number :* **541.183**

*Suggested additional number:* **541.128.13**

Butterworth & Co. (Publishers) Ltd.

1964

*Printed in Gt. Britain by Page Bros. (Norwich) Ltd., Norwich*

*To*
*SIR ERIC K. RIDEAL, F.R.S.*

# CONTENTS

# PREFACE TO SECOND EDITION

THE first edition of the book appeared eight years ago, and since then considerable advances have taken place, particularly in experimental techniques. The subject has always been very dependent upon the devising of sound and ingenious experiments, and the last decade has been most fruitful from this point of view. It has seen the investigation of surface layers by infra-red spectra, and developments in ultra-high vacuum techniques for use with metal filaments, in the field emission microscope, in electron diffraction techniques, and in magnetic methods. It has also seen the full realization of the importance of the semiconducting property in chemisorption on oxides. In addition, interesting new data have appeared using more established methods, such as the use of tracers, and the measurement of heats of chemisorption.

These developments have led to extensive advances in our understanding of fast chemisorptions on metals, of mechanisms of chemisorption on both metals and semiconductors, and of the mechanism of surface mobility.

A further point is that at the time of the first edition, no very adequate treatise on catalysis was available, and therefore it seemed useful to include two chapters showing how data relating to chemisorption could be applied to problems in catalysis. This gap in the literature has now been largely filled, making it possible for the present volume to be concerned purely with chemisorption.

The overall result is that in preparing a second edition a very considerable recasting of the first edition has been necessary. One additional change has also taken place. The first edition was a solo effort: the second edition has involved the use of double harness. Readers may like to know that wherever the English is incomprehensible the author is D.O.H., and that where the science is incorrect the author is unquestionably B.M.W.T.

D. O. HAYWARD

B. M. W. TRAPNELL

London,
*October 1963*

# PREFACE TO FIRST EDITION

T. E. LAWRENCE says in one of his letters that books are meant to be written not to be read, meaning, I imagine, that the greatest good to come out of their publication is the clarity with which the author should see his subject as a result of writing about it. Nevertheless, this book has been written to fill a gap in the existing literature, and so is primarily for the reader. A number of interesting discoveries have been made in the subject of chemisorption during the last 15 years, which are in the main available to scientists only as original papers. Neither a selective, nor an exhaustive treatment of chemisorption as a whole is available, and while this has given me a clear field, I have been conscious of the danger of attempting both treatments at the same time. In general, I have concentrated on the aspects of the subject which seem to me best understood, so that my treatment aims to be selective.

Chemisorption is closely related to heterogeneous catalysis, and the latter is bound to crop up in any treatise on the former. However, too many important problems in catalysis are at present *sub judice* for more than a very interim report to be possible, and such mention as I have made is largely to show how knowledge gained from chemisorption studies can be applied to problems in catalysis, and vice versa.

It is a pleasure to acknowledge three especial debts of gratitude. The first is to Sir Eric Rideal, to whom, in common with many other of his pupils, I owe not only an abiding interest in my subject, but also a great deal more besides. The second is to Dr. F. C. Tompkins, who first suggested that I should write the book, and who has been a source of encouragement on other occasions. The third is to my wife, who, while finding chemisorption an incomparably dull subject, has nevertheless converted my untidy longhand to neat typescript, and accepted with equanimity such antics as my writing has involved.

B. M. W. TRAPNELL

Oxford,
*September 1954*

# I

# INTRODUCTION

### CHEMISORPTION AND PHYSICAL ADSORPTION

WHEN two immiscible phases are brought into contact, it is nearly always found that the concentration of one phase is greater at the interface than in its bulk. This tendency for accumulation to take place at a surface is called *adsorption*. Its occurrence is due to the atoms in any surface being subject to unbalanced forces of attraction perpendicular to the surface plane, and therefore possessing a certain unsaturation.

Adsorption takes place with a decrease in surface free energy, $\Delta G$: also it normally takes place with a decrease in entropy, $\Delta S$, because by confining an adsorbed molecule to a thin surface layer, certain degrees of freedom are lost. Use of the equation

$$\Delta G = \Delta H - T.\Delta S \qquad (1.1)$$

then shows that $\Delta H$ is also negative, that is, adsorption is in general exothermic. Certainly no case of endothermic adsorption is definitely known, although DE BOER[1] has suggested that in one or two cases where a transient chemisorption takes place to a very limited extent, an endothermic process may be involved.

The main work of saturating a surface is usually accomplished by condensation of a single layer of molecules, and in such a case the adsorption is termed *unimolecular* or *monomolecular*. However, adsorptions involving the condensation of several layers are by no means infrequent, and these are called *multimolecular*.

Adsorption processes have a wide significance. The stabilization

1

of colloids, important not only in detergence, but also for the continued existence of biological organisms, is always achieved by adsorption, usually at a liquid–liquid interface. Examples where adsorption at solid surfaces is important are in lubrication, heterogeneous catalysis, and various processes of purification. The gas mask and chromatography also function through adsorption on solids.

Although the degree of unsaturation of surfaces can vary widely, and no doubt continuously, experience has taught that there are only two kinds of adsorption. The surfaces of many substances are inert in the sense that the valency requirements of their atoms may be thought to be satisfied by bonding with adjacent atoms. With this type of surface, adsorption tends to take place simply through forces of physical attraction, similar to those causing the deviations of real gases from ideal laws, the liquefaction of gases and so on. This kind of adsorption is called *physical* or *van der Waals adsorption*, and is very similar in nature and mechanism to the condensation of a vapour on the surface of its own liquid.

On the other hand many surfaces are much more unsaturated, and the valency requirements of their surface atoms may be thought not to be fully satisfied by bonding with nearby atoms. A rather oversimplified picture of a metal surface of this kind is shown in *Figure 1*. In adsorption such a surface will tend to form chemical bonds with a

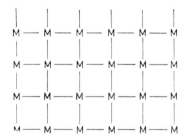

*Figure 1. Free valencies at a metal surface*

nearby phase and this process is called *chemisorption*. Although a kind of chemisorption takes place at liquid surfaces, particularly when the adsorbed molecules are ionized, the more important kind takes place at the surfaces of solids, notably metals, oxides and carbon, and the chemisorption of gases and vapours on these will be our main concern.

The difference between chemical and physical adsorption is that electron transfers take place between *adsorbent* and *adsorbate* in chemisorption, but do not take place in physical adsorption.

There are certain differences in the properties of the two kinds of adsorption, which can be used as experimental criteria for deciding the adsorption type. No single criterion proves to be so sharp as to enable decision to be made in all cases, but equally, there are few cases where it is uncertain which kind of adsorption is operating.

(1) The best single criterion is the magnitude of the heat of adsorption. Chemical bonds are normally stronger than physical forces of attraction: heats of chemisorption should therefore be large while heats of physical adsorption should be low, and in the neighbourhood of heats of liquefaction. Early determinations of heats of adsorption suggested that this was so. Heats of chemisorption of carbon monoxide and hydrogen, for example, seemed always to exceed some 20 and 15 kcal/mole respectively[2, 3], whereas the heats of physical adsorption were always less than about 6 and 2 kcal/mole[4, 5].

Although the distinction is in general valid, more recent work has shown that heats of chemisorption can be far smaller than was previously believed. For example, with hydrogen values as low as 3 kcal/mole[6,7] have been observed, and with carbon monoxide there is one case[8] where there appears to be no discontinuity in heat between the end of chemisorption and the beginning of physical adsorption on top of the chemisorbed layer.

Thus, although heats of van der Waals adsorption cannot exceed certain upper limits, so that high heats always indicate chemisorption, there may occasionally be uncertainty as to the nature of a weak adsorption.

(2) A similar criterion is the temperature range in which the adsorption proceeds. As physical adsorption and liquefaction are related, the former tends to occur only at temperatures near or below the boiling point of the adsorbate at the pressure considered. Chemisorption on the other hand can usually take place at temperatures far above the boiling point. More precisely, if an adsorption is studied at a pressure $p$, the saturation vapour pressure at the temperature concerned being $p_0$, appreciable fractions of a monolayer are formed by physical adsorption only when $p/p_0$ exceeds about 0·01. The criterion is not however infallible, for not only can the stronger and more active van der Waals adsorbents, particularly those possessing fine capillaries[9], adsorb gases and vapours at $p/p_0$ values as low as $10^{-8}$, but also the weaker chemisorptions occasionally take place only when $p/p_0$ approaches values at which van der Waals adsorption might be commencing.

(3) Chemisorption, being a chemical reaction, may require an

3

appreciable activation energy. In this case it will only proceed at a reasonable rate above a certain minimum temperature. Physical adsorption on the other hand requires no activation energy, just as condensation of liquid from vapour requires none. It should therefore be exceedingly rapid at any temperature, and take place as fast as the adsorbate reaches the surface.

Distinction between physical and chemical adsorption on grounds of velocity is, however, liable to be blurred for two reasons. First, many surfaces are so unsaturated that they undergo rapid chemisorption even at extremely low temperatures[10]. In some of these cases there is evidence that almost every molecule which strikes an uncovered surface atom is chemisorbed, so that the activation energy is effectively zero. A rapid adsorption need not therefore be physical in nature.

Second, if an adsorbent is porous, or possesses fine capillaries, penetration of adsorbate to the interior of the material may be an extremely slow process. This penetration may result in chemisorption at interior surfaces, but it may also be physical adsorption or even solution of gas—the problems raised by this effect are complex and are discussed later. It does, however, mean that a slow disappearance of gas is by no means certain to be chemisorption. Carbon, owing to its porosity, is a particularly difficult material with which to decide adsorption type on the basis of velocity measurements.

(4) Chemisorption possesses a certain specificity which physical adsorption does not. This is partly because it depends upon the adsorbent surface being clean, partly because not all surfaces, even when clean, are active in chemisorption. Physical adsorption on the other hand takes place on all surfaces under the correct conditions of temperature and pressure. Thus, with a metal powder adsorbent, extreme measures must be taken to free the surface of initial atmospheric contamination before chemisorption can proceed, and in general, unless there is good reason to believe that a surface is clean and unsaturated, it is extremely unlikely to be active in chemisorption.

(5) Chemisorption ceases when the adsorbate can no longer make direct contact with the surface, and is therefore a single layer process. With physical adsorption no such limitation applies, and under suitable conditions of temperature and pressure, physically adsorbed layers many molecules thick can be obtained. Therefore, if the extent of an adsorption is known to exceed a monolayer, it is certain that second and higher layers at least are physically adsorbed.

4

## ADSORPTION AND ABSORPTION

The contact of immiscible phases may, in addition to adsorption, result in the penetration of the bulk of one phase by the other. This is called *absorption*. If the *absorbent* is a liquid the process is solution and is relatively simple: with a solid the term covers wider and more diverse phenomena.

Absorption by solids divides into roughly three types. The first type is diffusion and adsorption along fine capillaries. In the limit this becomes the second type—diffusion along crystal grain boundaries. Of these, the first is normally non-activated, the second normally activated. The third type is penetration of gas between the atoms of a crystal to form a true solution.

The particular kind of absorption which predominates with any given solid depends on its nature. The metals do not often contain fine pores, and for this reason crystal boundary diffusion and solution in the lattice are more important. With carbon and clay adsorbents, capillary effects and sometimes solution tend to outweigh crystal boundary effects.

The extent of absorption is dependent on the form of the solid. Powders, being both bulky and porous, may absorb relatively large quantities of material. Thin film adsorbents, prepared by evaporation onto glass, tend to have a larger surface to volume ratio, are less bulky, and do not possess fine pores. As a result they usually absorb material to a much smaller extent. The same seems to be true of metal filaments.

One very important fact is that all phenomena normally classed as absorption proceed slowly except at elevated temperatures, because either an activation energy or a slow non-activated diffusion is involved. As a result there is always a possibility that an absorption may be thought to be a slow chemisorption on a free surface, or vice versa. However, absorptions have certain characteristics which in general enable them to be distinguished from adsorptions, and the most important of these are the following:

(*1*) True solution in a solid is usually endothermic and is distinguished by this from adsorption which is normally exothermic.

(*2*) For small diffused amounts, that is when the concentration of adsorbate at the centre of the solid particle is effectively zero, the quantity of absorbed gas is proportional to the square root of the time[11]. This relation only holds for slow adsorptions under very special circumstances[12].

(*3*) Absorption of the simpler gases such as hydrogen often takes

5

place with dissociation of the molecule to atoms, in which case the amount absorbed at equilibrium is proportional to the square root of the pressure[13]. This is very rarely true of adsorption even when dissociation of the molecule takes place. As shown in Chapter V the main reason is that the heat of adsorption varies with adsorbed amount.

(4) Certain diffusions obey Fick's Law and are non-activated. The rate of these [14] is proportional to $\sqrt{T}$, whereas slow adsorptions are activated and are exponentially dependent on temperature.

(5) If absorption is associated with formation of a compound with the solid, very large amounts of gas will be used, and measurement of the surface area would show these to be far in excess of the quantity which could possibly be adsorbed. An example is the formation of hydrides by the metals palladium, zirconium and titanium.

## LOCALIZED AND NON-LOCALIZED ADSORPTION

A surface may be represented diagrammatically as a plane, the potential energy of which fluctuates from point to point. When these fluctuations are appreciable the troughs represent *adsorption sites*, and adsorption is therefore said to be *localized*. If, however, the fluctuations are so small as effectively to vanish, there are no adsorption sites, and adsorption is said to be *non-localized*.

Chemisorption is always localized, and in localized adsorption two extreme conditions may be distinguished. If the energy fluctuation is the same between any pair of sites and all sites have the same

*Figure 2. A uniform surface*

energy, the surface is said to be *uniform* or *homogeneous*. If the fluctuation is irregular and the sites have different energies, the surface is said to be *non-uniform* or *heterogeneous*. Examples of the two types of surface are shown in *Figures 2* and *3*. Since homogeneous and heterogeneous surfaces have very different properties in adsorption and catalysis, it is important to know to which of these classes a given surface belongs.

In non-localized adsorption there is no energy barrier opposing movement of a particle from point to point on the surface, but in localized adsorption there is a barrier. Therefore, with non-localized layers, the kinetic thermal energy of the adsorbed particles is sufficient to ensure that they will be *mobile* and move over the surface, but localized layers may be mobile or *immobile*, according as the

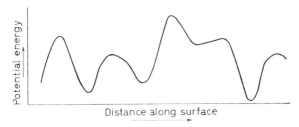

*Figure 3. A non-uniform surface*

thermal energy is greater or less than the energy barrier between sites. With localized adsorption, mobility reduces to a series of migrations from site to site, each requiring an activation energy. On a uniform surface, this energy will be the same for each migration, but on a non-uniform surface it will be different.

### THE SURFACE BOND

Chemisorption is an interaction between the electrons of the adsorbent and those of the adsorbate. As a result, the arrangement of electrons in the adsorbent may be crucial in deciding such properties as the ease and strength of chemisorption. Again, since metals, semiconductors and insulators represent three extreme types of electronic arrangement in solids, one might expect the surface properties of each category to show certain characteristic features. To some extent this proves to be the case.

In order to understand the nature of the surface bond it is necessary to know something of the theory of the solid state. The most important fact for our purposes is that solids possess electron bands. That is to say, whereas the electrons of isolated atoms have sharp, discrete energy values usually separated from one another by appreciable intervals, the levels broaden when the atoms

7

coalesce to form a crystal, giving a band of permitted energies. Thus the $3d$ levels of transition metal atoms become the $3d$ band of the crystal, while in an oxide the $2s$ and $2p$ levels of the oxygen atoms become an overlapping $sp$ band in the crystal.

Entry of electrons into a full band is obviously impossible, and as a result chemisorption, either through covalence or through positive ion formation, will be impossible. Again, if a band is virtually empty, chemisorption with negative ion formation may be limited simply on this account. These simple considerations have quite wide application. For example, the poor conductivity of oxides is due to the fact that their electron bands are either virtually full or virtually empty, thereby limiting the migration of electrons through the crystal. On account of this structure certain chemisorptions are precluded. Thus in zinc oxide the highest band is almost empty, and consequently chemisorption of oxygen as negative ions is limited[15]. Again, measurement of the change in magnetic suscepti-bility of transition metals during chemisorption suggests that an entry of electrons into the $d$-band takes place[16]. One might therefore expect the non-transition metals to be relatively inactive in chemi-sorption because their $d$-bands are full, and this proves to be the case[17].

However, rather more detailed consideration[18] of the energy levels is necessary to obtain an accurate picture in the case of the metals. For example, if the highest occupied level in the adsorbate lies above the highest occupied level (the Fermi level) in the metal, exothermic transfer of an electron from the adsorbate to the metal is clearly possible. A high metal work function $\phi$, and a low ionization potential, $I$, of the adsorbate will clearly make for strong chemi-sorption as positive ions, as shown in *Figure 4a*, while *Figure 4b* shows that under these conditions the activation energy of chemisorption, $E$, will be small. For negative ion formation $\phi$ should be low, and the electron affinity of the adsorbate $\xi$ should be large (*Figure 4c*).

Simple electrovalence is however uncommon. The surface dipoles formed on chemisorption are usually small, suggesting covalent surface bonds. Here (*Figure 4c*) one may consider the elevation of a metal electron to the Fermi level from a filled level at about the height of the occupied level of the adsorbate, and inter-action between the latter and the now unoccupied metal level to form a homopolar bond. In this way the exchange forces in forma-tion of the bond become appreciable. The accommodation of the promoted electron at the Fermi level will be assisted if the density of states there is large, while for a given adsorbate the promotion energy will be small if the work function is large. These two circumstances

8

should, in other words, assist covalent chemisorption, and in fact the high activity of transition metals in chemisorption may arise from the high density of states in the $d$-band at the Fermi level.

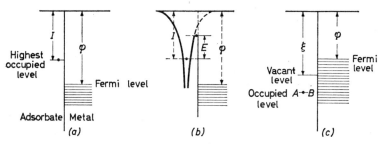

*Figure 4. Chemisorption with* (a) *and* (b) *positive ion formation; and* (c) *negative ion or covalent bond formation*

By courtesy of Stone, F. S. *Chemistry of the Solid State* (Ed. Garner) London; Butterworths, 1955

Similar considerations apply to some extent in the case of oxides, although the overriding factor is normally the simple availability of electrons and vacancies in the band system.

### SURFACE RADICALS

In chemisorption, the adsorbate is usually dissociated into independent fragments. Radicals and atoms are thus the units of which chemisorbed layers are made, and their nature must be considered when dealing with mechanisms of chemisorption. The question is important because the nature of chemisorbed radicals decides the mechanisms of catalytic reactions. In general it is easier to discover the nature of surface radicals with carbon and the metals than with the oxides, because they possess only one type of adsorption centre whereas the oxides possess two types. Thus, chemisorption of the simple diatomic gases hydrogen, oxygen and nitrogen on metals can only reasonably take place with formation of atoms, according to such equations as

$$2M + H_2 \rightarrow 2MH$$

On the oxides, however, hydrogen chemisorption may take place either on the metal ions, according to the above equation, or on the oxygen ions[19], with reduction to hydroxide and a valence change at a neighbouring cation.

9

$$O^{2-} + \tfrac{1}{2}H_2 \rightarrow OH^- + \epsilon$$

$$M^{2+} + \epsilon \rightarrow M^+$$

Sometimes both mechanisms operate simultaneously, and it is difficult to decide the relative proportions of each.

With larger molecules, more than one mechanism is usually possible even with the metals. Thus with ethane, either ethyl or methyl radicals might be produced at low temperatures

$$2M + C_2H_6 \rightarrow MC_2H_5 + MH$$

$$2M + C_2H_6 \rightarrow 2MCH_3$$

and only detailed experiments on the exchange of deuterium with ethane[20] suggest that the former mechanism is probably correct.

### VELOCITIES OF ADSORPTION AND DESORPTION

Chemisorption presents a wide range of velocities, and a number of these have been measured. The slower activated chemisorptions may be studied with ease at room temperatures and above. With very fast chemisorptions, the velocity may be measured provided a steady low pressure of adsorbate can be maintained at the surface. With gases this may be done by diffusion through a fine orifice to the surface. In the chemisorption of metal vapours (e.g. of sodium vapour on a tungsten surface) it may be done by warming a source of sodium so that it gives a small vapour pressure. The methods require considerable delicacy of technique, but have given reliable rates of several rapid chemisorptions.

Initially, the reason for studying rates of chemisorption was to discover whether chemisorption, like an ordinary chemical reaction, requires an activation energy. Nowadays there are two further reasons for studying velocities of chemisorption.

The first applies to the very fast chemisorptions on metals where the activation energy approaches zero. Here elucidation of the sticking probability and its variation with coverage is important. This quantity, defined as the fraction of those molecules colliding with the surface which is adsorbed, often approaches 0·3 on bare surfaces, though it usually falls as the surface coverage increases[21].

The second reason is to discover whether the slowest step in a catalytic reaction is chemisorption of a reactant. In two cases,

10

ammonia synthesis[22] and hydrogen–deuterium exchange[7] at metal surfaces

$$N_2+3H_2\rightarrow2NH_3$$

$$H_2+D_2\rightarrow2HD$$

the rate of catalytic reaction appears to be equal to the rate of chemisorption of nitrogen and hydrogen respectively, so that these processes determine the rate of reaction.

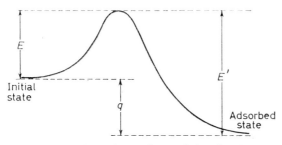

*Figure 5. Change of potential energy during adsorption*

Desorption, unlike adsorption, is always activated. If the heat of adsorption is $q$, and the activation energy of adsorption is $E$, *Figure 5* shows that the activation energy of desorption, $E'$, is given by

$$E'=q+E \qquad (1.2)$$

Thus, even in the limiting case where $E=0$,

$$E'=q \qquad (1.3)$$

Equation (1.3) is of some importance, because it suggests that with very fast chemisorptions $(E=0)$ determination of $E'$ from the temperature coefficient of desorption velocity gives the heat of chemisorption. The first determination of a heat of chemisorption on a clean metal surface, that of oxygen on tungsten, was made in this way[23]. However, with adsorbates such as oxygen which dissociate upon adsorption, equation (1.3) must be used with care. If the atoms recombine and desorb as molecules the equation applies, but if the atoms desorb as such the equation becomes

$$E'=\tfrac{1}{2}(q+E_D)$$

where $E_D$ is the heat of dissociation of the molecule. In addition Chapter IV gives further reasons why equation (1.3) must be used with care.

11

## EQUILIBRIUM AT SURFACES

For a given weight of adsorbent, the volume of gas, $v$, adsorbed at equilibrium is determined by the pressure and temperature alone. That is,

$$v = f(p, T) \qquad (1.4)$$

Experimentally, a family of curves is usually determined, each referring to a particular fixed value of one of the three variables $v$, $p$ and $T$. Frequently the volume is measured as a function of pressure at a number of fixed temperatures. In this case a family of *adsorption isotherms* is obtained, each given by

$$v = f(p) \quad , \quad T = \text{constant} \qquad (1.5)$$

If the volume is measured as a function of temperature at a number of fixed pressures, the curves are *adsorption isobars*:

$$v = f(T) \quad , \quad p = \text{constant} \qquad (1.6)$$

If the pressure is measured as a function of temperature at a number of fixed adsorbed volumes, the curves are *adsorption isosteres*:

$$p = f(T) \quad , \quad v = \text{constant} \qquad (1.7)$$

Clearly, a family of curves of any one type can, by replotting, be converted to a family of either of the other two types.

Measurements of equilibrium are difficult to make with many chemisorptions because extremely high temperatures are required before the equilibrium pressure achieves values large enough to measure. These temperatures may either be inaccessible, or introduce some complicating effect. With hydrocarbon chemisorption, reversibility is rarely attainable because the necessary temperatures produce a carbonized surface with hydrogen in the gas phase[24]. Carbon monoxide is often only desorbed from oxides as $CO_2$, owing to interaction with the oxygen ions of the lattice[19].

In general, it is possible to obtain equilibrium data only on very weak chemisorptions, and the number of these so far discovered is rather few. However, the lack of experimental data is to some extent compensated by the availability of a number of theoretical isotherms.

The Clausius–Clapeyron equation may be applied to experimental isotherms to give $q$, the heat of adsorption at particular values of $v$:

$$\left(\frac{d \ln p}{dT}\right)_v = \frac{q}{RT^2} \qquad (1.8)$$

As adsorption is exothermic it should, at constant pressure, decrease continuously with increasing temperature. With many systems this is so, but others, notably those where chemisorption may be expected, show more complex features. A very frequent type of behaviour is that minima and maxima appear as the temperature is raised. An example, obtained for hydrogen adsorption on a nickel powder[25], is shown in *Figure 6*.

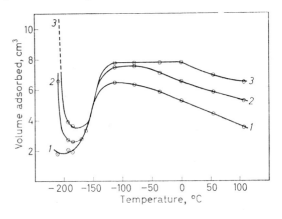

Curve 1—2·5 cm pressure
Curve 2— 20 cm pressure
Curve 3— 60 cm pressure
*Figure 6. Isobars for hydrogen on a nickel powder*
By courtesy of Benton, A. F. and White, T. A. *J. Amer. Chem. Soc.* **52**, 2325, 1930

These results are explicable if two different processes predominate in different temperature ranges, but the nature of the two processes is still uncertain. According to one school of thought, the low temperature process is physical adsorption, and the high temperature process activated chemisorption[26]: according to a second, the low temperature process is both physical and non-activated chemical adsorption, and the high temperature process absorption[27]. According to a third, chemisorption is in part non-activated and in part activated and operates on both sides of the minimum[28].

13

## THE HEAT OF ADSORPTION

The magnitude of the heat is the most significant single property of an adsorption, and determination of reliable heats is therefore of considerable importance.

If the heat is low, so that chemisorption may be studied under conditions where it is reversible, it may best be determined from isotherms using the Clausius–Clapeyron equation. Such heats are called *isosteric* or *isothermal heats*.

For non-activated adsorptions, heats may also be determined by measurement of the temperature coefficient of the velocity of desorption, as already explained.

For the majority of adsorptions, however, calorimetric methods are best. In these, a small quantity of gas is admitted to the adsorbent, and the liberated heat is measured. Such a heat is an *integral heat*, as it is the average value of the heat over the part of the surface covered during the adsorption. It differs from an isosteric heat, which is a *differential heat*, and refers to a particular value of the adsorbed amount. Clearly, by making the quantity of gas admitted to the surface very small in a calorimetric measurement, the integral heat which is obtained approximates to a differential heat.

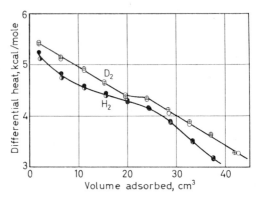

*Figure 7. Hydrogen and deuterium chemisorption on chromia at −183°C*
By courtesy of Beebe, R. A. and Dowden, D. A. *J. Amer. Chem. Soc.* **60**, 2912, 1938

Heats of chemisorption vary widely, even on closely related solids (e.g. different metals). By determining the heats of chemisorption of a particular gas on different solids, and relating these to the structure of the solid, information may be gained as to the factors making for high chemisorptive and catalytic activity, the nature of the surface bond and so forth[29].

Again, the differential heat of chemisorption falls markedly as the volume adsorbed increases and, as shown in *Figure 7*, the $q$–$v$ relation may be quite complex[6]. This fall has been attributed by some to surface heterogeneity, with sites of lessening activity covered as adsorption proceeds, but others have suggested that the surface is uniform and that the effect is due to increasing surface repulsions between neighbouring adsorbed atoms. Other possibilities are that different electron levels in the solid are being used, and that different mechanisms of chemisorption are operating.

## ELECTRICAL PROPERTIES

Among the electrical properties of adsorbed layers, the magnitude of the dipole moment, $\mu$, which is produced on adsorption is of interest. This is obtained by measurement of the change in work function on adsorption.

Values of $\mu$ have been obtained for a number of systems. Many measurements have been made with gas layers on metals, usually using saturated layers for which the fraction of the surface covered, $\theta$, approaches unity[30, 31]. However, for certain layers of metal vapours adsorbed on tungsten $\mu$ has been measured as a function of $\theta$, and found to decrease markedly as $\theta$ increases, owing to mutual depolarization of dipoles. Results for caesium and thorium layers are shown in Table 1[12]. From these it has been calculated that the fields causing depolarization are of the order of $8 \times 10^7$ and $5 \times 10^7$ volts/cm respectively.

TABLE 1

Dipole Moments of Caesium and Thorium
Layers on Tungsten

| $\theta$ | $\mu$(D)<br>Cs *on* W | $\mu$(D)<br>Th *on* W |
|---|---|---|
| 0·0 | 8·1 | 2·0 |
| 0·1 | 6·5 | 1·7 |
| 0·5 | 4·1 | 1·0 |
| 0·7 | 3·1 | 0·8 |
| 0·9 | 2·3 | — |
| 1·0 | 1·8 | — |

Electrical measurements are important for two reasons. First, the

15

magnitude of the dipole is in itself an indication of bond type: large $\mu$ values suggest ionic bonds, and low $\mu$ values suggest covalent bonds.

Second, aligned dipoles repel, and the repulsion energy increases as $\theta$ increases. The effect amounts to a decrease in the heat of adsorption as $\theta$ increases. By calculating the magnitude of these and other interactions, it is in principle possible to decide whether the entire experimental fall in heat can be attributed to interactions, and so to decide whether the surface is uniform.

## REFERENCES

[1] De Boer, J. H. *Adv. in Catalysis* **9**, 472, 1957
[2] Beebe, R. A. *Trans. Faraday Soc.* **28**, 761, 1932
[3] Beebe, R. A. and Taylor, H. S. *J. Amer. Chem. Soc.* **46**, 43, 1924
[4] Beebe, R. A. and Stevens, N. P. *J. Amer. Chem. Soc.* **62**, 2134, 1940
[5] Taylor, H. S. and Williamson, A. T. *J. Amer. Chem. Soc.* **53**, 2168, 1931
[6] Beebe, R. A. and Dowden, D. A. *J. Amer. Chem. Soc.* **60**, 2912, 1938
[7] Trapnell, B. M. W. *Proc. Roy. Soc.* A**206**, 39, 1951
[8] Rideal, E. K. and Trapnell, B. M. W. *Proc. Roy. Soc.* A**205**, 409, 1951
[9] Brunauer, S. *Physical adsorption of gases and vapours* p. 69. London; Oxford University Press, 1944
[10] Roberts, J. K. *Proc. Roy. Soc.* A**152**, 445, 1935
[11] Ward, A. F. H. *Proc. Roy. Soc.* A**133**, 522, 1931
[12] Langmuir, I. *J. Chem. Soc.* 511, 1940
[13] Smithells, C. J. *Gases and Metals* p. 155, London; Chapman & Hall, 1937
[14] Barrer, R. M. and Rideal, E. K. *Proc. Roy. Soc.* A**149**, 231, 1935
[15] Barry T. I. and Stone, F. S. *Proc. Roy. Soc.* A**255**, 124, 1960
[16] Dilke, M. H., Maxted, E. D. and Eley, D. D. *Nature, Lond.* **161**, 804, 1948
[17] Trapnell, B. M. W. *Proc. Roy. Soc.* A**218**, 566, 1953
[18] Dowden, D. A. *J. Chem. Soc.* 242, 1950
[19] Garner, W. E. *J. Chem. Soc.* 1239, 1947
[20] Kemball, C. and Taylor, H. S. *J. Amer. Chem. Soc.* **70**, 345, 1948
[21] Becker, J. A. and Hartman, C. D. *J. Phys. Chem.* **57**, 153, 1953
[22] Zwietering, P. and Roukens, J. J. *Trans. Faraday Soc.* **50**, 178, 1954
[23] Langmuir, I. and Villars, D. S. *J. Amer. Chem. Soc.* **53**, 486, 1931
[24] Wright, M. M. and Taylor, H. S. *Can. J. Res.* **27**, 303, 1949
[25] Benton, A. F. and White, T. A. *J. Amer. Chem. Soc.* **52**, 2325, 1930
[26] Taylor, H. S. *J. Amer. Chem. Soc.* **53**, 578, 1931
[27] Beeck, O., Ritchie, A. W. and Wheeler, A. *J. Coll. Sci.* **3**, 505, 1948
[28] Porter, A. S. and Tompkins, F. C. *Proc. Roy. Soc.* A**217**, 529, 1953
[29] Beeck, O. *Disc. Faraday Soc.* **8**, 118, 1950
[30] Culver, R. V. and Tompkins, F. C. *Adv. in Catalysis* **11**, 67, 1959.
[31] Eberhagen, A. *Fortschr. Phys.* **8**, 245, 1960

## II

# EXPERIMENTAL METHODS

### THE PREPARATION OF CLEAN SURFACES

WHEREAS all surfaces are active in physical adsorption, relatively few are sufficiently active to enter into chemisorption, and these, by virtue of their high unsaturation, are very prone to contamination. Exposure of a chemisorbing surface to the atmosphere at room temperature will almost certainly cover it with a complete layer of oxygen or nitrogen, and unless this is removed before starting an experiment, either the solid will not take up gas at all or, if it does,

17

the effect will be due to some process other than chemisorption, such as absorption or reaction of adsorbate with the layer already present on the surface.

Methods for obtaining a clean surface are of two types. In the first a contaminated surface is cleaned. This has been carried out successfully with oxide powders, cleaning of which seems to be easy, and to some extent with the metals and with carbon.

In the second category, a fresh surface is generated in vacuo, usually by evaporating a small specimen of adsorbent on to a glass surface to form a thin film. The method seems to be applicable to all metals and also to carbon: there is no reason why it should not also be applicable to the oxides.

Having produced a clean surface it is essential to maintain it in this condition for the duration of the experiment. Metal surfaces, in particular, are extremely reactive, and in many cases nearly every molecule of the ambient gas striking the surface is chemisorbed. On the average there are $10^{15}$ adsorption sites per square centimetre of a metal surface, and assuming the sticking probability of the gas molecules approaches unity a complete monolayer of adsorbed gas will be formed in about 20 seconds at a pressure of $10^{-7}$ mm of Hg. In such cases, the pressure of residual active gases immediately above the metal surface must be reduced below $10^{-9}$ mm otherwise the surface may be seriously contaminated before measurements can be made.

CLEANING A CONTAMINATED SURFACE

The first step towards cleaning a contaminated powder is to heat it strongly in vacuo. This will undoubtedly remove much of the dissolved gas, an important procedure as such gas will often otherwise diffuse to a cleaned surface and poison it.

With the oxides, heating in vacuo is also likely to produce at least a partly cleaned surface. For example chromium and copper oxides[1, 2], outgassed at 400 °C and 150 °C respectively, have fair activity in chemisorption.

However, with the metals, heating in vacuo may not remove surface contamination even if it is carried out at the highest possible temperatures. Oxygen chemisorbed on nickel and iron filaments is not appreciably desorbed even at temperatures at which evaporation of the metal itself commences[3, 4], and on a tungsten filament it requires several years to desorb[5] at 1,200 °C.

After heating in vacuo, reduction of adsorbed oxygen or nitrogen in hydrogen is often attempted. This is then followed by further

18

heating in vacuo to remove any hydrogen which has been chemisorbed. With oxides, this treatment usually gives surfaces active in chemisorption[6], though of somewhat irreproducible properties. Care must of course be taken that the oxide is not bodily reduced to the metal.

With carbon, chemisorbed oxygen seems to be removed as CO and $CO_2$ at temperatures below 900 °C, whereas hydrogen is not removed until about 1,000 °C[7]. For this reason reduction is not usually attempted with carbon.

With the metals, reduction is more likely to be effective in removing surface impurity than outgassing, and furthermore any hydrogen which is chemisorbed will be at least partly removed by the subsequent heating in vacuo—most chemisorbed hydrogen is removable from metals at 500 °C[8]. However, reduction is not certain to remove contamination even at very high temperatures. The original contamination on an iron filament cannot, for example, be removed by hydrogen below the melting point of the metal[4]. Furthermore, at these temperatures there is always a danger that traces of solid impurity in an adsorbent will diffuse to the surface and poison it.

The simple methods so far outlined are thus only likely to produce active powder surfaces with oxides. With the metals and with carbon, the following more rigorous methods of purification have been developed. In all these methods, the possibility of contamination of the surface by the vapour of tap grease, or by mercury or water vapour from the apparatus, is always rigidly excluded by placing cold traps between the adsorbent and any possible source of such vapours.

*(a) Reduction techniques*

Certain more vigorous reduction techniques are now available for powders. In these, the very purest hydrogen must be used as the presence of even 0·01 % of oxygen or water vapour has been found to be a perpetual source of recontamination[9].

In direct outgassing and reduction of powders, silica or very hard glass vessels are used to enable reduction to be carried out up to 1,000 °C. Double-walled vessels are employed, with the annulus evacuated, to prevent contamination by diffusion of air through the glass at these high temperatures.

The simplest form of reaction vessel, due to BARRER[10], and used by BARRER and RIDEAL[11] to outgas carbon at 1,000 °C, is shown in *Figure 8*. A more elaborate apparatus, essentially a vacuum furnace, and due to FRANKENBURG[12] is shown in *Figure 9*. The adsorption vessel *AV* is surrounded by a furnace, the lower part of which is a steel-lined oven. The upper part is water-cooled, and is joined to the lower part by screws *B* and a rubber gasket *RG*. The delivery tube from *AV* passes through holes in the top of the furnace sealed

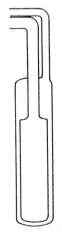

Figure 8.
*Double-walled reaction vessel*
By courtesy of Barrer, R. M.
*J. Chem. Soc.* 378, 1934

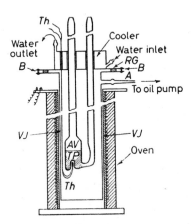

Figure 9.
*Vacuum furnace for outgassing powders*
By courtesy of Frankenburg, W. G.
*J. Amer. Chem. Soc.* **66**, 1827, 1944

by picein. The whole furnace is evacuated through the side tube *A*. The temperature of the furnace is measured by the thermocouple *Th*, the leads of which also pass through a picein-sealed hole in the upper half of the furnace. With this apparatus Frankenburg carried out reductions at temperatures approaching 750 °C and obtained moderately clean tungsten powder surfaces.

An alternative method of reduction is to use atomic hydrogen, produced in the reaction vessel by an electrodeless discharge[13]. This may be done by winding the outside of the vessel with a few turns of wire connected to a 15 Mc/sec oscillator, filling the vessel with 0·1 mm hydrogen, and then passing a current sufficient to give a luminous discharge. In this way, even the most strongly adsorbed contaminations may be reduced, very often at room temperatures. However, hydrogen is bound to be dissolved and chemisorbed by the adsorbent, and the treatment must be followed by stringent outgassing. Chemisorbed hydrogen is removable in this way, but dissolved hydrogen may be difficult to remove completely, even at temperatures of 750 °C or more[14].

*(b) Bombardment techniques*

When reduction by molecular or atomic hydrogen is ineffective, bombardment of the surface with positive ions of a non-adsorbed gas, normally argon or neon, may be successful.

The normal procedure is to introduce about 0·1 mm pressure of inert gas into the system and to start a glow discharge (400–1,000 volts) between the adsorbent surface and a secondary electrode, the adsorbent being the cathode. Normally an ion current of 100 microamperes per cm² of surface is adequate[15, 16], although much higher current densities have been used[4].

The method was first used by LANGMUIR and KINGDON[17] to remove thorium atoms from tungsten, and has since been used to obtain allegedly clean surfaces of platinum[18], iron[4], titanium[19], germanium[15, 19, 20], silicon[16, 20] and nickel[21, 22]. In all cases, except thorium on tungsten, however, simple bombardment after outgassing the adsorbent near its melting point was insufficient to give a clean surface.

With platinum[18], bombardment of the surface with oxygen ions prior to bombardment with argon ions was claimed to give a clean surface, as judged by work function measurements. However, the vacuum conditions used were indifferent and the work function of the supposedly clean surface does not in fact agree with the best values now available.

In later work using an iron wire[4], successive oxygen and neon bombardments were only partially effective in cleaning the wire, but when nitrogen was used in place of oxygen the value of the neon accommodation coefficient suggested that a clean surface had been obtained. A vigorous outgassing procedure was followed and active gases were removed from the neon by circulation over activated carbon at liquid nitrogen temperature. In all probability the surfaces obtained by this technique were genuinely clean.

The ineffectiveness of the simple bombardment procedure seems to have been due to incomplete outgassing, so that as soon as surface contamination was removed it was replaced by gas diffusing from the interior of the metal. In the initial bombardment with oxygen or nitrogen a subsurface barrier is probably formed, which prevents the diffusion of other more mobile contaminants to the surface.

If this explanation is correct, the diffusion of contaminants from

C

the interior of metals to the surface may be quite large even at room temperature and after thorough outgassing. This has very serious implications in relation to the cleanliness of powder surfaces produced in the manner described earlier.

FARNSWORTH and co-workers[15, 16, 19-22] have used single crystal faces in their studies, and the criterion of cleanliness has been the low energy diffraction pattern of the clean metal surface. After bombardment with argon ions no low energy diffraction maxima could be observed owing to the large number of defects introduced into the lattice. It was necessary to anneal at an elevated temperature to remove the defects together with occluded argon ions. Even so, a clean surface did not result, again mainly due to diffusion from the bulk to the surface during the annealing period. To reduce this diffusion to a very low level, a cycle of ion bombardments and anneals was performed. The difficulties which arise are illustrated by nickel[21, 22]. This metal was found to be covered with a layer of carbon after heating at temperatures up to 1,100 °C. A clean surface was produced by argon ion bombardment and subsequent annealing, but further high temperature treatment caused more carbon to diffuse from the interior and many cycles were necessary to reduce the carbon density near the surface. Altogether the nickel crystal was outgassed at 800 °C for a total of 400 hours and at 1,100 °C for 5 hours. The total bombardment time was 3 hours and vacua of the order of $10^{-10}$ mm were obtained. Even so, there is considerable dispute as to whether surfaces prepared in this way are really clean[23].

### (c) Flashing a filament

A clean surface of some metals may be obtained by heating a filament electrically in vacuo near to its melting point. With the higher melting metals, these temperatures are above those at which impurity can remain on the surface or in the bulk of the filament. For example, a tungsten filament can be heated to 3,300 °C without melting: it outgasses efficiently above about 2,800 °C[24]: the most stable chemisorbed layer, that of oxygen, evaporates rapidly at 2,000 °C[25]: tungstic oxide is volatile above 1,200 °C[5], and the normal boiling point of silica, which is often present in small amounts in tungsten, is 2,230 °C.

This method of obtaining a clean surface has been extremely important, and the main features of chemisorption by clean metals have been elucidated using a flashed tungsten filament. Since the area of the filament is very small it is highly susceptible to contamination and therefore the residual gas pressure should not exceed $10^{-9}$ mm. This calls for ultra high vacuum techniques.

The method is mainly restricted to the high melting point metals such as tungsten and molybdenum although nickel[26] and silicon[27] have been cleaned in this way. It is ideal for the measurement of desorption rates since a filament can be heated so easily to the requisite high temperature. Also, a fresh surface is readily obtained for successive measurements by flashing.

### THE EVAPORATED FILM TECHNIQUE

The most widely applicable method of obtaining clean surfaces is to outgas a small specimen of the solid in vacuo at temperatures just below those at which it becomes volatile, and then to heat it to a slightly higher temperature to form an evaporated film on the surface of the containing vessel[28, 29]. Occasionally, the evaporation is carried out in the presence of a small pressure ($\sim0.5$ mm) of a non-adsorbed gas, such as argon[29]. In either case an appreciable area of fresh, clean surface is generated. Up to now the method has been applied mainly to the metals, and to some extent to carbon.

Methods of preparing metal films have been reviewed by ALLEN[30]. Films of many metals (W, Mo, Ta, Nb, Ti, Pd, Fe, Co, Ni, Ag) may be made by direct evaporation from an electrically heated filament (*Figure 10a*). With other metals this may not be possible, either because the metal melts before it evaporates, or because filaments are not available. Here the simplest method is to use a tungsten filament as a support and, if wire is available, to wind it round the tungsten (*Figure 10b*); otherwise small pieces of the metal may be hung over a suitably bent filament (*Figure 10c*). If the metal alloys with tungsten some other high melting point metal should be used as a support. Alternatively, a bead of metal supported in a refractory crucible can be used, this method being particularly useful when large quantities of metal need to be evaporated (*Figure 10d*).

Germanium and silicon[31] have been evaporated from small pieces of the material lodged in tightly coiled tungsten filaments (*Figure 10e*). Films of potassium[32], arsenic, antimony and selenium[33] have been prepared by distillation from a side tube into a larger vessel. Electron bombardment heating has been used successfully to evaporate carbon[34], using the electrode arrangement shown in *Figure 10f*. The guard electrode, which is held at a negative potential, prevents excessive heating of the tungsten support.

Most evaporated films are porous with a high surface area to weight ratio. If formed at low temperatures they may be somewhat unstable due to their high surface energy and should, therefore, be sintered at a temperature above that reached in any subsequent part of the experiment.

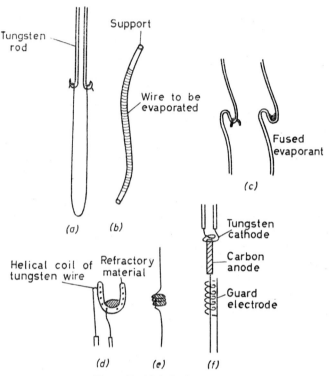

*Figure 10. Methods of evaporation*

With the transition metals the area of films deposited at a given temperature is proportional to their weight[29, 35] and may be as high as 60 sq.m per g[36].   The low melting point metals[32] and the group 1B metals[37] differ in that the surface area of films deposited above −80 °C is roughly equal to the apparent area whatever the weight, so that the surfaces must be virtually flat.

The surface area of an average film will be not less than 1,000 sq. cm and approximately $10^{18}$ molecules are needed to form a monolayer on this surface.  Since this number of molecules is far in excess of the reservoir of gas adsorbed on the glass walls of a well outgassed system, the surface can be expected to remain substantially clean for quite long periods.

WHEELER[38] has suggested that the following results indicate film surfaces to be clean:

(a) The general reproducibility of results by workers in different laboratories.

(b) The linear increase in the amount of gas chemisorbed with film thickness. If films are contaminated this would be worse with the thinner ones which would adsorb less gas in proportion to their weight.

(c) Surface areas calculated from physical adsorption data agree with those found from chemisorption data. Since physical adsorption will occur on contaminated as well as uncontaminated surface sites this agreement would not arise unless films were substantially clean.

HICKMOTT and EHRLICH[39], however, have concluded that tungsten films may be contaminated. Using an ultra-high vacuum system, a pressure of $5 \times 10^{-10}$ mm could be maintained with the tungsten filament hot. During evaporation, with the reaction vessel isolated from the pumps, the pressure rose to about $4 \times 10^{-8}$ mm, and did not return to its initial low value until the heating current was switched off. Since most gases are rapidly chemisorbed by tungsten it was concluded that the film was contaminated, probably by desorption from the glass walls. If the evaporation was carried out in short bursts, however, the initial pressure was never exceeded and the film was presumed clean.

This behaviour has not been confirmed by more recent experiments[40] in which, during a continuous evaporation, the initial pressure of $5 \times 10^{-10}$ mm dropped in the first few minutes to about $1 \times 10^{-10}$ mm and remained there for the remainder of the deposition.

OTHER TECHNIQUES

Single crystal discs of germanium have been crushed in vacuo by a glass covered drop-hammer operated by a solenoid[41]. 5,000–7,000 cm$^2$ of fresh surface were obtained in this way from 2 g of germanium, the latter being first sliced into thin wafers and then crushed in a sealed-off, evacuated apparatus.

Fresh germanium surfaces have also been prepared by decomposition of germane on clean Pyrex glass wool at 300 °C, followed by evacuation at the same temperature for several hours to remove hydrogen[42].

## THE ATTAINMENT OF ULTRA-HIGH VACUA

In order to maintain a clean metal surface the pressure of active gas above it should not exceed $10^{-9}$ mm. In the evaporated film technique a fresh surface of considerable area is generated which produces its own high vacuum by gettering. Thus it is not essential (although it is desirable) to use ultra-high vacuum techniques. However, with the very small surfaces of filaments and single crystal faces, these techniques must be used.

The essence of ultra-high vacuum techniques is a high pumping rate and complete outgassing of all parts of the apparatus past the diffusion pumps. Bakeable metal valves are therefore used instead of greased stopcocks or mercury cut-offs, while the high pumping rate can be obtained by a fast diffusion pump backed by another diffusion pump and by using large bore Pyrex tubing throughout the high vacuum line. All glass parts should be baked at 450 °C and all metal parts at as high a temperature as possible. Cold traps should be placed before the diffusion pumps to trap condensible vapours. In very high vacuum work the top part of the diffusion pump is baked[43].

Pressures as low as $5 \times 10^{-11}$ mm may be measured with a Bayard–Alpert ionization gauge[44]. For lower pressures an inverted magnetron gauge should be used[45]. If the nature of the residual gas is required, an omegatron radio-frequency mass spectrometer[46] is useful.

For sealed-off systems, immersion in liquid helium is very effective, the vapour pressure of all other gases being effectively zero at such low temperatures[47]. However, precautions should be taken to prevent the diffusion of helium through the glass[46] during the cooling down period.

Two dangers must be avoided in the use of hot filament ionization gauges. First, misleading results may arise because the filament decomposes certain gases. For example, hydrogen is atomized and may then be chemisorbed on germanium, whereas hydrogen molecules are not adsorbed[48, 49].

Second, SCHLIER[50] has shown that oxygen pressures cannot be measured satisfactorily, partly because of the high pumping rate of oxygen by the hot filament, and partly because of the formation of carbon monoxide by interaction with carbon in the filament. This effect can however be minimized by heating the filament in oxygen at $10^{-6}$ mm for 48 hours[51].

MEASUREMENT OF THE QUANTITY OF GAS ADSORBED

THE VOLUME ADSORBED

The previous section indicated that there are three main types of clean surface—those of the powder, the evaporated film and the filament—and these normally differ greatly in surface area. An average 40 g powder sample may chemisorb up to 100 cm³ of gas measured at N.T.P., whereas a 30 mg film adsorbs about 0·1 cm³ and an average filament only $10^{-5}$ cm³ of gas. On this account different designs of apparatus are required for volumetric work with the different adsorbents.

*(a) Powders*[12]

A series of admissions of gas is normally made, the quantity of each being determined before contacting it with the adsorbent by reading the pressure exerted in a known volume. In order to obtain the amount adsorbed, it is essential to know how much gas is used in filling the evacuated portions of the apparatus. These are called dead spaces, and are often largely made up of the pore space within the adsorbent itself. They are determined by expanding a known quantity of non-adsorbed gas, usually helium, into the various evacuated parts of the apparatus and measuring the pressure. Calibrations are usually carried out with the reaction vessel at different temperatures, corrections being applied for Charles' Law and also for 'thermomolecular flow'. The latter arises from the fact that if a tube of diameter $d$ connects two parts of a system at temperatures $T_1$ and $T_2$, the pressures $p_1$ and $p_2$ in these parts are equal only if $d \gg \lambda$, the mean free path of the gas molecules. This normally holds only above pressures of 0·1 mm, and below this value it is very important to determine the extent of pressure inequality by calibration experiments, otherwise it may introduce the most serious single error into the measurements[52]. The effect is largest below about $10^{-4}$ mm, when $d \ll \lambda$ and $p_1/p_2 = \sqrt{(T_1/T_2)}$.

In volumetric work with powders, pressures from one atmosphere down to $10^{-5}$ mm are usually measured. For pressures between about 10 and 750 mm a U-tube may be used in conjunction with a barometer, while two McLeod gauges are sufficient to cover the rest of the range.

*(b) Evaporated metal films*

An apparatus for the volumetric determination of adsorption on films, due to RIDEAL and TRAPNELL[53] is shown in *Figure 11*. In this, a series of admissions of gas is again made, and mercury seals are used instead of taps. With an average evaporated film, adsorption can only be studied at pressures up to about $10^{-1}$ mm: if gas is admitted to a film sufficient to exert a pressure greater than this, the fraction of it which is adsorbed becomes so small that it cannot be determined with any accuracy. Consequently it is sufficient for the system to contain a single McLeod gauge, covering the pressure range $10^{-6}$–$10^{-1}$ mm. However, to allow observation of rapid pressure changes a Pirani gauge is incorporated.

The method of operation is then as follows. A small quantity of adsorbate is extracted from $R2$, previously filled to some 30 mm, by lowering and raising $S5$. This is expanded into the evacuated reservoir $R1$ by lowering $S4$. In $R1$ the gas exerts some 0·1 mm pressure. A small fraction is extracted using $S2$ and $S3$. This quantity is admitted to the film, and is sufficient to cover some 10–15 per cent of an average surface area.

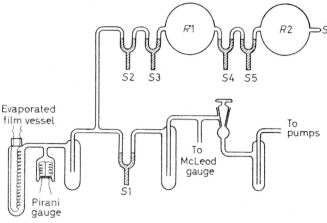

Figure 11. Volumetric measurement of adsorption on evaporated metal films
By courtesy of Rideal, E. K. and Trapnell, B. M. W. Proc. Roy. Soc. A**205**, 409, 1951

Suitable calibrations are first carried out in the absence of the film to obtain dead spaces and the magnitude of each admission. The film is then prepared, and a series of admissions of gas made, the equilibrium pressure being measured after each admission.

The apparatus permits isotherms covering several pressure magnitudes to be determined with fair accuracy. High gas purity is, however, important, for if almost all an admission is adsorbed, it is important to be certain that the residual pressure is a true equilibrium value, and not due to a trace of non-adsorbed impurity.

## (c) Filaments

The volumetric determination of chemisorption on filaments is rather difficult, owing to their minute surface areas, and is liable to be inaccurate. The volume of gas needed to cover a filament of surface area 0·5 cm² with a complete monolayer fills even a small apparatus, of volume 250 cm³, to a pressure of only $4 \times 10^{-5}$ mm. Thus the merest traces of residual gas or of impurity in the system may poison an appreciable part of the surface. Small amounts of adsorption taking place in cold traps also affect the results, and for this reason measurements are only feasible with the least condensible gases.

The apparatus used by ROBERTS[24] is shown in *Figure 12*. The filament is contained in the tube *W* and is protected by cold traps

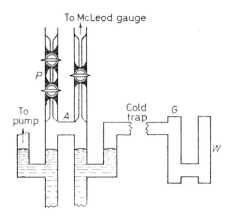

*Figure 12. Volumetric measurement of adsorption on filaments*
By courtesy of Roberts, J. K. *Proc. Roy. Soc.* **A152**, 445, 1935

which are not shown. This tube, together with the tube *G* in which there is a sensitive Pirani gauge, is connected to a pumping system and to a gas pipette *P* leading to a reservoir.

The filament is flashed, and when the flashing current is switched off, connected to a sensitive Wheatstone bridge. As the filament cools, the bridge galvanometer drifts—after a few minutes this may easily be followed. The apparatus is then cut off from the pump and a charge of gas is admitted. Adsorption is detected by a rise in temperature of the filament due to liberation of the heat of adsorption, and is confirmed by showing that the Pirani gauge indicates no permanent gas pressure. Further charges are admitted until a small permanent pressure results, and no further heat is liberated. The volume adsorbed at this stage is calculated.

The method has only been used for the determination of the total extent of a fast irreversible chemisorption. Such determinations Roberts found to be reproducible to about 15 per cent.

BECKER and HARTMAN[54] have measured the velocity of the rapid chemisorption of nitrogen on a tungsten ribbon filament by a volumetric technique. The experimental system, shown in *Figure 13*, consists of a bulb containing the filament *FF* connected to a gas

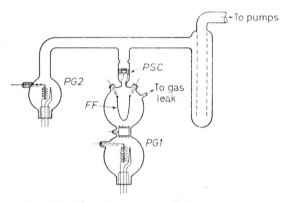

*Figure 13. Volumetric measurement of adsorption on filaments*
By courtesy of Becker, J. A. and Hartman, C. D., *J. Phys. Chem.* **57**, 153, 1953

leak for admission of nitrogen, a sensitive and rapidly responding ionization gauge *PG1*, and a pumping system. Between the filament bulb and the pumping system is a device *PSC* which controls the pumping speed. The success of the method depends on obtaining a steady low pressure of nitrogen in the bulb by simultaneous use of gas leak and pumps, and on the speed of response and sensitivity of *PG1*, with which this low pressure is measured.

In an experiment nitrogen is allowed to leak into the bulb. After a while the pressure reaches a steady value $p_0$, when the rate of removal by pumping is equal to the rate of supply through the leak. The magnitude of $p_0$ is decided by the setting of *PSC*. The filament is then flashed to clean it—this causes a temporary rise in the pressure owing to liberation of desorbed gas, but after some time the pressure again returns to the value $p_0$. Then, at $t=0$, the flashing current is turned off. Thereafter the ribbon adsorbs nitrogen. The pressure drops below $p_0$ for a while on this account, but then rises again, asympotically approaching $p_0$.

To determine the adsorption, the filament is flashed and the rise in pressure $\Delta p$ measured. The adsorption is then given approximately by

$$nV\Delta p = AM\theta \qquad (2.1)$$

where $n =$ no. of molecules per litre in the bulb at $p = 1$ mm, $V$ the volume of the bulb, $A$ is area of the filament, and $M$ the number of

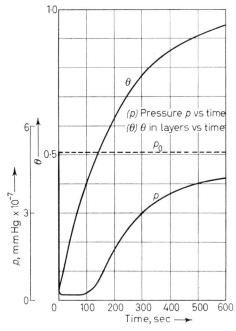

*Figure 14. The adsorption of nitrogen on a tungsten filament*
By courtesy of Becker, J. A. and Hartman, C. D. *J. Phys. Chem.* **57**, 153, 1953

molecules adsorbed per cm² when $\theta$, the fraction of the surface covered, is unity. Assuming the usual roughness factor for a tungsten filament, 1·4, it is then possible to convert $\Delta p$ values to $\theta$ values.

From the results, two curves are therefore obtained, one of $\theta$ against time, one of pressure against time. Examples are shown in *Figure 14*. From these, a sticking probability, $s$, is derived, defined as the fraction of molecules colliding with the surface which is adsorbed. This is done using the equation

$$M \cdot \frac{\mathrm{d}\theta}{\mathrm{d}t} = \frac{p}{\sqrt{(2\pi m k T)}} \cdot s \tag{2.2}$$

where $m$ is the mass of the molecule and $p/\sqrt{(2\pi m k T)}$ is the rate of collision of gas with unit area of surface.

Great care is necessary if this technique is to yield accurate results. Corrections should be applied for evaporation from and adsorption on the glass walls of the containing vessel. The amount of gas on the glass walls will be a function of the pressure in the system.

Most work has been done on the adsorption of nitrogen on tungsten[39, 54, 55] although the adsorption of hydrogen[56], oxygen[57] and CO[58] have also been studied. A difficulty with oxygen is that not all gas is desorbed as oxygen molecules. With hydrogen, atomic hydrogen, produced when the gas is introduced into an ionization gauge, is strongly adsorbed on glass and also reacts with it to give CO, $H_2O$ and $CH_4$[59]. If a lanthanum boride coated tantalum filament is used in the gauge, a lower filament temperature is possible and no atomization of hydrogen occurs[56].

### THE WEIGHT ADSORBED

The gravimetric method is ideally suited to the determination of adsorptions on low surface areas (e.g. of evaporated films) at high pressures, where the volumetric method is inapplicable. For example, it is possible to measure gravimetrically the adsorption on a surface area of a few square centimetres at pressures approaching an atmosphere[60], where volumetric measurements would be limited to pressures below about $10^{-3}$ mm.

The weight of gas adsorbed by a solid may be measured either by the extension of a spring from which the adsorbent is suspended[61], or by the deflection of a beam microbalance[62]. Of these, the first is easier to use, but only the second has sufficient sensitivity for the problem in hand. Beam microbalances also have the advantage that by skilful designing the buoyancy correction may be eliminated, whereas with spring balances this is impossible.

Beam microbalances are of two types. In the first, the beam is supported on knife edges: in the second, it is attached to a fine torsionless wire. A balance of the second type, due to GULBRANSEN[63], is illustrated in *Figure 15*.

The beam and frame are made of 1·5 mm diameter quartz rod. Attached to one end of the beam is a fine pointer for following its movement relative to a second pointer attached to the frame. Specimen and counterweight supports are made of fine tungsten wire and are attached to the beam using fused AgCl. Two slots ground into the centre of the frame serve as mounting points for the beam support wire, which is 0·025 mm diameter tungsten. This is mounted using fused AgCl, and then the beam is attached to the wire by the same means.

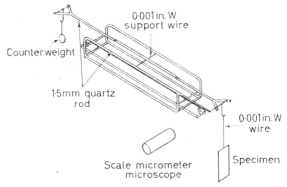

*Figure 15. Gravimetric determination of adsorption*
By courtesy of Gulbransen, E. A. *Rev. Sci. Inst.* **15**, 261, 1944

The balance weighs to within $0·3 \times 10^{-6}$ of a g and the pressure coefficient is less than $0·3 \times 10^{-6}$ g for a 1 atmosphere change. The temperature coefficient is, however, about $0·8 \times 10^{-6}$ g/deg. and this is sufficiently high to necessitate temperature control.

RHODIN[60] has increased the balance sensitivity by a factor of six, by raising the centre of gravity of the beam and by decreasing the diameter of the tungsten crosswire to 0·01 mm. This enables adsorption isotherms to be obtained on 10 cm² areas at pressures up to 700 mm. In Rhodin's work, sample and counterweight are maintained at the same temperature to minimize thermal eddy currents.

Accumulation of electrostatic charge on the surface of a balance is liable to cause serious errors. This is best avoided by placing a small sample of a radioactive substance in the reaction tube, when ionization of the gas removes the charge. Also, it is advisable to have some means of adjusting the balance in vacuo: this may be accomplished by having a partly hollow beam with a small counterweight of iron wire in the hollow portion[64]. The beam may then be tilted by moving the wire with a solenoid.

33

RADIOACTIVE TRACER TECHNIQUES

Very small amounts of radioactive chemisorbed gas can be detected with a Geiger counter. DILLON and FARNSWORTH[65] have studied the adsorption of radioactive $CO_2$ on single crystal nickel surfaces using a counter with a very thin mica window, sealed into the adsorption chamber. Recently CROWELL[66] has followed the adsorption of $^{14}CO$ on nickel by a similar technique. In this case the metal specimen was exposed to the gas, and then moved magnetically in front of a mica window in the reaction vessel. The window was thin enough to pass a measurable amount of radiation and yet strong enough to withstand atmospheric pressure.

SURFACE AREA MEASUREMENTS ON FILMS AND POWDERS

Since physical adsorption is non-specific it can be used to measure the total area of surface exposed to the gas phase. This is important in determining the degree of coverage of the chemisorbed layer.

The method normally used for surface area measurements employs the well known B.E.T. isotherm for multilayer physical adsorption[67]

$$\frac{p}{(p_0-p)v} = \frac{1}{v_m c} + \frac{c-1}{v_m c} \cdot \frac{p}{p_0} \tag{2.3}$$

In this equation $v_m$ is the volume necessary to form a monolayer, $v$ is the volume of gas adsorbed (reduced to N.T.P.) at a pressure $p$, $p_0$ is the vapour pressure of the adsorbate at the temperature of the experiment and $c$ is a constant which depends on the nature of the adsorbate–adsorbent system.

By plotting $p/(p_0-p)v$ against $p/p_0$ it is possible to calculate $v_m$. Then if the area occupied by the adsorbed molecule on the surface is known or can be estimated, $v_m$ can be converted to a surface area.

While the basic assumptions underlying the B.E.T. equation have been questioned[68], there is considerable evidence that values of $v_m$ obtained with weakly adsorbed molecules on heterogeneous surfaces are acceptable[69].

In order to obtain accurate results, the amount of gas adsorbed and the amount in the gas phase should be of the same order of magnitude. This means making a suitable choice of gas and temperature, taking into account the dead space and the estimated surface area of the adsorbent. For small surface areas, such as those of films, adsorption of krypton at the temperature of boiling nitrogen has been used[70, 71], since its vapour pressure at this temperature is only 2–3 mm. In addition there is no possibility of chemisorption of krypton. For powders, adsorption of nitrogen at −195°C is often suitable[72].

## MEASUREMENT OF THE HEAT OF ADSORPTION

Heats of adsorption may be determined from isotherms, from desorption rates, or measured calorimetrically. Calorimetric measurements are of two kinds. First, the heat liberated by adsorption may be used to produce a phase change in a surrounding solid or liquid. In this case the heat is derived from the volume change in the surrounding substance, and the measurement is isothermal. Second, escape of heat from the adsorbent may be prevented, and the heat determined from the rise in the adsorbent temperature. Such measurements are adiabatic.

Whether isothermal or adiabatic methods are used depends to some extent on the form of the adsorbent. If it is a film or a filament, the adsorption is very small, and the liberated heat is insufficient to produce a measurable extent of phase change. Adiabatic methods must therefore be used. With powders, however, the surface area is normally sufficiently large to render either method possible.

### HEAT MEASUREMENTS USING POWDERS

Isothermal measurements may be made over a wide range of temperatures by using suitable working substances. DEWAR[73] measured heats of adsorption at −185 °C by observing the volume of liquid air vaporized on adsorption. FAVRE[74] made measurements at −40°C by causing the adsorption to melt mercury: many observers have used ice calorimeters for determinations at 0°C[75]. Heats have also been measured at 26°C[76] and 40°C[77], the melting points of diphenyl ether and phenol respectively. In all cases the apparatus is essentially a variation of the Bunsen ice calorimeter.

With all adiabatic calorimeters, loss of heat is prevented by sur rounding the adsorbent by a vacuum. However, two distinct types of adiabatic calorimeter may be distinguished. In the first, the adsorbate is admitted to the evacuated space between calorimeter and containing vessel, that is, to the *outside* of the radiating surface[78]. In this way, particularly if the adsorbent is contained in a fine gauze, it is often easier to promote uniform adsorption throughout the powder, and hence uniform temperature rise. However, if the adsorption is reversible, the equilibrium gas pressure may be high enough to cause too large a loss of heat from the calorimeter. Again, if the adsorption is slow, so that the gas pressure outside the radiating surface continually varies, the cooling coefficient of the calorimeter also varies, and the results cannot readily be interpreted. In both these cases it is necessary to use the second type of adiabatic calorimeter[79, 80], where the gas is admitted to the inside of the adsorbent, that is, to the *inside* of the radiating surface, and to maintain a hard vacuum round the exterior surface.

An experimental difficulty with fine powders arises from their very poor thermal conductivity. This means that if adsorption does not take place uniformly throughout the powder, as may well be the case if it is rapid, heating may not be uniform. In this case the temperature rise registered by a thermocouple may give a fallacious heat of adsorption.

There are two ways of overcoming this difficulty. First, the adsorbent may be mixed with a quantity of a good thermal conductor, which is inactive in adsorption—copper shot has in some cases been used with success[80]. Second, a small quantity of a non-adsorbed gas, usually helium, may be added to the adsorbate to assist heat transfer[78].

### HEAT MEASUREMENTS USING EVAPORATED FILMS

The low surface areas of evaporated films require the use of an adiabatic calorimeter of the very smallest heat capacity. Even so, the best designs only allow heat measurements with fast, irreversible adsorptions—with slow or reversible chemisorptions, the heat losses by radiation and by conduction through residual gas respectively are too large to allow satisfactory measurements.

The calorimeter of BEECK, COLE and WHEELER[81] is shown in *Figure 16*. The calorimeter proper is the lower portion of the inner tube, and is made from eggshell glass: a little above it is a constriction to minimize heat losses to the upper part of the tube.

Fine platinum wire is wound round the outside of the calorimeter, and cemented in place with a thin layer of sodium silicate. This wire serves as a resistance thermometer, and is connected to a bridge circuit. The metal film is deposited on the inside of the eggshell tube from a heated filament—during this process cooling water is passed through the outer jacket to prevent softening and collapse of the thin glass. The jacket is then evacuated, turning the assembly into a vacuum calorimeter. The calorimeter is next surrounded by a thermostat, gas admitted and the temperature rise measured. Heat losses are considerable, and it proves necessary to have a fast responding galvanometer in the bridge circuit so as to be able to take temperature readings at 5 or 6 second intervals.

The thermal capacity of the calorimeter has been determined by weighing the component parts and multiplying by the respective specific heats[81], and also by passing a known current through the platinum wire and observing first the steady temperature which the calorimeter attains and then the rate of cooling when the current is switched off[82]. However, these methods give unsatisfactory results, and the best method would seem to be a modification of that used by BAGG and TOMPKINS[83]. In this[36], a metal film is evaporated on to the inside of the eggshell glass and used as a

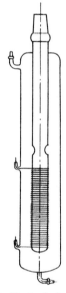

*Figure 16. Measurement of heats of adsorption on evaporated films*
By courtesy of Beeck, O., Cole, W. A. and Wheeler, A. *Disc. Faraday Soc.* **8**, 314, 1950

resistance heater. An electric current is passed either for a few seconds and the temperature rise noted, or until equilibrium is achieved, when the rate of cooling is followed on switching off the current.

Recent observations[36] have shown that certain precautions must be taken with film calorimeters. Many chemisorptions occur very rapidly, forming an immobile layer, in which case successive

D

adsorptions may not occur uniformly throughout the metal film. Because of the high rate of cooling and the poor thermal conductivity of the eggshell glass, the calorimeter does not reach a uniform temperature. It is essential, therefore, that the change in resistance of the platinum windings should be dependent only on the total quantity of heat liberated and not on its distribution in the calorimeter. This can only be achieved if the eggshell glass is strictly uniform in thickness and the platinum windings are accurately spaced.

## HEAT MEASUREMENTS USING FILAMENTS

Heats of chemisorption on filaments may be measured using the filament itself as the calorimeter. Knowing the mass and specific heat of the filament, the heat of adsorption may be calculated from the observed temperature rise. As with films, heats on filaments may only be measured for fast, irreversible adsorptions.

The apparatus used by ROBERTS[24] has already been illustrated in *Figure 12*. The method of measurement is to flash the filament, and then when its rate of cooling has dropped to an observable limit, a small known charge of gas is admitted. The liberation of the heat of adsorption causes an increase in the filament resistance, which is measured in a bridge circuit. From this, the temperature rise $\Delta T$ may be calculated, knowing the temperature coefficient of resistance of the filament. The heat liberated on adsorption is therefore $m \cdot s \cdot \Delta T$ where $m$ is the mass of the filament and $s$ the specific heat. The molar heat of chemisorption, $q$ is then

$$q = \frac{m \cdot s \cdot \Delta T}{n} \tag{2.4}$$

where $n$ is the amount of the charge, measured in moles.

More recently, KISLIUK[84] has measured the heat of adsorption of nitrogen on a tungsten ribbon by a similar technique to that used by Roberts, the main differences being in the use of ultra-high vacuum equipment and more sophisticated electronic controls.

## MEASUREMENT OF WORK FUNCTION CHANGES[85, 86]

The electron work function of a solid, $e\phi$, is defined as the work necessary to remove an electron from the highest occupied level inside the solid to a point in vacuo just outside its surface. It varies with the surface state of the solid because adsorption creates dipoles which alter the potential barrier through which the electron passes in escaping from the surface. If the negative end of the dipole produced on adsorption is directed away from the surface (electro-negative layer), $\phi$ is increased: if towards the surface (electropositive layer), it is decreased.

By considering the dipolar adsorbed layer as a parallel plate condenser, it may readily be shown that the potential drop across the layer is

$$\Delta V = 4\pi n_s \theta \mu \qquad (2.5)$$

where $n_s$ is the number of surface sites per cm², $\theta$ is the fraction of surface covered, and $\mu$ is the dipole moment of an adsorbed molecule. $e\Delta V$ is equal to the change in work function, $e\Delta\phi$, because it is the change in energy needed to remove an electron from the solid after forming the adsorbed layer. Thus

$$\Delta\phi = 4\pi n_s \theta \mu \qquad (2.6)$$

This equation is important because it allows $\mu$ to be calculated from $\Delta\phi$, provided $\theta$ is known. This in turn indicates whether the surface bonding is predominantly ionic, covalent or physical. It can also be seen that $\Delta\phi$ is directly proportional to $\theta$ only if $\mu$ is independent of $\theta$, and as shown in Table 1 this may be far from the case.

Even clean surfaces have electrical double layers associated with them because the asymmetric environment of the surface atoms produces an overall shift of the electronic charge relative to the positive nuclei[87]. Since, for crystalline materials, this double layer will vary with crystal face, there will be a variation in work function over any surface that exposes more than one face to the vacuum, and any experimental value will be some sort of average over the surface.

The investigation of work function changes has been of greatest importance in studying chemisorbed layers on metals. Methods of measurement may be divided into two groups: electron emission methods and condenser methods.

ELECTRON EMISSION METHODS

Electron emission may be induced by heating, by irradiation with light of suitable wavelength or by applying sufficiently strong electrical fields for electrons to tunnel through the potential barrier at the surface. When accelerating collector fields are employed, it is normally the work function change of the cathode that is measured, although if the collecting field is very small it is possible to measure the change in work function of the anode.

## (a) Thermionic saturation current method

For thermionic emission from a uniform surface, the saturation current density $j$ at a temperature $T$, extrapolated to zero applied field, is given by

$$j = A(1-\bar{r})\, T^2 \exp\,(-e\phi/kT) \qquad (2.7)$$

where $\bar{r}$ is the average reflection coefficient of electrons at the surface and $A$ is a universal constant equal to 120 amps/cm$^2$/$^\circ$K$^2$.

If $j$ is measured as a function of $T$ and $\ln(j/T^2)$ plotted against $1/T$, a straight line is usually obtained even though $\bar{r}$ may vary somewhat with temperature. The slope of this 'Richardson plot' is $-e\phi^*/k$, where $e\phi^*$ is known as the apparent work function.

The method is limited because the temperatures needed to obtain measurable emission currents destroy many adsorbed layers. This is particularly true of electronegative layers of high work function. It has proved very useful, however, for studying electropositive layers of alkali metals on tungsten[88]. Here the low work functions make emission possible at quite moderate temperatures (150 °C for Cs on W).

A suitable electrode assembly for use with metal filaments has been described by Becker[89].

## (b) Photoelectric method

If electron emission from a surface with work function, $e\phi$, is brought about by irradiation with light of variable frequency, $\nu$, there is no emission below a certain threshold frequency, $\nu_0$, given by

$$h\nu_0 = e\phi \qquad (2.8)$$

This relationship arises because the incident photons must have at least sufficient energy to impart to the electrons to enable them to overcome the potential barrier at the metal surface. At normal temperatures, however, the threshold is blurred because of the emission of thermally excited electrons with energies above the Fermi level. This considerably complicates the determination of photoelectric thresholds since a true threshold exists only at 0 °K. However, if the quantum yield $I$ (i.e. the number of electrons liberated per incident photon) is plotted against the frequency of the incident light a spectral distribution curve is obtained. For this Fowler[90] has derived the equation

$$\log\,(I/T^2) = B + F(x) \qquad (2.9)$$

where $B$ is a constant independent of $\nu$ and $F(x)$ is a universal function of $x$, $x$ being equal to $h(\nu - \nu_0)/kT$.

The procedure in finding $\nu_0$ is then to plot log $(I/T^2)$ against $h\nu/kT$. The resulting curve should be identical in shape with the theoretical plot of $F(x)$ against $x$ and coincide with it if moved horizontally by an amount $h\nu_0/kT$ and vertically by an amount $B$. The horizontal shift thus gives $\nu_0$ and hence the work function.

An alternative method is to plot $\sqrt{I}$ against the photon energy[91]. Normally a straight line is obtained for $(h\nu - e\phi) < 1\cdot0$ e.V., and its intercept on the $h\nu$-axis yields $e\phi$.

The photoelectric method suffers from two practical difficulties. First, photocurrents as low as $10^{-14}$ amp have to be measured accurately. Second, for $\phi > 5V$, $\nu_0$ lies in the far ultraviolet.

A suitable photocell for adsorption studies has been described by SUHRMANN and SACHTLER[92] and is shown in *Figure 17*. The

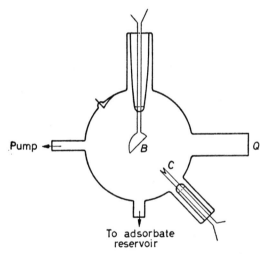

*Figure 17. Photocell for measuring the photoelectric work function*

By courtesy of Suhrmann, R. and Sachtler, W. M. H. *Proc. Intern. Symp. on Reactivity of Solids*, Gothenburg (1952), p. 601, 1954

cathode $B$ may be a metal foil, or an evaporated metal film deposited from the filament $C$, while a metal coating inside the cell serves as anode. Monochromatic light passes through the quartz window $Q$ and strikes the cathode $B$. Its energy can be measured by a calibrated photocell and the photoelectric yield obtained as a function of frequency.

*(c)  The field emission microscope*

The presence of a high external field $(3-6 \times 10^7$ V/cm) can reduce the width of the potential barrier at a metal surface to such an extent that electrons approaching the surface may well tunnel *through* the barrier and be emitted. This phenomenon is known as field emission and differs fundamentally from thermionic or photo-emission, where only electrons with sufficient energy to go *over* the barrier are emitted.

The attainment of the very high fields is possible only in the immediate vicinity of surfaces of high curvature. In the field emission microscope[93] the surface is in the form of a sharp tip with a radius of curvature of the order of 1,000 Å and is surrounded by a conducting fluorescent screen, as shown in *Figure 18a*. The field $F$ at the surface of the tip is related to the potential $V$ applied between it and the screen by

$$F = KV \qquad (2.10)$$

where $K$ is a constant depending mainly on the radius of curvature of the emitting surface. Electrons that have tunnelled through the potential barrier have very little kinetic energy and therefore follow the lines of force which diverge radially outwards from the tip (*Figure 18b*). Thus a highly magnified picture of the emission is obtained. Bright areas represent regions of low work function and dark areas represent regions of high work function.

The electron emission from the tip is described approximately by the Fowler–Nordheim equation[94]

$$i/V^2 = ab \, \exp \, (-6 \cdot 84 \times 10^7 (e\phi)^{3/2}/KV) \qquad (2.11)$$

where $i$ is the total current, $a$ is the emitting area and $b$ is equal to $6 \cdot 2 \times 10^6 K^2 (E_F/e\phi)^{\frac{1}{2}}/(E_F + e\phi)$. $e\phi$ refers to an 'average' work function for the whole surface, while $E_F$ is the energy distance of the Fermi level above the bottom of the band. The equation applies strictly only at $0\,^\circ$K but may be applied up to room temperature as field emission is almost independent of temperature in this range.

The slope of the plot of $\ln \, (i/V^2)$ against $1/V$ yields $(e\phi)^{3/2}/K$. Unfortunately $K$ is not normally known. However, if the work function, $e\phi_M$, of the clean metal is known, the change in work function upon adsorption, $e\Delta\phi$, can be calculated from

$$\Delta\phi = \phi_M \left[ \left( \frac{S_{ad}}{S_M} \right)^{2/3} - 1 \right] \qquad (2.12)$$

where $S_M$ and $S_{ad}$ are the slopes of the plots before and after adsorption[93].

Since the electrical double layer formed upon adsorption consists of discrete dipoles, the potential increment reaches its full value only at some distance from the surface. This slow build-up of potential lessens the barrier for tunnelling so that values of $\Delta\phi$ are slightly smaller than the true values[95].

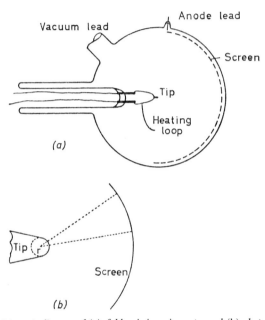

*Figure 18. Schematic diagram of* (a) *field-emission microscope, and* (b) *electron trajectories in a field-emission tube, showing mechanism of image formation*

By courtesy of Gomer, R. *Field Emission and Field Ionization.* Cambridge, Mass.; Harvard University Press, 1961

*(d) The space-charge limited diode*

When a small accelerating potential is applied between the anode and the cathode of a diode, the emission current is controlled by the negative space charge near the cathode surface. This is because the electrostatic barrier due to this charge is higher than the surface barrier. GYSAE and WAGENER[96] have shown that in this region the current collected by the anode depends mainly on the applied voltage, $V$, and on the mean anode work function, $e\phi_A$, and only slightly, if at all, on the work function of the cathode.

If current–voltage characteristics are plotted before and after adsorption of gas[86], as in *Figure 19*, there is a displacement along the voltage axis, $\Delta V$, equal to the change in $\phi_A$, $\Delta\phi_A$. This is because for a given current

$$V+\phi_A=(V+\Delta V)+(\phi_A+\Delta\phi_A) \qquad (2.13)$$

and therefore $-\Delta V=\Delta\phi_A$.

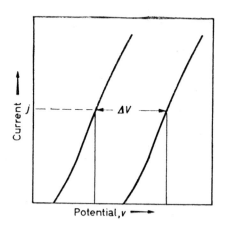

*Figure 19. Current–voltage curves obtained in the space-charge-limited diode*
By courtesy of Culver, R. V. and Tompkins, F. C. *Adv. in Catalysis* **11**, 67, 1959

Various forms of electrode assembly have been used[97–102]. The cathode is usually a tungsten filament maintained at a temperature above that at which adsorption occurs, so that its surface remains clean and therefore constant during the adsorption process. The anode may be a second filament[97–99, 102] or an evaporated metal film[100, 101].

CONDENSER METHODS

If two metals with work functions $e\phi_1$ and $e\phi_2$ are connected electrically through a circuit containing no source of e.m.f., the electrostatic potentials just outside the surfaces of the two metals are different. This potential difference, $V_{12}$, is known as the contact potential difference and arises because of the transfer of electrons from one metal to the other until, at equilibrium, the highest occupied levels in the two metals are equal. The origin of the contact potential difference is illustrated in *Figures 20a* and *20b*, where the metals are shown as the plates of a condenser. It can be seen that

$$V_{12} = \phi_2 - \phi_1 \qquad (2.14)$$

If a compensating potential, $V_a$, equal to $-V_{12}$, is applied across the plates the field between them will disappear, as shown in *Figure 20c*. The condenser methods measure the change in this potential during the adsorption of gas on one of the plates. The

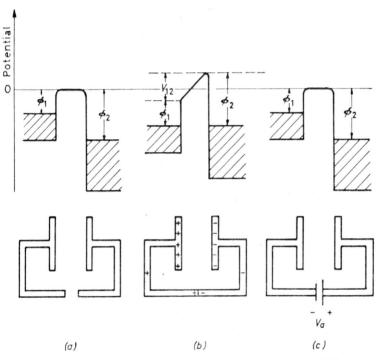

(a)                    (b)                    (c)

*Figure 20. Compensation of the contact potential by an applied voltage $V_a$[85]*

second plate is a reference electrode whose work function does not alter during adsorption. The change in contact potential is then equal to the change in work function of the other electrode. That is, $\Delta V_{12} = \Delta \phi$.

The disappearance of the electrical field between the two plates may be detected in two ways.

45

(a) *Vibrating condenser method*

When the field between the two surfaces is zero, no current is produced in the circuit connecting the plates on changing the capacity of the condenser. The capacity is usually changed by altering the distance between the electrodes. By vibrating one of these an a.c. signal is produced, which vanishes when the correct compensating potential is applied.

*Figure 21* shows a vibrating condenser cell used by MIGNOLET[103] It consists of a hollow glass tuning fork, the upper part of which is

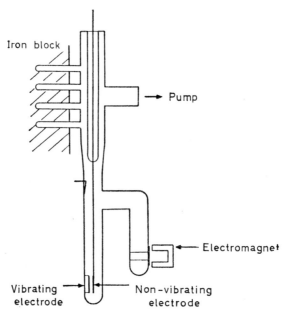

*Figure 21. Cell for contact potential difference measurement by the capacitor method*
By courtesy of Mignolet, J. C. P. *Disc. Faraday Soc.* **8**, 326, 1950

rigidly cemented into a metal block, while the two free ends are made to vibrate by an electromagnet. The vibrating capacitor plate is joined to the inside wall of one limb and the adjacent non-vibrating plate is fixed to the rigid part of the cell. The metal to be investigated is evaporated on to the vibrating plate from a filament (not shown), the other plate being shielded during this process.

## (b) Steady condenser method[104, 105]

With this method it is only possible to measure contact potential *changes*. The current flowing between the electrodes during the build-up of the adsorbed layer is used to regulate the compensating potential, the final value of which is equal to the change in contact potential. In the ideal case no charge would flow at all since the compensating potential and the contact potential difference would be exactly equal and opposite throughout.

This method has an advantage over the vibrating condenser method in that it avoids changing the capacity of the condenser, which is experimentally troublesome.

### 'AVERAGE' WORK FUNCTIONS

Since the work function varies with crystal face there will be contact potential differences between the various faces of the same metal, the areas of high work function becoming negatively charged with respect to those of low work function. The electrical fields arising between the areas of different work function are known as 'patch' fields. Most work function measurements are made on polycrystalline materials exposing a variety of crystal faces, and the effect of patch fields must therefore be considered.

At a distance from the surface which is large compared with the dimensions of the patches, the electrostatic potential $\Phi$ becomes constant and is equal to $\Sigma_i f_i \Phi_i$, where $f_i$ is the fraction of the surface occupied by patches of type $i$, and $\Phi_i$ is the electrostatic potential just outside them. The contact potential difference between two electrically connected metals, 1 and 2, both with patch surfaces and separated by a distance large compared with the patch dimensions is therefore given by

$$V = \Phi_1 - \Phi_2 = \bar{\phi}_2 - \bar{\phi}_1 \qquad (2.15)$$

where $\bar{\phi}_2$ and $\bar{\phi}_1$ are average values, equal to $\Sigma_i f_i \phi_i$, $e\phi_i$ being the work function of patches of type $i$. Hence the condenser methods measure changes in a true average work function upon adsorption.

In the electron emission methods the use of the emission equations (2.7), (2.9) and (2.11) is strictly correct only if the work function is constant over the whole emitting surface, and this is seldom the case. However, in practice the equations hold over small ranges of current for patch surfaces, and work functions can be obtained. Since the current is exponentially dependent on the work function, patches of low $\phi$ make contributions out of proportion to their area and the experimental value of $\phi$ is heavily weighted in favour of the

47

highly emitting, that is, the low work function regions. It is not a true average value.

For the calculation of average work function changes upon adsorption to have real meaning, the relative emission anisotropy of the surface before and after adsorption must remain unaltered and, as the field emission microscope demonstrates[106], this is only approximately true.

## MEASUREMENT OF ACCOMMODATION COEFFICIENTS

When a gas molecule at a temperature $T_1$ strikes a surface at a different temperature $T_2$, there is in general an energy interchange before the molecule leaves the surface. On departing, the molecule will therefore have a temperature $T_2'$ intermediate between $T_1$ and $T_2$. The accommodation coefficient, $a$, which is a measure of the extent of energy interchange, is then defined by

$$a = \frac{T_2' - T_1}{T_2 - T_1} \qquad (2.16)$$

The two extreme cases of no energy interchange $(T_2' = T_1)$ and complete equilibration $(T_2' = T_2)$ correspond respectively to $a=0$ and $a=1$. If $T_1$ and $T_2$ do not differ very greatly, $a$ is, to a good first approximation, independent of $(T_2 - T_1)$. It is, however, dependent on the absolute value of $T_2$.

Theory suggested [107] that for a monatomic gas striking a clean metal on which it is not adsorbed, $a$ should be about 0·05 when $T_1$ and $T_2$ are in the neighbourhood of room temperature. Early measurements however gave values around 0·3. The disagreement was shown by ROBERTS[24] to be due to the surfaces never having been properly cleaned, for when a contaminated tungsten filament was properly cleaned by flashing, the neon accommodation coefficient fell from 0·3 to about 0·08. $a$ therefore depends on the surface state, and measurement of the change in $a$ may be used to study adsorption.

The method has only been used with metals; in addition the method is only applicable to irreversible chemisorption. This is because $a$ is determined by measurement of the quantity of heat removed from the adsorbent by a small pressure of inert gas, and the method would be invalidated by an appreciable pressure of a second gas.

The experimental method is as follows[108]. A filament of diameter $d$ is placed axially in a cylindrical glass vessel whose temperature is

$T_1$ and is maintained electrically at a temperature $T_2$ slightly above $T_1$. A small pressure of neon is admitted, sufficiently low for the mean free path of the gas molecules to be much larger than $d$. It may then be shown that the heat loss from the wire by conduction to the gas, in calories/cm²/sec is

$$q^* = 1.74 \times 10^{-4} \frac{ap}{\sqrt{(MT_1)}} (T_2 - T_1) \qquad (2.17)$$

where $M$ is the molecular weight and $p$ is measured in dynes/cm². All the quantities in this equation except $a$ may be measured, and thus $a$ is determined.

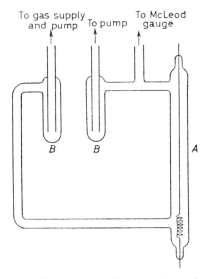

*Figure 22. The measurement of accommodation coefficients*
By courtesy of Miller, A. R. *The Adsorption of Gases on Solids* London; Cambridge
University Press, 1949

The apparatus[108] used by ROBERTS is shown in *Figure 22*. A tungsten filament of diameter 0·06 mm and length about 18 cm is contained in the tube $A$, and over it a pressure of about 0·1 mm neon is continuously circulated. Traces of oxygen are removed by charcoal in the liquid air traps $BB$: a further trap is placed between $A$ and the McLeod gauge. The filament is flashed to clean the surface and allowed to cool. It is then connected to a Wheatstone bridge, in which the current is sufficient to raise its temperature ($T_2$) some $20°$ above that of the oilbath ($T_1$) in which the tube $A$ is immersed. $T_2$ is obtained from the filament resistance. Under these conditions, the main heat loss is by conduction to the gas, radiation and end losses being small. After allowing for these, the heat supplied to the wire by the current is equal to $q^*$, and the accommodation coefficient can be calculated. A small quantity of adsorbate is then admitted, and the change in accommodation coefficient followed.

The method has been modified to investigate rates of adsorption and desorption. Initially, the velocities were measured qualitatively, but subsequently MORRISON and ROBERTS[25] succeeded, by observing the change in $a$ with time, in measuring the rate of the fast irreversible chemisorption of oxygen on tungsten.

A steady, partial pressure of oxygen between 2 and $5 \times 10^{-9}$ mm is maintained at the filament surface by allowing oxygen to diffuse into the circulating neon system through a fine capillary. The oxygen which is not adsorbed by the filament is taken up by the charcoal traps and the partial pressure of oxygen is obtained by calculation of the rates of flow of gas through the various parts of the system. The change in accommodation coefficient is assumed to be proportional to the amount adsorbed.

Even with the best vacuum conditions, accommodation coefficients slowly increased with time after flashing, presumably because of contamination. Values of $a$ for the clean surface were obtained by extrapolating back to zero time. For accurate extrapolation, measurements have to be taken within a few minutes of flashing and this is possible only if there is a rapid attainment of a thermal steady state. Correct design of reaction tube is important in this respect[109, 110].

Recently, evaporated films of aluminium have been used to remove active gases. Values of $a$ for helium on a clean tungsten surface were around 0·016 and showed little variation with temperature[111]. These results are in contrast with those of ROBERTS[112] who found that $a$ decreased with decreasing temperature, approaching 0·015 only at $70°$K. There is still some doubt, therefore, as to the cleanliness of Roberts' surfaces at the higher temperatures where it is more difficult to maintain adequate vacuum conditions.

A variation of the Roberts' method, due to BLODGETT and LANGMUIR[113], is to measure changes in the accommodation coefficient of gases which are themselves being adsorbed. The method is less powerful than the Roberts' method.

MEASUREMENT OF CHANGES IN ELECTRICAL CONDUCTIVITY

METALS

The adsorption of a gas on a metal may involve localization of electrons from the conduction band of the metal at the surface, or the adsorbate may contribute electrons to the conduction band. In either case the conductivity of the metal will alter. However, the change will be appreciable only if the surface-to-bulk ratio is large.

Strictly, measurements should be carried out on single crystals, but in practice this is difficult and thin evaporated metal films between 30 and 80 atom layers thick are normally used instead[114]. The metal is evaporated on to the walls of a bulb containing two platinum contacts and the film resistance between them measured. Films should be annealed rather above adsorption temperature as their resistance may otherwise alter slowly with time. As the films must be thin, and have to be annealed for some time, ultra-high vacuum techniques should be used, and outgassing should be particularly thorough. SACHTLER[115] has shown that the adsorption of hydrogen on thin films of nickel formed under moderate vacuum conditions causes an increase in conductivity, whereas on films deposited under high vacua there is a decrease.

The change in the number of conduction electrons per adsorbed atom can be calculated from the results only if certain rather doubtful assumptions are made[116]. Firstly, it must be assumed that the film is of uniform thickness and that grain boundary resistance is negligible. In fact, evaporated metal films are porous and their resistance may well be concentrated at crystallite contacts. The second assumption is that the only effect of chemisorption is to change the number of conduction electrons. However, gases with high heats of adsorption, such as oxygen, are known to cause considerable sintering of films even after they have been annealed[36], and this may well have an effect on the conducting properties of the film.

SEMI-CONDUCTORS

Methods of measuring changes in semi-conductivity have been discussed by GRAY[117], with special reference to oxides, and by LAW[118], with special reference to the elemental semi-conductors, silicon and germanium. With these materials, the surface electrical double layer penetrates the crystal to a considerable distance ($\sim 10^{-4}$ cm), and the mobility as well as the number of charge carriers in this region may be altered by adsorption processes. As a result, conductivity measurements alone are insufficient to determine quantitatively the extent of charge transfer across the surface.

For a simple $n$-type semi-conductor (see Chapter VIII) the conductivity increases on adsorption of gases which donate electrons to the surface layer and decreases on adsorption of gases which accept electrons. For $p$-type semi-conductors the conductivity changes are reversed. However, in the case of a dual nature semi-conductor, conductivity measurements do not determine even the direction of electron transfer. If the semi-conductor has, for example, $n$-type bulk conductivity, it cannot be assumed that the surface region is also $n$-type without confirmatory evidence. If the semi-conductor is intrinsic, adsorption of either donor or acceptor gases will lead to an increased conductivity. For these reasons conductivity measurements are often carried out in conjunction with measurements of other quantities, such as work functions or field effect mobilities.

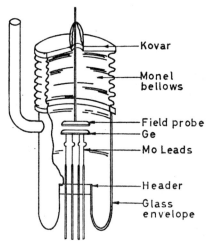

*Figure 23. A schematic diagram of an experimental tube used for measurement of the surface conductance and the field effect mobility*

By courtesy of Handler, P. *Semiconductor Surface Physics*. Philadelphia; University of Pennsylvania Press, 1957

Measurement of the d.c. resistance of semi-conductor powders may be of little significance, since the contact resistance between grains frequently determines the overall resistance[117]. Unfortunately much of the work on powders has ignored this effect. The problem may be overcome by making a.c. resistance measurements over a range of frequencies, the high frequency resistance approximating to that of the bulk material.

GRAY[119] has described a method for measuring the semi-conductivity of thin oxide films. The apparatus consists of a glass tube with two platinum electrodes fused to the inside of the glass and a means of depositing between these a uniform film of metal, which is then oxidized. The thickness of the metal film is obtained from its resistance, values between 1,200 and 2,000 Å proving most convenient. After oxidation, the film is outgassed, and adsorption followed by measurement of the resistance change.

With germanium and silicon, thin slices are often used, and to eliminate contact errors a four-point system is employed in which the current passes through the end leads and the potential drop is measured across the other two. It is also usual to measure the field effect mobility at the same time[120]: this is the change in conductivity of the sample produced by a field applied normal to its surface as shown in *Figure 23*. The field induces a charge on the semi-conductor surface: if this is positive the conductivity of a $p$-type surface increases, whereas the conductivity of an $n$-type surface decreases.

## MAGNETIC MEASUREMENTS

Chemisorption often involves the unpaired electrons in solids, with a consequent change in their magnetic properties. From these may be calculated the change in the number of unpaired electrons per adsorbed atom or molecule. Since the magnetic properties are bulk and not surface properties the surface/volume ratio must be high, otherwise the effect of adsorption is not detectable. For this reason magnetic measurements are nearly always carried out on fine powder samples.

In paramagnetic substances the relationship between the atomic or molecular moment, $\mu$, and the magnetic susceptibility per mole of substance, $\chi_M$, is

$$\mu = 2 \cdot 84 \sqrt{[\chi_M(T+\Delta)]} \tag{2.18}$$

where $T$ is the temperature and $\Delta$ is a constant[121].

For the transition metals $\mu$ is equal to $\sqrt{[n(n+2)]}$ where $n$ is the number of unpaired electrons per atom[121]. Hence, by making susceptibility measurements at a number of temperatures before and after chemisorption, the number of unpaired electron spins cancelled or created per adsorbed molecule may be obtained.

The necessity for a vacuum complicates susceptibility measurements. However, the Faraday method has been modified by

E

Selwood and his co-workers[121-124] for chemisorption work. In this method the force exerted on the sample in a non-uniform field is measured. If the field gradient is $\partial H/\partial s$ and $m$ is the mass of the sample, the force exerted is

$$f = m\chi H \partial H/\partial s \qquad (2.19)$$

This force is measured by the extension of a spiral spring, and the apparatus may be operated at any temperature from 20 °K to 1,200 °K.

With ferromagnetic materials the magnetic susceptibility is large and dependent on field strength. On the latter account the specific magnetization is often measured. This is equal to $\chi H$. However, it is more desirable to obtain the saturation magnetization, i.e. the magnetization at zero temperature and infinite field, since the saturation moment per atom, $\mu$, is directly equal to the number of unpaired electrons, $n$.

Since it is impossible to realize the saturation magnetization experimentally, extrapolation is necessary. The system[125] shown in *Figure 24* operates at field strengths up to 10,000 G and at temperatures down to 4·2 °K, magnetization being measured by moving the sample from one set of sensing coils to another set with the same number of turns wound in opposition. The current induced in the coils is measured by a ballistic galvanometer and is directly proportional to the specific magnetization of the sample. Extrapolations to infinite field are made from plots of magnetization versus $1/H$ or $1/H^2$ and a series of measurements is made before and after chemisorption.

For the system $H_2/Ni$ Dietz and Selwood[125] calculate that to a first approximation the number of electron spins cancelled per hydrogen atom, $\epsilon$, by pairing in the $d$-band, is given by

$$\epsilon = \left(\frac{\Delta M_0}{M_0}\right)\left(\frac{\mu_{Ni}\, N_{Ni}}{N_H}\right) \qquad (2.20)$$

where $\Delta M_0/M_0$ is the fractional change in the saturation magnetization due to adsorption of hydrogen, $\mu_{Ni}$ is the saturation moment of nickel per atom in Bohr magnetons, and $N_{Ni}/N_H$ is the ratio of the number of nickel atoms present in the sample to the number of hydrogen atoms chemisorbed.

RESONANCE METHODS

Although the potentialities of magnetic resonance techniques in chemisorption studies are considerable, little work has been done to date.

Nuclear magnetic resonance could be useful in the determination of the structure of adsorbents. The best nuclei for such studies are those with resultant spin $\frac{1}{2}$ but, unfortunately, the majority of transition metals, which are very active in chemisorption, are

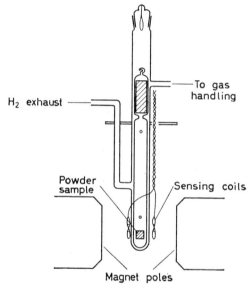

H₂ exhaust

To gas handling

Powder sample

Sensing coils

Magnet poles

*Figure 24. Schematic diagram of apparatus for measurements of magnetization*[125]

unfavourable[126]. An interesting study would be the determination of nuclear magnetic resonance spectra of adsorbed hydrogen, since the hydrogen nucleus has spin $\frac{1}{2}$. This would give information concerning the immediate environment of the proton in the surface.

Electron spin resonance has been applied to the adsorption of gases on carbon[127], and could be very useful in chemisorption studies on transition metals. From the area under the resonance peak the number of unpaired electrons in the sample can be calculated, and hence the change during chemisorption.

## INFRA-RED MEASUREMENTS[128]

Two types of band may be observed in the infra-red spectra of chemisorbed, molecules; one due to bonds within the adsorbed molecule itself and the other due to the bond between the adsorbate and the surface. Interest has tended to centre on the former, since by comparing such spectra with those of molecules and complexes of known structure it is possible actually to identify the adsorbed radicals.

Bands due to the surface bond have not often been observed[129, 130]. Whether this is because they occur at long wavelengths, outside the range of most investigations, or because of the special nature of the surface bond is not clear.

Since chemisorption results only in formation of a monolayer, the infra-red radiation must traverse many layers for the absorption bands to be detectable. This may be achieved in three ways:

(a) by transmission through a highly dispersed adsorbent.

(b) by multiple reflections.

(c) by a series of total internal reflections along a 'light pipe'.

TRANSMISSION METHODS

A schematic diagram of the type of cell used by EISCHENS and his co-workers[129] is shown in *Figure 25*. The sample is supported on a calcium fluoride plate which is placed in a quartz tube wound with tungsten wire to act as a heating element. The rest of the cell is made of Pyrex with calcium fluoride windows sealed to the two ends.

The samples usually consist of finely dispersed metals on supports of silica, alumina or titania. The support must have a small particle size to reduce losses of radiation by scattering. Cabosil ($SiO_2$) and Alon C ($\gamma Al_2O_3$), with particle sizes less than 200 Å, are suitable. The metal is deposited by treating the support with a solution of a metal salt, drying, transferring to the cell and reducing in hydrogen. The size of the metal particles is normally in the range 50–100 Å. If the size is much above 100 Å an excessive amount of radiation is lost by scattering.

It is an advantage if the partially dried powder is pressed into a disc before being placed in the cell, as the scattering is reduced, and the need for a supporting plate is eliminated.

The cell shown in *Figure 25* is unsuited to ultra-high vacuum work as the seals between the calcium fluoride windows and the cell body are normally made with glyptal resin, which will not withstand baking out at high temperatures. A further disadvantage is the long path length.

O'NEILL and YATES[131] have used a much improved cell with magnesium oxide windows sealed directly to soda glass. This cell can be baked out at 400 °C. Also, the sample holder can be moved magnetically in and out of the light beam so that it is possible to differentiate between bands due to adsorbed molecules and those due to molecules in the gas phase.

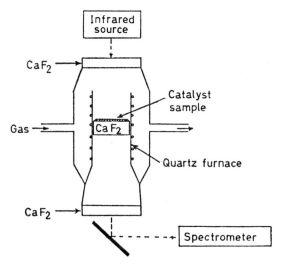

*Figure 25. Cell for infra-red study of chemisorbed gases*
By courtesy of Eischens, R. P. and Pliskin, W. A. *Adv. in Catalysis* **10**, 1, 1958

Even with good vacuum conditions it is doubtful whether metal surfaces produced in this way are completely free from impurity, and unfortunately it is difficult to obtain a sufficiently small particle size with evaporated metal films. However, this situation can be improved by evaporation in a small pressure of inert gas or by evaporating a support material such as $CaF_2$ at the same time as the metal. Bands for the adsorption of carbon monoxide on a number of transition metals have been obtained with the latter technique[132].

REFLECTION METHODS

An advantage of reflection methods over transmission methods is that the spectra of molecules adsorbed on bulk metal can be studied. However, the absorption for one reflection is unlikely to exceed 0·5 per cent of the incident intensity and this is below the noise level in conventional spectrometers. Hence multiple reflection methods are necessary, together with techniques for increasing the sensitivity of the spectrometer.

PICKERING and ECKSTROM[133] evaporated films of nickel and rhodium on to the mirrors of a multiple reflection system in a vacuum cell. Even with 15–35 reflections the bands due to chemisorbed molecules corresponded to only 1 per cent absorption.

### TOTAL INTERNAL REFLECTION METHOD

This method is suitable only for optically transparent media and has not yet been used in chemisorption although it has potentialities in the study of adsorbed gases on semi-conductors[134]. It involves using a series of total internal reflections inside a specially shaped adsorbent. As each reflection is total, the number is limited only by absorption in the medium itself. The angle of incidence of the beam must not of course be less than the critical angle, otherwise the beam is lost. Since, as Maxwell's theory predicts, the totally reflected beam penetrates into the rarer medium, the beam is sensitive to adsorbed layers on the surface.

### ELECTRON DIFFRACTION

Electron waves are more powerfully diffracted by crystals than X-rays, and consequently give patterns due to the surface layers. The method is, therefore, well suited to the investigation of adsorbed layers. Since chemisorption is normally localized at definite sites in the crystal surface, the layer will have a structure related to but somewhat different from the underlying crystal, and the diffraction patterns will arise from interference of the radiation from the two lattices as well as from the supporting crystal alone.

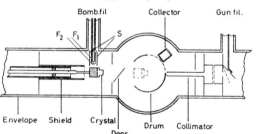

*Figure 26. Electron diffraction tube for chemisorption studies*
By courtesy of Farnsworth, H. E., *et al. J. Appl. Phys.* **29**, 1150, 1958

A major difficulty with the method is in obtaining clean, single crystal faces. This subject has been dealt with at some length earlier in the chapter.

An electron diffraction tube, developed for adsorption studies by FARNSWORTH and his co-workers[135], is shown in *Figure 26*. It consists essentially of an electron gun, a crystal target and an electron collector. Electrons of controlled energy strike the crystal face at normal incidence, and the diffracted electrons are picked up by a Faraday collector which can be rotated about a drum by remote magnetic control. Further, the crystal itself can be rotated about the axis of the incident beam so that scattering in all directions is covered.

During cleaning, the crystal is withdrawn into the side tube and outgassed for many hours by electron bombardment from the filament $F_2$ and by conduction heating. This is followed by a series of ion bombardments and anneals until the electron diffraction pattern shows the surface to be clean.

For a complete analysis of the surface the collector current must be measured as a function of three variables; the energy of the incident electrons, the angle between the incident and diffracted beams, and the azimuthal angle, which is the orientation of the crystal face with respect to the plane made by the two beams. It is important to vary the beam energy as this determines the depth of penetration of the electrons into the crystal and helps to give, as it were, a three dimensional view of the surface. Normally, for any one crystal face, there will be at least two azimuths in which well developed diffraction patterns are observed.

FARNSWORTH et al.[15] have developed an automatic scanning and recording mechanism for taking the readings for any one azimuth. Even so the total data for one azimuth takes 12 hours to record and there must be some doubt concerning the cleanliness of these surfaces after such a long period.

For certain azimuthal orientations there will be rows of surface atoms at right angles to the plane containing the incident and diffracted beams. If the separation of the rows is $d$ the condition for diffraction maxima is

$$n\lambda = d \sin \theta \qquad (2.21)$$

where the symbols have their usual significance. This leads to the equation

$$V = \frac{150n^2}{d^2 \sin^2 \theta} \qquad (2.22)$$

where $V$ is the energy of the electron beam in electron-volts and $d$ is in Angstroms.

Normally, collector current is plotted against beam energy for each collector angle[15], as shown in *Figure 27*. From a series of these plots the position of diffraction maxima may be obtained as a function of collector angle and beam energy.

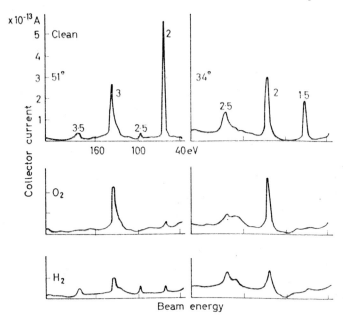

*Figure 27. Diffraction maxima in the (001) azimuth of a germanium surface. Representative curves obtained after cleaning, exposure to $O_2$ and exposure to $H_2$, for collector angles of 51° and 34°. Numbers next to the peaks are the orders of reflection from the surface grating*

By courtesy of Schlier, R. E. and Farnsworth, H. E. *Semiconductor Surface Physics* (Ed. Kingston) Philadelphia; University of Pennsylvania Press, 1957

On adsorption the relative intensities and positions of the diffraction maxima may change and from this it is possible to obtain information concerning the positions of the adsorbed molecules on the surface.

Recently, GERMER and his co-workers[136] have developed an ultra-high vacuum diffraction tube in which the diffracted electrons are accelerated by a potential difference of 3–4 kV, impinge on a fluorescent screen and can be photographed.

## SURFACE DIFFUSION STUDIES WITH THE FIELD
### EMISSION MICROSCOPE

The field emission microscope has been used not only in measuring changes in work function on adsorption, but also in studying surface diffusions[106]. The gas to be investigated is evaporated on to one side of the tip, altering the emission characteristics in this region. On heating the tip the ensuing surface diffusion can be followed visually.

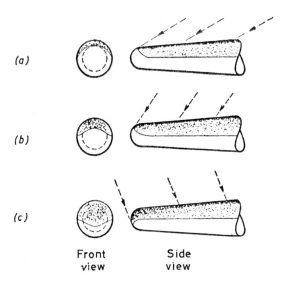

(a)

(b)

(c)

Front view    Side view

Figure 28.   Deposit geometrics. (a) Beam from source misses emitting portion of tip (dotted circle in front view), (b) Source slightly aft of tip, (c) Source ahead of tip
By courtesy of Gomer, R., Wortman, R. and Lundy, R. *J. Chem. Phys.* **26**, 1147, 1957

A sealed-off field-emission tube is immersed in liquid helium or hydrogen and the tip is cleaned by flashing. Gas is then produced from an electrically heated source. Since all gases have high sticking coefficients on the glass walls at very low temperatures, only those portions of the tip 'visible' to the gas source receive a deposit, as shown in *Figure 28*. *Figure 29* shows a field-emission tube suitable for surface diffusion studies, incorporating a universal gas source[137].

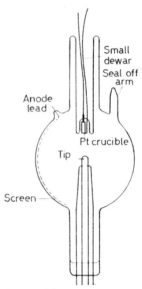

*Figure 29. Schematic diagram of field-emission tube for surface diffusion studies*

The tube is sealed off with 10–30 mm of gas in it and the small Dewar shown is filled with the refrigerant. After all the gas has been condensed in the platinum crucible, the whole bulb is cooled and the gas evaporated on to the tip as required.

REFERENCES

[1] Beebe, R. A. and Dowden, D. A. *J. Amer. Chem. Soc.* **60**, 2912, 1938

[2] Garner, W. E., Gray, T. J. and Stone, F. S. *Proc. Roy. Soc.* A**197**, 294, 1949

[3] Bosworth, R. C. L. *Trans. Faraday Soc.* **35**, 397, 1939

[4] Eggleton, A. E. J. and Tompkins, F. C. *Trans. Faraday Soc.* **48**, 738, 1952

[5] Langmuir, I. *J. Chem. Soc.* 511, 1940

[6] Garner, W. E. and Veal, F. J. *J. Chem. Soc.* 1487, 1935

[7] Anderson, R. B. and Emmett, P. H. *J. Phys. Chem.* **56**, 753, 1952

[8] Kummer, J. T. and Emmett, P. H. *J. Phys. Chem.* **55**, 337, 1951

[9] Taylor, H. S. *Disc. Faraday Soc.* **8**, 9, 1950

[10] Barrer, R. M. *J. Chem. Soc.* 378, 1934

[11] Barrer, R. M. and Rideal, E. K. *Proc. Roy. Soc.* A**149**, 231, 1935

[12] Frankenburg, W. G. *J. Amer. Chem. Soc.* **66**, 1827, 1944

[13] Couper, A. and Eley, D. D. *Disc. Faraday Soc.* **8**, 172, 1950

[14] Farkas, A. and Farkas, L. *Trans. Faraday Soc.* **31**, 821, 1935

[15] Schlier, R. E. and Farnsworth, H. E. in *Semiconductor Surface Physics* (ed. R. H. Kingston) Philadelphia; University of Pennsylvania Press, 1957, p. 3

[16] Farnsworth, H. E., Schlier, R. E. and Dillon, J. A. *J. Phys. Chem. Solids* **8**, 116, 1959

[17] Langmuir, I. and Kingdon, K. H. *Phys. Rev.* **22**, 148, 1923

[18] Oatley, C. W. *Proc. Phys. Soc.* **51**, 318, 1939

[19] Farnsworth, H. E., Schlier, R. E., George, T. H. and Burger, R. M. *J. Appl. Phys.* **26**, 252, 1955

[20] Schlier, R. E. and Farnsworth, H. E. *J. Chem. Phys.* **30**, 917, 1959

[21] Schlier, R. E. and Farnsworth, H. E. *Adv. in Catalysis* **9**, 434, 1957

[22] Farnsworth, H. E. and Tuul, J. *J. Phys. Chem. Solids* **9**, 48, 1959

[23] Autler, S. H. and McWhorter, A. L. in *Semiconductor Surface Physics* (ed. R. H. Kingston) Philadelphia; University of Pennsylvania Press, 1957, p. 47

[24] Roberts, J. K. *Proc. Roy. Soc.* A**152**, 445, 1935

[25] Morrison, J. L. and Roberts, J. K. *Proc. Roy. Soc.* A**173**, 1, 1939

[26] Gomer, R. *J. Chem. Phys.* **21**, 293, 1953

[27] Allen, F. G., Eisinger, J., Hagstrum, H. D. and Law, J. T. *J. Appl. Phys.* **30**, 1563, 1959

[28] Farkas, A. *Trans. Faraday Soc.* **32**, 416, 1936

[29] Beeck, O., Smith, A. E. and Wheeler, A. *Proc. Roy. Soc.* A**177**, 62, 1940

[30] Allen, J. A. *Revs. Pure and Appl. Chem. (Australia)* **4**, 133, 1954

[31] Brennan, D., Hayward, D. O. and Trapnell, B. M. W. *J. Phys. Chem. Solids* **14**, 117, 1960

[32] Trapnell, B. M. W. *Proc. Roy. Soc.* A**218**, 566, 1953

[33] Greenhalgh, E. and Trapnell, B. M. W. *Adv. in Catalysis* **9**, 238, 1957

[34] Bell, A. E., Pritchard, J. and Sykes, K. W. *Nature, Lond.* **191**, 487, 1961

[35] Porter, A. S. and Tompkins, F. C. *Proc. Roy. Soc.* A**217**, 544, 1953

[36] Brennan, D., Hayward, D. O. and Trapnell, B. M. W. *Proc. Roy. Soc.* A**256**, 81, 1960

[37] Allen, J. A. and Mitchell, J. W. *Disc. Faraday Soc.* **8**, 309, 1950

[38] Wheeler, A. in *Structure and Properties of Solid Surfaces* (eds. R. Gomer and C. S. Smith) Chicago; University of Chicago Press, 1952, p. 439

[39] Hickmott, T. W. and Ehrlich, G. *J. Phys. Chem. Solids* **5**, 47, 1958

[40] Hayward, D. O.—Unpublished results

[41] Green, M., Kafalas, J. A. and Robinson, P. H. in *Semiconductor Surface Physics* (ed. R. H. Kingston) Philadelphia; University of Pennsylvania Press, 1957, p. 349

[42] Tamaru, K. *J. Phys. Chem.* **61**, 647, 1957

[43] Venema, A. *Vacuum* **9**, 54, 1959

[44] Alpert, D. *J. Appl. Phys.* **24**, 860, 1953

[45] Redhead, P. A. *Can. J. Phys.* **36**, 255, 1958

[46] Alpert, D. and Buritz, R. S. *J. Appl. Phys.* **25**, 202, 1954

[47] Gomer, R., Wortman, R. and Lundy, R. *J. Chem. Phys.* **26**, 1147, 1957

[48] Law, J. T. *J. Phys. Chem.* **59**, 543, 1955

[49] Bennett, M. J. and Tompkins, F. C. *Trans. Faraday Soc.* **58**, 816, 1962

[50] Schlier, R. E. *J. Appl. Phys.* **29**, 1162, 1958

[51] Becker, J. A., Becker, E. J. and Brandes, R. G. *J. Appl. Phys.* **32**, 411, 1961

[52] Porter, A. S. *Disc. Faraday Soc.* **8**, 358, 1950

[53] Rideal, E. K. and Trapnell, B. M. W. *Proc. Roy. Soc.* A**205**, 409, 1951

[54] Becker, J. A. and Hartman, C. D. *J. Phys. Chem.* **57**, 153, 1953

[55] Ehrlich, G. *J. Chem. Phys.* **34**, 29, 1961

[56] Hickmott, T. W. *J. Chem. Phys.* **32**, 810, 1960

[57] Eisinger, J. *J. Chem. Phys.* **30**, 412, 1959

[58] Ehrlich, G. *J. Chem. Phys.* **34**, 39, 1961

[59] Hickmott, T. W. *J. Appl. Phys.* **31**, 128, 1960

[60] Rhodin, T. J. *J. Amer. Chem. Soc.* **72**, 4343, 1950

[61] McBain, J. W. and Bakr, A. M. *J. Amer. Chem. Soc.* **48**, 690, 1926

[62] McBain, J. W. and Tanner, H. G. *Proc. Roy. Soc.* A**125**, 579, 1929

[63] Gulbransen, E. A. *Rev. Sci. Instr.* **15**, 201, 1944

[64] Barrett, H. M., Birnie, A. W. and Cohen, M. *J. Amer. Chem. Soc.* **62**, 2839, 1940

[65] Dillon, J. A. and Farnsworth, H. E. *J. Chem. Phys.* **22**, 1601, 1954

[66] Crowell, A. D. *J. Chem. Phys.* **32**, 1576, 1960

[67] Brunauer, S., Emmett, P. H. and Teller, E. *J. Amer. Chem. Soc.* **60**, 309, 1938

[68] Hill, T. L. *Adv. in Catalysis* **4**, 211, 1952

[69] Harkins, W. D. and Jura, G. *J. Amer. Chem. Soc.* **66**, 1362, 1944

[70] Beebe, R. A., Beckwith, J. B. and Honig, J. M. *J. Amer. Chem. Soc.* **67**, 1554, 1945

[71] Rosenberg, A. J. *J. Amer. Chem. Soc.* **78**, 2929, 1956

[72] Livingstone, H. K. *J. Colloid Sci.* **4**, 447, 1949

[73] Dewar, J. *Proc. Roy. Soc.* A**74**, 122, 1904

[74] Favre, P. A. *Ann. Chim. Phys.* **1**, 209, 1874

[75] Marshall, M. J. and Bramston-Cook, H. E. *J. Amer. Chem. Soc.* **51**, 2019, 1929

[76] Sachse, H. *Z. physik. Chem.* A**143**, 94, 1929

[77] Gregg, S. J. *J. Chem. Soc.* 1494, 1927

[78] Bull, H. I., Hall, M. H. and Garner, W. E. *J. Chem. Soc.* 837, 1931

[79] Garner, W. E. and Veal, F. J. *J. Chem. Soc.* 1436, 1935

[80] Beebe, R. A., Biscoe, J., Smith, N. P. and Wendell, C. B. *J. Amer. Chem. Soc.* **69**, 96, 1947

[81] Beeck, O., Cole, W. A. and Wheeler, A. *Disc. Faraday Soc.* **8**, 314, 1950

[82] Wahba, M. and Kemball, C. *Trans. Faraday Soc.* **49**, 1351, 1953

[83] Bagg, J. and Tompkins, F. C. *Trans. Faraday Soc.* **51**, 1071, 1955

[84] Kisliuk, P. *J. Chem. Phys.* **31**, 1605, 1959

[85] Eberhagen, A. *Fortschr. Phys.* **8**, 245, 1960

[86] Culver, R. V. and Tompkins, F. C. *Adv. in Catalysis* **11**, 67, 1959

[87] Herring, C. and Nichols, M. H. *Rev. Mod. Phys.* **21**, 185, 1949

[88] Reimann, A. L. *Thermionic Emission* London; Chapman and Hall, 1934, Chapter III

[89] Becker, J. A. *Adv. in Catalysis* **7**, 135, 1955

[90] Fowler, R. H. *Phys. Rev.* **38**, 45, 1931

[91] Eisinger, J. *J. Chem. Phys.* **29**, 1154, 1958

[92] Suhrmann, R. and Sachtler, W. M. H. *Proc. Intern. Symposium on Reactivity of Solids, Gothenburg (1952)*, 1954, p. 601

[93] Gomer, R. *Field Emission and Field Ionization*. Cambridge, U.S.A.; Harvard University Press, 1961, Chapter II

[94] Fowler, R. H. and Nordheim, L. W. *Proc. Roy. Soc.* A**119**, 173, 1928

[95] Gomer, R. *J. Chem. Phys.* **21**, 1869, 1953

[96] Gysae, B. and Wagener, S. *Z. tech. Physik.* **19**, 264, 1938; *Z. Physik.* **115**, 296, 1940

[97] Langmuir, I. and Kingdon, K. H., *Phys. Rev.* **34**, 129, 1929

[98] Reimann, A. L. *Phil. Mag.* **20**, 594, 1935

[99] Bosworth, R. C. L. and Rideal, E. K. *Proc. Roy. Soc.* A**162**, 1, 1937

[100] Mignolet, J. C. P. *Rec. Trav. chim.* **74**, 685, 1955

[101] Culver, R. V., Pritchard, J. and Tompkins, F. C. in *Surface Activity* Vol. 2 (ed. J. H. Schulman) New York; Academic Press, 1958, p. 243

[102] Jones, P. L. and Pethica, B. A. *Proc. Roy. Soc.* A**256**, 454, 1960

[103] Mignolet, J. C. P. *Disc. Faraday Soc.* **8**, 326, 1950

[104] Eberhagen, A., Jaeckel, R. and Strier, F. *Z. angew. Phys.* **11**, 131, 1959

[105] Delchar, T. A., Eberhagen, A. and Tompkins, F. C. *J. Sci. Instr.* **40**, 105, 1963

[106] Gomer, R. *Field Emission and Field Ionization*. Cambridge, U.S.A.; Harvard University Press, 1961, Chapter IV

[107] Jackson, J. M. *Proc. Camb. Phil. Soc.* **28**, 136, 1932

[108] Miller, A. R. *The Adsorption of Gases on Solids*. London; Cambridge University Press, 1949

[109] Eggleton, A. E. J., Tompkins, F. C. and Wanford, D. W. B. *Proc. Roy. Soc.* A**213**, 266, 1952

[110] Bremner, J. G. M. *Proc. Roy. Soc.* A**201**, 305, 1950

[111] Thomas, L. B. and Schofield, E. B. *J. Chem. Phys.* **23**, 861, 1955

[112] Roberts, J. K. *Proc. Roy. Soc.* A**142**, 518, 1933

[113] Blodgett, K. B. and Langmuir, I. *Phys. Rev.* **40**, 78, 1932

[114] Suhrmann, R. *Adv. in Catalysis* **7**, 303, 1955

[115] Sachtler, W. M. H. *J. Chem. Phys.* **25**, 751, 1956

[116] Ehrlich, G. *J. Chem. Phys.* **35**, 2165, 1961

[117] Gray, T. J. in *Chemistry of the Solid State* (ed. W. E. Garner). London; Butterworths, 1955, p. 123.

[118] Law, J. T. in *Semiconductors* (ed. N. B. Hannay). New York; Reinhold, 1959, p. 676

[119] Gray, T. J. *Proc. Roy. Soc.* A**197**, 314, 1949

[120] Handler, P. in *Semiconductor Surface Physics* (ed. R. H. Kingston). Philadelphia; University of Pennsylvania Press, 1957, p. 23

[121] Selwood, P. W. *Adv. in Catalysis* **3**, 27, 1951

[122] Jacobson, P. E. and Selwood, P. W. *J. Amer. Chem. Soc.* **76**, 2641, 1954

[123] Sabatka, J. A. and Selwood, P. W. *J. Amer. Chem. Soc.* **77**, 5799, 1955

[124] Moore, L. E. and Selwood, P. W. *J. Amer. Chem. Soc.* **78**, 697, 1956

[125] Dietz, R. E. and Selwood, P. W. *J. Chem. Phys.* **35**, 270, 1961

[126] O'Reilly, D. E. *Adv. in Catalysis* **12**, 31, 1960

[127] Ingram, D. J. E. in *Chemisorption* (ed. W. E. Garner). London; Butterworths, 1957, p. 260

[128] Crawford, V. *Quart. Rev.* **14**, 378, 1960

[129] Eischens, R. P. and Pliskin, W. A. *Adv. in Catalysis* **10**, 1, 1958

[130] Pliskin, W. A. and Eischens, R. P. *Z. phys. Chem. (Frankfurt)* **24**, 11, 1960

[131] O'Neill, C. E. and Yates, D. J. C. *J. Phys. Chem.* **65**, 901, 1961

[132] Eberhagen, A., Hayward, D. O. and Tompkins, F. C.—To be published

[133] Pickering, H. L. and Eckstrom, H. C. *J. Phys. Chem.* **63**, 512, 1959

[134] Harrick, N. J. *J. Phys. Chem.* **64**, 1110, 1960

[135] Farnsworth, H. E., Schlier, R. E., George, T. H. and Burger, R. M. *J. Appl. Phys.* **29**, 1150, 1958

[136] Germer, L. H. *Adv. in Catalysis* **13**, 191, 1962

[137] Gomer, R. *J. Chem. Phys.* **28**, 168, 1958

# III

# VELOCITIES OF ADSORPTION

I T is convenient to consider the more qualitative aspects of adsorption velocities before giving a detailed, quantitative account of them. Consequently, this chapter has been divided into two main sections. The first classifies the different adsorbate–adsorbent combinations qualitatively according as adsorption is (*a*) fast and non-activated, (*b*) slow and activated, (*c*) so slow as to be undetectable in a reasonable length of time or (*d*) thermodynamically not feasible. The second gives a fairly detailed quantitative account of the various experimental kinetics and of the theories that can explain them.

## QUALITATIVE TREATMENT

### THE THEORY OF ACTIVATED ADSORPTION

Early investigations of adsorption used powder surfaces and appeared to show that many solids adsorbed the same gas in different ways at different temperatures. Two kinds of evidence pointed to this conclusion. The first was that the magnitude of the heat of adsorption often varied greatly with the temperature. For example DEWAR[1] found that the heat of oxygen adsorption on charcoal at liquid air temperatures was 3·75 kcal/mole, whereas for adsorption at 0°C, several investigators[2, 3] have recorded heats in the neighbourhood of 80 kcal/mole. The second kind of evidence arose from the study of adsorption isobars. If only one type of adsorption operates, the quantity adsorbed at constant pressure will fall continuously with increasing temperature: if two or more kinds operate in different temperature ranges the adsorption may increase with temperature between these ranges, and the isobar show maxima and minima. A typical example is illustrated in *Figure 6*. Such isobars have been observed with almost all adsorptions studied on powders and foils. The first recorded examples are for the adsorption of oxygen and carbon monoxide on platinum foil[4].

A simple explanation of these phenomena is that the low temperature adsorptions, which are limited to temperatures near the boiling point of the gas concerned and are associated with low heat changes, are reversible physical adsorption, while the higher temperature adsorptions with the high heats are chemisorption. This was first suggested by LANGMUIR[4], and subsequently in more explicit form by TAYLOR[5]. It is Taylor in particular who emphasized that as chemisorption seemed to proceed to a measurable extent only above certain minimum temperatures, it must involve an appreciable activation energy.

Taylor and his co-workers have aimed at showing that adsorption isobars in general show maxima and minima, with the higher temperature adsorption proceeding with an activation energy, and with a heat too large for physical adsorption. Work by TAYLOR and WILLIAMSON[6] on various manganous oxides exemplifies the method. Pure manganous oxide shows no hydrogen adsorption at 0 °C, but at 184 °C and above there are slow activated uptakes of gas. The activation energies increase with increasing adsorbed amount from 12·4 kcal/mole for the initial adsorption to 20·8 kcal/mole for the largest adsorptions. With a mixed manganous-chromic oxide, heats of hydrogen adsorption were obtained from isotherms using the Clausius–Clapeyron equation. At liquid air temperatures, the heat of adsorption is 1·9 kcal/mole and adsorption is therefore physical, while from isotherms between 305 and 440 °C, heats amounting to 19 kcal/mole were obtained, showing that chemisorption takes place. With this oxide, carbon monoxide chemisorption is also activated.

Precisely similar results to these have been recorded with a number of gases on a variety of powder surfaces[7], and differences between adsorbents are of degree rather than kind. With the metals, activated adsorptions of hydrogen have been reported on Cu, Ni, Fe and W: of oxygen on Ag and Au: of carbon monoxide on Pd, Fe and Cu: of nitrogen on Fe and W, and of hydrocarbons on many metals.

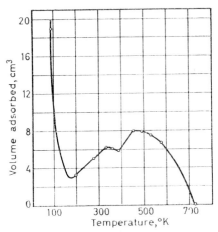

*Figure 30. Adsorption isobar of hydrogen on* ZnO *at 760 mm pressure*
By courtesy of Taylor, H. S. and Strother, C.O. *J. Amer. Chem. Soc.* **56**, 586, 1934

With the oxides, activated adsorptions of hydrogen have been recorded on ZnO, $Cr_2O_3$, $Al_2O_3$, $V_2O_3$ and many mixed oxides, of carbon monoxide on mixed zinc-molybdenum and manganese-chromium oxides, of water on alumina, and of ethylene on $Cr_2O_3$.

With ZnO[8] and with certain iron catalysts[9], the hydrogen isobar showed two minima and two maxima, as shown in *Figures 30* and *31*.

69

This suggested that two different kinds of activated chemisorption operate on these surfaces, and the two types were shown to behave differently in catalytic reactions[10, 11]. With zinc oxide[10] the activation energy of chemisorption lay between 3 and 6 kcal/mole for the

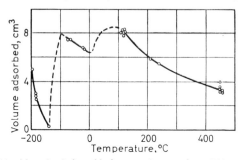

*Figure 31. Adsorption isobar of hydrogen on iron powder at 760 mm pressure*
By courtesy of Emmett, P. H. and Harkness, R. W. *J. Amer. Chem. Soc.* **57**, 1631, 1935

adsorption between 0 and 110 °C, and between 8 and 15 kcal/mole for the adsorption above 180 °C.

CRITICISMS OF THEORY

As early as 1932, the activated adsorption theory had been questioned on two grounds. The first doubt arose from work by WARD on the adsorption of hydrogen on copper[12]. In this work, an extremely rapid adsorption was observed at 0 °C followed by a slow uptake. The heat of the rapid adsorption was 10 kcal/mole, and the process therefore chemisorption: the speed of adsorption indicated that the activation energy was exceedingly low.

The extent of the slow uptake was found to be proportional to the square root of the time, and this relationship Ward showed to be characteristic of a diffusion or solution process. Thus, slow processes may in certain cases be absorption, not adsorption, and chemisorption may be extremely rapid at quite moderate temperatures.

The second criticism of the Taylor viewpoint was made by ALLMAND and CHAPLIN[13], who suggested that what was then the conventional technique for cleaning powders, namely to outgas and reduce them at temperatures of 500 °C, was inadequate. The surfaces might therefore have been contaminated with oxygen, and slow processes, particularly with hydrogen, carbon monoxide and hydrocarbons, might be due to reaction with initial contamination or displacement of it. Allmand and Chaplin actually showed that during slow 'adsorptions' of various hydrocarbons on charcoal, oxides of carbon, which had been displaced from the surface, appeared in the gas phase.

Slow effects at imperfectly cleaned powder surfaces may, therefore, be due to contamination.

Similar effects arise when an adsorption is studied on a deliberately dirtied film or filament. SCHUIT and DE BOER[14] have found that when a carefully cleaned nickel powder is deliberately contaminated with oxygen, there are slow adsorptions of hydrogen, the extent of which increase roughly linearly with the amount of prior oxygen contamination. On clean tungsten filaments and nickel films, hydrogen chemisorption is rapid and apparently non-activated, but at an oxygenated surface there is a considerable slow uptake of hydrogen[15, 16]. TRAPNELL[17] has found that clean potassium and silver films do not chemisorb hydrogen at all at room temperatures or below, but that oxygenated films take up hydrogen slowly. Silver films show an identical effect with ethylene.

A third criticism of the Taylor theory is that in the low temperature region, where adsorption was thought to be wholly physical, chemisorption is now known to operate. For example, in the adsorption of hydrogen on $Cr_2O_3$ at liquid air temperatures, *Figure* 7 shows the heat to be rather too large for physical adsorption[18], and the oxide has been found to catalyse $H_2/D_2$ exchange even at $-195°C$,

$$H_2 + D_2 \rightarrow 2HD$$

indicating that chemisorption as atoms must be taking place[19, 20]. Iron powders[11] likewise catalyse $H_2/D_2$ exchange at $-195°C$.

Modern investigations of chemisorption arise from these criticisms of the older work. Many of them have been carried out with clean metal filaments and evaporated films. These, in addition to presenting pure surfaces, do not appear to dissolve gas in large quantities.

### CHEMISORPTION ON CLEAN METAL FILAMENTS

The first studies of fast chemisorption on clean metal surfaces are due to ROBERTS[15], who used a flashed tungsten filament as adsorbent. He followed the adsorption of hydrogen, oxygen and nitrogen both volumetrically and by measurement of the change in the neon accommodation coefficient.

Previous workers had found the chemisorption of hydrogen and nitrogen on tungsten powders, outgassed and reduced at $750°C$, to be strongly activated[21, 22]. The hydrogen isobar showed a minimum at 75 °C and a maximum at 150 °C, while with nitrogen there was no adsorption at all at 0 °C and very little at 100 °C.

The results with the filament were entirely different. First, when a small charge of hydrogen, sufficient to fill the apparatus to a pressure of 4 . $10^{-4}$ mm, was admitted to the filament at either room temperature or liquid air temperature, the accommodation coefficient rose rapidly, as shown in *Figure 32*, and achieved a steady

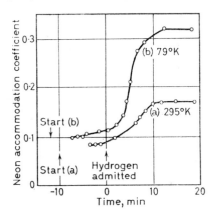

*Figure 32. Hydrogen adsorption on a tungsten filament*
By courtesy of Roberts, J. K. *Proc. Roy. Soc.* **A152**, 445, 1935

value in a few minutes. After this no further change took place, that is, there were no slow adsorptions. Moreover, when the equilibrium hydrogen pressure was increased from 3 . $10^{-4}$ to 3 . $10^{-3}$ mm there was no further rise in accommodation coefficient, suggesting that the adsorbed layer was saturated at these very low pressures.

In order to decide whether the rapid adsorption was chemical or physical in nature small known charges of hydrogen were admitted, and the heat of adsorption of each measured. This was continued until there was a residual pressure owing to the layer being complete. Heats were found to fall from 34 kcal/mole at low coverages to about 17 kcal/mole for densely packed layers. These values confirm that chemisorption was taking place, as the upper limit for the heat of physical adsorption is some 2 kcal/mole.

The volume of gas chemisorbed is also of importance. The work of JOHNSON[23] has shown that in the surface of aged tungsten filaments (110) and (100) planes predominate. The numbers of atoms per cm² in these planes are respectively $14 \cdot 24 \times 10^{14}$ and $10 \cdot 07 \times 10^{14}$, giving

72

an average of $12\cdot15 \times 10^{14}$. The apparent surface area of the filament which Roberts used was $0\cdot55$ cm$^2$: the roughness factor of an aged tungsten filament, deduced by TAYLOR and LANGMUIR[24] from experiments on caesium adsorption, is $1\cdot4$. The number of atoms in the surface of Roberts' filament was therefore $1\cdot4 \times 0\cdot55 \times 12\cdot15 \times 10^{14}$, or $9\cdot3 \times 10^{14}$. The number of hydrogen atoms adsorbed, averaged over a series of experiments, was $8\cdot6 \times 10^{14}$. The volume of hydrogen chemisorbed therefore corresponds closely with one hydrogen atom per surface tungsten atom, that is, with the equation

$$2W + H_2 \rightarrow 2WH$$

where W represents a surface atom.

As not more than one atom of hydrogen per surface atom can be chemisorbed, the rapid chemisorption extends over most, if not quite all, of the surface.

With oxygen[25] similar results were obtained. Some $4\cdot9 \times 10^{14}$ molecules were adsorbed on the same filament with great rapidity at room temperatures, with an initial heat between 155 and 112 kcal/mole. This high heat again shows the process to be chemisorption, and the volume adsorbed suggests that a mechanism $2W + O_2 \rightarrow 2WO$ is operating over most of the surface. Nitrogen was likewise chemisorbed with great rapidity at room temperatures[26].

Recently, rapid chemisorption has also been observed for carbon monoxide on a tungsten filament[27] and for hydrogen on a molybdenum ribbon[28].

## CHEMISORPTION ON EVAPORATED METAL FILMS

The results obtained with filaments have been considerably extended using evaporated films. In qualitative work these have two advantages over filaments. The first is that a wide variety of metals can be employed, whereas with filaments only high melting point metals can be used with any certainty. The second is that clean film surfaces can still be preserved if protecting cold traps are held at $-78\,^{\circ}$C, whereas with filaments traps must be held at $-183\,^{\circ}$C. As a result, the chemisorption of quite condensable gases, such as ammonia and ethylene, may be studied using films, whereas this would be extremely difficult with filaments.

Two general results have emerged from these investigations.

(*1*) Although fast chemisorption is very widespread, it is not, as might be imagined from filament work, universal with all gases on all metals provided the surface is clean.

(*2*) Once fast chemisorption is over, it is very often followed by slow activated effects. The amount of gas taken up slowly is usually so small as to be undetectable using filaments.

These results are treated in the following two sections.

## INITIAL VELOCITIES OF CHEMISORPTION ON FILMS

The available data concerning initial velocities of chemisorption on metal films may be divided conveniently into three categories.

(a) Chemisorption is often so fast as effectively to be non-activated. These velocities have usually been measured qualitatively with films, but the normal result, namely that a small quantity of gas, sufficient to exert a pressure of about $10^{-3}$ mm in the apparatus, is quantitatively adsorbed at room temperatures and below in a very few seconds, shows that if an activation energy is involved it must be exceedingly small.

(b) In some cases chemisorption is definitely activated.

(c) In many cases, no adsorption has been recorded up to a certain temperature, normally $0\,^{\circ}C$.

Results due to ALLEN and MITCHELL[29], BEECK et al.[16, 30, 31], BENNETT and TOMPKINS[32], ELEY and WILKINSON[33], KEMBALL et al.[34–37], TRAPNELL et al.[17, 38–40], and WAGENER[41], are summarized in Table 2.

The number of slow chemisorptions is seen to be relatively small. Those of hydrogen and nitrogen on calcium are under some doubt because the films may have been contaminated.

The rate of adsorption of ammonia on tungsten, nickel and iron is reported[35] to be measurably slower than that of hydrogen. However, this is probably due to a slow diffusion of ammonia through the protective cold trap placed before the film, and consequently these adsorptions have been classified in the table as fast.

Slow chemisorptions are probably activated and this has been confirmed in some cases by measuring rates at different temperatures. In this way the activation energies shown in Table 3 have been obtained.

With methane and ethane, chemisorption becomes slow on all metals once a certain fraction of the surface has been covered, this fraction varying from metal to metal[36, 38]. The reason why these chemisorptions tend to be activated may be that formation of metal-to-carbon bonds is hindered by the presence of the hydrogen atoms surrounding the carbon atom.

The cases where no chemisorption is observed up to $0\,^{\circ}C$ cannot be interpreted with certainty. Possibly the activation energies are in some cases so large that chemisorption will proceed only at

TABLE 2

Chemisorption on Metal Films

| Gas | Very fast chemisorption | Slow chemisorption | No chemisorption up to 0 °C |
|---|---|---|---|
| $H_2$ | Ti, Zr, Nb, Ta, Cr, Mo, W, Fe, Co, Ni, Rh, Pd, Pt, Ba | Mn, ?Ca, Ge | K, Cu, Ag, Au, Zn, Cd, Al, In, Pb, Sn |
| $O_2$ | All metals except Au | — | Au |
| $N_2$ | La, Ti, Zr, Nb, Ta, Mo, W | Fe, ?Ca, Ba | As for $H_2$ plus Ni, Rh, Pd, Pt |
| CO | As for $H_2$ plus La, Mn, ?(Cu, Ag, Au) | Al | K, Zn, Cd, In, Pb, Sn |
| $CO_2$ | As for $H_2$ less Rh, Pd, Pt | Al | Rh, Pd, Pt, Cu, Zn, Cd |
| $CH_4$ | Ti, Ta, Cr, Mo, W, Rh | Fe, Co, Ni, ?Pd | — |
| $C_2H_6$ | As for $CH_4$ plus Ni ?Pd | Fe, Co, | — |
| $C_2H_4$ | As for $H_2$ plus Cu, Au | Al | As for CO |
| $C_2H_2$ | As for $H_2$ plus Cu, Au, K | Al | As for CO less K |
| $NH_3$ | ?(W, Ni, Fe) | — | — |
| $H_2S$ | W, Ni | — | — |

temperatures well above 0 °C, but it is equally likely in others that chemisorption is endothermic, in which case it will not occur however high the temperature. In other cases still, both an appreciable activation energy and a low heat may be operating. Thus, hydrogen atoms are adsorbed on a copper film at low temperatures but desorb as molecules if the film is warmed to room temperature[42], suggesting that the system has become unstable except perhaps at very low coverages and high ambient pressures. On the other hand, hydrogen molecules are not adsorbed at all. Combining these results it would seem that molecular hydrogen is not adsorbed at low temperatures because of an activation energy and at higher temperatures because adsorption involves an increase in free energy.

### TABLE 3

Activated Chemisorption on Metal Films

| System | Activation energy (kcal/mole) | Reference |
|--------|-------------------------------|-----------|
| $H_2$/Mn | 0·9 | 40 |
| $H_2$/Ca | 1·7–4·0 | 17 |
| $H_2$/Ge | 16·6 | 32 |
| $N_2$/Ca | 1·5–3·8 | 17 |
| $N_2$/Ba | 2–4 | 41 |
| CO/Al | 4·2 | 33 |
| $CH_4$/Ni | 11 | 34 |

#### SLOW EFFECTS ON METAL FILMS FOLLOWING RAPID CHEMISORPTION

Although the initial chemisorption at the surface of a clean metal film is often non-activated, the systems so far studied show subsequent slow effects at all temperatures. Some of these systems are listed in Table 4.

### TABLE 4

Systems showing 'Slow Effects' following Rapid Chemisorption

| Gas | Metals |
|-----|--------|
| $H_2$ | W[43], Fe[44], Ni[45, 46], Pd[47] |
| $O_2$ | most metals[17, 48] |
| CO | W[49], Fe[44], Ni[45] |
| $N_2$ | Ta[50], W[31, 51], Cr[50], Fe[50] |

With certain oxygen adsorptions, there is good evidence[52] that several layers of oxide have been rapidly formed before the slow effect commences, so that the latter is almost certain to be further oxidation. In these cases kinetics characteristic of metal oxidation are often found to be obeyed[48]. However, in other oxygen adsorptions, and also with hydrogen, carbon monoxide and nitrogen, slow effects commence at about the monolayer stage. These may be grouped together on this account and also because they are usually small in extent, amounting to only 15–20 per cent of the fast chemisorption. They may be due either to slow, surface processes (adsorption) or to penetration of the lattice (absorption or compound formation).

The relative extents of the fast and slow processes may be obtained from adsorption isobars (see *Figure 33*). The extent of the fast, non-activated adsorption, $n_f$, is measured at some low temperature (usually $-195\,°C$ or $-183\,°C$). The film is then warmed to a higher temperature in the presence of the gas, when the slow process rapidly reaches equilibrium. This causes more gas to be

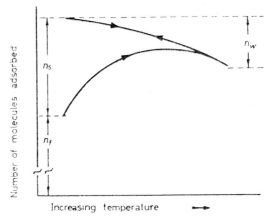

*Figure 33. Diagrammatic representation of an adsorption isobar*

$$n_f = \text{number of molecules adsorbed in fast process}$$
$$n_w = \text{  ,,  ,,  ,, reversibly adsorbed}$$
$$n_s = \text{  ,,  ,,  ,, adsorbed in slow process}$$

taken up, although at the same time any weakly held gas may be desorbed. On cooling again to the low temperature the latter readsorbs and the difference between the two uptakes measured at this temperature, $n_s$, represents the amount of slow uptake.

In the adsorption of hydrogen on nickel it was originally found by BEECK, RITCHIE and WHEELER[46] that, for a given weight of film, the amount of slow uptake was independent of the degree of sintering, i.e. independent of the surface area. Similar behaviour has been reported for the adsorption of hydrogen on tungsten films[43]. These results suggest that the slow effect is not connected with the surface but with the weight or volume of the film, and is, therefore, solution.

However, in a more detailed study of the hydrogen–nickel system by GUNDRY and TOMPKINS[45] the slow uptake was found to fall on sintering in proportion to the fall in the fast chemisorption, provided the sintering temperature was below $33\,°C$. A 15-fold decrease in the surface/bulk ratio caused only a 47 per cent decrease in the ratio of the fast to the slow uptake. Similar results were obtained with carbon monoxide on nickel and with both gases on iron[44], where the critical sintering temperature was 158 °C. These results suggest that both fast and slow processes may be surface phenomena.

The difference between the two sets of results for the hydrogen–nickel system is probably due to the different sintering temperatures employed. BEECK *et al.* sintered their films at temperatures between 25 and 400 °C whereas GUNDRY and TOMPKINS worked mostly between −196 °C and 33 °C. When the latter worked at higher temperatures, they observed similar behaviour to that observed by BEECK *et al.* It would appear, therefore, that both absorption and adsorption may be responsible for the slow effect, but that the former makes an insignificant contribution at lower temperatures.

### ADSORPTION ON MERCURY

Mercury offers the only ready possibility of studying adsorption on the surface of a liquid metal. Furthermore the surface area of liquid mercury may be taken to be equal to its apparent area, and is thus definite and known. Adsorptions on mercury have been studied volumetrically[53], and by indirect methods, notably measurement of the change in surface tension[54-56] and work function[57] on adsorption.

Much of the work using mercury is difficult to interpret. In some cases, a fresh mercury surface was generated in the presence of the gas in question, and although this may have ensured contact of adsorbate with bare mercury atoms, it greatly increases the possibility of absorption. In other cases, the surface tension of the 'clean' surface differed considerably from what is now known to be the true value, so that the surface was not pure.

The adsorption of $H_2$, $O_2$ and $CO_2$ on mercury has been studied by COOK[54], using a surface tension method, and volumetrically by BURDON[53]. Both workers agree that there is rapid, strong adsorption at room temperatures. Cook found that when a fresh mercury surface was generated in the presence of gas, the surface tension was much lower than when the surface was formed in vacuo. In vacuo, however, the surface tension (515 dynes/cm) differed from the true value (484 dynes/cm) for a clean surface[55]. The extent of the lowering depended on the gas pressure: on pumping out the gas the surface tension rose, but did not achieve the value 515 dynes/cm. The adsorptions therefore appear to be partly reversible and partly irreversible.

Rapid irreversible adsorption of these gases has also been claimed by BURDON[53], who generated fresh surfaces in the presence of air, $H_2$ and $CO_2$. The gas was then pumped out, and the mercury surface broken by running the mercury out of the reaction vessel. In all cases a quantity of gas was liberated roughly equal to the quantity which would have been adsorbed into a monolayer.

These results suggest rapid chemisorption at room temperatures, but should perhaps be accepted with reserve, particularly as recent careful work by KEMBALL[56, 57] shows that mercury is relatively inert in chemisorption. In this work definitely clean mercury surfaces were obtained by continuous distillation in vacuo for 15 days with pumping. These could be maintained for long periods of time, and so gases and vapours could be admitted to static mercury. Heats of adsorption were obtained, and these showed that acetone, the alcohols, benzene, toluene and heptane were only physically adsorbed at room temperatures. Only certain halides, notably $CCl_4$ and $CHCl_3$, were chemisorbed, and here the process was non-activated in the initial stages, but activated when more than about half the surface was covered.

## CHEMISORPTION ON CARBON

Carbon is a similar adsorbent to metals in that only surfaces free of contamination are active in chemisorption. With carbon, however, films and filaments have not been used to any extent, and carbon powders are both extremely porous and extremely difficult to clean. Probably the best method so far used for cleaning a carbon powder, namely to outgas it between 900 and 1,000 °C for 24 hours, is insufficient to obtain more than a partially clean surface. The available data may therefore suggest that carbon has a somewhat lower activity in chemisorption than would be the case for a truly pure surface.

Early work, which gives a qualitative indication of the rate of chemisorption of some simple gases by charcoal powders, is due to KEYES and MARSHALL[2], who measured differential heats of adsorption in an ice calorimeter. Initial values are given in Table 5, together with latent heats of evaporation of the gases at their normal boiling points.

With carbon dioxide and water the heats of adsorption are near the latent heat, and this indicates that the adsorption is physical. With oxygen, chlorine and ammonia, however, the heats of adsorption exceed the latent heats sufficiently to ensure that chemisorption is operating. This must have taken place fairly rapidly to permit heat measurements to be made, and indicates that the activation energy of chemisorption must be quite small.

TABLE 5

Heats of Adsorption of Gases on Charcoal

| Gas | $O_2$ | $Cl_2$ | $CO_2$ | $NH_3$ | $H_2O$ |
|---|---|---|---|---|---|
| Initial heat (kcal/mole) | 72 | 31·9 | 8·4 | 16·9 | 9·4 |
| Latent heat (kcal/mole) | 1·6 | 4·4 | 6·0 | 5·5 | 10·6 |

Later, BULL, HALL and GARNER[3] found that at room temperatures a charcoal powder chemisorbed quantitatively a charge of oxygen in 10 to 30 seconds, again pointing to a very low activation energy.

At about this time it was discovered that the ortho–para hydrogen conversion could be catalysed by the inhomogeneous magnetic fields existing in the neighbourhood of paramagnetic substances. This discovery afforded a novel way of investigating the adsorption of oxygen on charcoal[58]. If oxygen is chemisorbed as atoms, the surface will be diamagnetic and a poor conversion catalyst: if it is physically adsorbed as molecules, the surface will be paramagnetic and a good conversion catalyst. Oxygen adsorption at liquid air temperatures was in this way found to be physical, and at room temperatures to be chemical. Subsequently, chemisorption was shown to take place only above −70 °C, and this indicates that a definite albeit small activation energy is involved.

The same conclusion was reached independently by BARRER[59], who used both graphite and diamond as adsorbent. On diamond, the activation energy increased markedly with adsorbed amount, as shown in Table 6. At very low amounts, it must have been almost zero.

TABLE 6

Oxygen Chemisorption by Diamond

| Volume adsorbed ($\times 10^3$ cm³ at N.T.P.) | 35 | 59 | 73 | 93 |
|---|---|---|---|---|
| $E$ (kcal/mole) | 4·3 | 12·0 | 18·6 | 23·0 |

BARRER and RIDEAL[60] have carried out detailed work on hydrogen adsorption on carbon. Below about $-78°C$, hydrogen is physically adsorbed on charcoal, the heat lying between 1,380 and 1,650 cal/mole. Between $-78$ and $300°C$ there is little adsorption, but above $300°C$, slow effects are observed. Above $700°C$, equilibrium is rapidly established, and isotherms may be obtained. From these the heat of adsorption is found to be some 50 kcal/mole, so that chemisorption is taking place.

The kinetics of adsorption are complex. Between 300 and $600°C$, the velocity is exponentially dependent on temperature, and the activation energy increases continuously with adsorbed amount from 10 to 30 kcal/mole. Above about $600°C$, the rate ceases to be exponentially dependent on temperature, and commences instead to increase in proportion with $\sqrt{T}$. This is characteristic of a diffusion, and indicates that passage of gas to interior surfaces is slower than chemisorption and determines the rate. The results are shown in *Figure 34*.

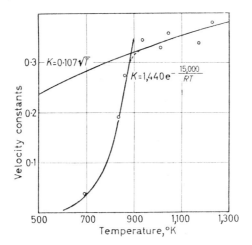

*Figure 34. The adsorption of hydrogen on carbon powders.*
*The points are experimental, the lines calculated*
By courtesy of Barrer, R. M. *Proc. Roy. Soc.* **A149**, 253, 1935

Hydrogen chemisorption on diamond and graphite is likewise activated, with the activation energy increasing with adsorbed amount from 13·7 to 22·4 kcal/mole with diamond, and from 22·0 to 33·8 kcal/mole with graphite. The heats of adsorption are respectively 58 and 45 kcal/mole.

RIDEAL and TRAPNELL[61] have recorded that hydrogen chemisorption on an evaporated carbon film can only be detected well above room temperatures, and this confirms that the chemisorption is activated.

Chemisorption of CO, $CO_2$ and $CH_4$ on various carbons appears to commence only at temperatures approaching 700 °C, and is therefore strongly activated[59, 60]. For methane the activation energy is 53 kcal/mole.

### CHEMISORPTION ON OXIDES

As adsorbents the oxides differ from carbon and the metals in two important respects.

The first is that they possess more than one chemical type of adsorption centre. Not only are the metal ions and the oxide ions potential sites for chemisorption, but in addition adsorption may be closely connected with the defects which oxides usually contain. Because of this the same gas is often chemisorbed in more than one way, and a particular experiment may well result in a composite process which it is not easy to disentangle. However, a weak, fast adsorption and a slow, strong adsorption are quite frequently found, and these can be separated by studies at different temperatures—the former will occur only at low temperatures and the latter only at high temperatures.

Second, with the oxides, the term 'active surface' need not mean a surface free of adsorbed gas. Sometimes chemisorption of one gas will assist and create sites for the adsorption of a second. Partly on this account active oxide surfaces are more easily prepared than active metal or carbon surfaces. However, chemisorption on oxides has been studied only on powders and since these are porous, it is normally impossible to measure absolute velocities of fast chemisorptions because a slow diffusion through pores is rate determining.

For purposes of discussion the available data may be divided into three categories.

(*1*) Certain chemisorptions have been shown by various techniques to be effectively non-activated.

(*2*) In many cases chemisorption at room temperatures is partly rapid and partly slow.

(*3*) Sometimes chemisorption seems to be slow even at elevated temperatures.

Chemisorptions in category (*2*) may possess a low activation energy: those in category (*3*) are probably fairly strongly activated.

## NON-ACTIVATED CHEMISORPTIONS ON OXIDES

Three types of evidence show that some chemisorptions on oxides are, to a first approximation, non-activated.

(1) Sometimes gases are chemisorbed on oxides with great rapidity at liquid air temperatures.

Thus, chromia outgassed at 400 °C quantitatively adsorbs small charges of hydrogen, deuterium and carbon monoxide at $-183$ °C in less than 2 minutes, and the heats of adsorption are respectively 5·1, 5·4 and 12·7 kcal/mole[18]. The maximum possible heats of physical adsorption are about 2 kcal/mole for hydrogen and deuterium, and 6 kcal/mole for carbon monoxide, so in all three cases chemisorption is operating. With oxygen and nitrogen, the adsorptions are not quite so rapid: the heats are respectively 27 and 9·2 kcal/mole which are again larger than can be ascribed to physical adsorption. Possibly chemisorption of these two gases involves an activation energy of a few hundred calories.

(2) A number of isotopic exchange reactions are catalysed by oxides at very low temperatures, implying the occurrence of rapid, virtually non-activated chemisorption. Examples are given in Table 7.

TABLE 7

Exchange Reactions on Oxides at Low Temperatures

| Reaction | Oxide | Temperature (°C) | Reference |
|---|---|---|---|
| (a) $H_2 + D_2 \rightleftharpoons 2HD$ | $Cr_2O_3$ | $-195$ | 20 |
|  | $Co_3O_4$ | $-195$ | 20 |
|  | NiO | $-195$ | 20 |
|  | ZnO | $-130$ | 10 |
|  | $Al_2O_3$ | $-100$ | 62 |
| (b) $^{16}O_2 + ^{18}O_2 \rightleftharpoons 2^{16}O^{18}O$ | ZnO | $-195$ | 63 |
| (c) $C^{18}O +$ oxygen ions of oxide | $Cu_2O$ | $-78$ | 64 |
| (d) $C^{18}O_2 +$ oxygen ions of oxide | $Cu_2O$ | $-78$ | 64 |

An important difference between the first two and the last two reactions is that the former could be taking place on a very few surface sites, whereas the extensive exchange of oxygen with surface oxide ions in the latter implies a fast chemisorption over a large fraction of the surface.

(3) Provided adsorption does not involve dissociation, the activation energy of adsorption, $E$, is equal to $(E'-q)$ where $E'$ is the activation energy for desorption and $q$ is the heat of adsorption.

Since $E'$ can be calculated from experimental rates of desorption, as shown in Chapter IV, and $q$ can be measured calorimetrically, $E$ can be found.

This method of obtaining $E$ was used with success by GARNER, notably with carbon dioxide chemisorption on oxides[65]. This takes place at oxygen ions to form surface carbonate, and has been studied on zinc, chromium and manganese oxides, on the spinel $ZnO.Cr_2O_3$ and on the mixed oxide $MnO_{1.5}.Cr_2O_3$. In all cases adsorption is rapid. Desorption takes place at room temperatures, and the calculated activation energy is equal to the heat of chemisorption to within a few hundred calories. To this accuracy, chemisorption is therefore non-activated.

The technique has also been applied to the chemisorption of carbon monoxide on zinc oxide[65]. Usually carbon monoxide is desorbed from oxides, at least in part, as $CO_2$, and in such cases the method is inapplicable, since it assumes that mechanisms of adsorption and desorption are the same, On zinc oxide, however, desorption takes place at room temperatures wholly as CO and the value of $E'$ is again equal to the heat of chemisorption to within a few hundred calories.

Possibly fast low temperature chemisorptions on oxides are more common than the present, rather sparse data imply. It is tempting to suggest that, by analogy with fast chemisorption on metals, this type of adsorption takes place on metal ions. With hydrogen some evidence for this idea has been provided by DOWDEN, MACKENZIE and TRAPNELL[20], but with CO and $CO_2$ the occurrence of exchange with the oxygen ions of the adsorbent is difficult to explain in such terms.

OTHER CHEMISORPTIONS ON OXIDES

The remaining data on oxides are of two kinds. They consist either of adsorption isobars or of rates of disappearance of gas at room temperatures or above. The results occasionally differ from those of the previous sections, even for identical systems. For example, section (2) showed the existence of rapid low temperature chemisorptions of $H_2$ and $O_2$ on ZnO and of $H_2$ on $Al_2O_3$. Volumetric work, however, leads to the conclusion that these chemisorptions are strongly activated, occurring at a measurable rate only well above room temperature[7, 66, 67]. In the case of $O_2$ on ZnO an activation energy of about 15 kcal/mole has been recorded[66, 67]. Possibly two mechanisms are involved. In the case of $H_2$ on ZnO this is very likely, as the low temperature chemisorption does not alter the semiconductivity of the oxide, whereas the high temperature chemisorption does[68, 69]. Again, on several oxides, $H_2$ can be desorbed as such at low temperatures but only as water at higher temperatures[70]. With CO, desorption may take place[70] as CO or $CO_2$. With $N_2O$ there is an instantaneous reversible adsorption on NiO and CoO[71, 72] at room temperatures, the heat for CoO being 13 kcal/mole, but there is also a slow chemisorption with a heat of 46 kcal/mole for NiO and 50 kcal/mole for CoO[72]. The latter values correspond closely with those expected for the process

$$N_2O \rightarrow N_2 \uparrow + O^{2-}_{ads}$$

Presumably the weaker adsorption must involve a different mechanism.

TABLE 8

Chemisorptions on Oxides Initially Fast at Room Temperature

| Gas | Oxide | Initial heat of adsorption (kcal/mole) | Velocity of adsorption |
|---|---|---|---|
| $O_2$ | NiO | 54 | Initially rapid, $E \rightarrow O$, then slow with $E$ rising |
| $O_2$ | $Cr_2O_3$ and $Fe_2O_3$ | — | As for NiO |
| $O_2$ | MnO | 24 | Small, very rapid adsorption |
| $O_2$ | $ZnO.Cr_2O_3$ | 42·9 | Extremely rapid |
| CO | NiO | 26 | Rapid adsorption, coverage $<1·5\%$ at $20°C$ |
| CO | CoO | 20 | Rapid adsorption, coverage $3\%$ at $25°C$ and $0·1$ mm pressure |
| CO | ZnO | 9–13 | Rapid, reversible adsorption |
| CO | $Cu_2O$ | 20 | Rapid adsorption, $30\%$ coverage at $20°C$ and $0·2$ mm pressure |
| CO | MnO | 64·4 | Rapid adsorption |
| CO | $Cr_2O_3$ | 28 | Adsorption $90\%$ complete in 5 minutes |
| CO | $ZnO.Cr_2O_3$ | 14·9 | Adsorption $90\%$ complete in 5 minutes |
| $CO_2$ | NiO | 28 | $10\%$ limiting coverage at $20°C$ |
| $CO_2$ | CoO | 23 | $6\%$ limiting coverage at $20°C$ |
| $N_2O$ | NiO | — | Instantaneous reversible adsorption |
| $N_2O$ | CoO | 13 | Instantaneous reversible adsorption |
| $C_2H_4$ | CoO | 13 | Completely reversible at $20°C$ |
| $C_2H_4$ | ZnO | 25·2 | $90\%$ of charge adsorbed in 2 minutes |
| $C_2H_4$ | $ZnO.Cr_2O_3$ | 11 | Charge adsorbed in 8 minutes |
| $C_2H_4$ | $Cu_2O$ | 20 | Rapid adsorption |
| $SO_2$ | $Cu_2O$ | 37 | Rapid adsorption |

G

However, there may be cases where only one mechanism is involved, adsorption being fast at low coverages but activated once a certain coverage has been exceeded. In the case of $O_2$ chemisorption on NiO, $Cr_2O_3$ and $Fe_2O_3$, WINTER[73] concludes from kinetic data that the activation energy is initially zero, but then rises continuously with adsorbed amount to 35 kcal/mole for NiO and $Cr_2O_3$, and to 12 kcal/mole in the case of $Fe_2O_3$.

TABLE 9

Slow Chemisorptions on Oxides at Room Temperatures or Above

| Gas | Oxide | Initial heat of adsorption (kcal/mole) | Velocity of adsorption |
|---|---|---|---|
| $H_2$ | ZnO $Cr_2O_3$ $Al_2O_3$ $V_2O_3$ | — | Slow at elevated temperatures |
| $H_2$ | $ZnO.Cr_2O_3$ (oxidized) | 49·7 | Very slow at room temperatures |
| $O_2$ | $Cu_2O$ | 62 | $E=7$ kcal/mole |
| $O_2$ | CoO | 65 | Slow at room temperatures |
| $O_2$ | ZnO | 110 | $E \simeq 15$ kcal/mole initially |
| $O_2$ | MgO | — | $E=14$ kcal/mole |
| CO | $MnO.Cr_2O_3$ | — | Slow at elevated temperatures |
| $C_2H_4$ | $Cr_2O_3$ | — | Slow at elevated temperatures |
| $C_2H_6$ | $ZnO.Cr_2O_3$ (oxidized) | 28·7 | Very slow at room temperatures |
| $N_2O$ | NiO | 46 | Slow at room temperatures |
| $N_2O$ | CoO | 50 | Slow at room temperatures |

Data due to GARNER and his co-workers[65, 74], KUBOKAWA et al.[67], STONE and his co-workers[72, 75-77], TAYLOR and his co-workers[7], and to WINTER et al.[64, 66, 71, 73, 78] are summarized in Tables 8 and 9 according as adsorption is initially fast or entirely slow at room temperature, suggesting respectively a low and an appreciable initial activation energy.

## QUANTITATIVE TREATMENT

### GENERAL CONSIDERATIONS

#### STICKING PROBABILITIES

At an ambient pressure, $p$, the number of gas phase molecules colliding with unit area of a surface per second is equal to

$p/\sqrt{(2\pi mkT)}$, $m$ being the mass of a molecule and $k$ the Boltzmann constant. The sticking probability, $s$, is defined as the fraction of these collisions resulting in chemisorption. The rate of adsorption, $u$ (expressed in molecules adsorbed per cm$^2$ per second), may therefore be written as

$$u = \frac{sp}{\sqrt{(2\pi mkT)}} \qquad (3.1)$$

Only rarely is $s$ equal to unity and one or more of the following factors may be responsible for lower values of $s$.

*(a) Activation energy*

If chemisorption is an activated process only those molecules possessing the necessary activation energy can be chemisorbed. Most chemisorptions on clean metal surfaces, however, are non-activated, as seen in the previous section.

*(b) Probability or steric factor*

Not every molecule possessing the required activation energy will necessarily be chemisorbed but only those passing through the particular configuration of the 'activated complex'. Because of this $s$ may be considerably less than one, even though the activation energy for chemisorption approaches or is equal to zero.

*(c) Efficiency of energy transfer*

For a molecule or atom to become permanently chemisorbed it must lose, during its impact with the surface, an amount of energy exceeding its original thermal energy. Otherwise it will remain in the chemisorbed state merely for the duration of one vibration and then desorb. In chemisorption the energy of interaction between the molecule and the surface is fairly high and collisions are generally inelastic, resulting in efficient energy transfer. However, this factor may be important in physical adsorption and, since the latter is often a precursor to chemisorption, it may influence the sticking probability.

*(d) Surface heterogeneity*

Activity in chemisorption may vary from site to site on the surface and the overall sticking probability will be a function of this variation.

*(e) Collision with an occupied site*

Until recently collision with an occupied site was thought to preclude chemisorption, but it is now known that molecules can be adsorbed into a weakly held second layer and migrate over the covered portions of the surface until a vacant site is reached. However, some molecules almost certainly desorb before finding a vacant site, particularly at higher coverages.

POTENTIAL ENERGY CURVES

The curve relating the potential energy of an atom or molecule and its distance from the surface usually shows a rather shallow minimum corresponding to physical adsorption and a deeper one corresponding to chemisorption. This is illustrated in *Figure 35* for the dissociative adsorption of a diatomic molecule, $X_2$. In both (*a*) and (*b*), curve 1 gives the potential energy of the molecule $X_2$ if physical forces of attraction only are operating, while curve 2 corresponds to the interaction of two X atoms with the surface, the separation between them being the same as for curve 1.

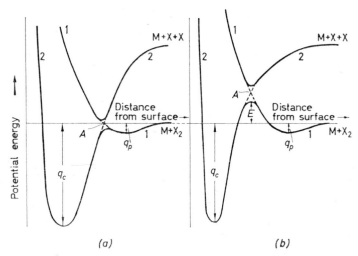

*Figure 35. Potential energy curves for physical adsorption and chemisorption*

Thus, for any particular configuration of the X nuclei with respect to the surface there are two ways of arranging the bonding electrons —one consists predominantly of bond formation between the X atoms to form a molecule, with only a small interaction with the surface; the other corresponds to bond formation with the surface and only repulsive terms between the X atoms. These two circumstances are illustrated in *Figure 36* for hydrogen.

88

Returning to *Figure 35*, at *A* the two potential energy curves cross, implying that for this particular configuration of the nuclei there are two electronic states of the system with the same energy. This degeneracy is normally not allowed, the two levels splitting as shown, with the incoming $X_2$ molecules following the lower solid

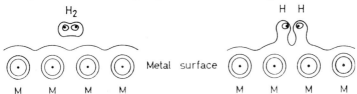

*Figure 36. Two possible electronic states for a particular nuclear configuration of the system* H + H + *metal. The contour lines represent electron density*

line. To the right of *A* the equilibrium internuclear separation is always close to that in the unperturbed molecule $X_2$ but to the left of *A* the separation increases and can become infinite. If the second curve crosses the first while the van der Waals forces are still attractive, as in *Figure 35a*, there is no activation energy for chemisorption, but if the forces are already repulsive an activation energy, *E*, is introduced as in *Figure 35b*.

No activation energy is anticipated for the adsorption of an atom since little electronic rearrangement is required within the atom before the adsorption bond can be formed. This, of course, assumes that the adsorbent surface itself has free valencies and this often seems to be true, in particular with the transition metals. In this case the adsorption process is really a combination of two free radicals. If, however, electrons within the adsorbent have to be promoted to higher energy levels before interaction can occur, even the adsorption of atoms may be activated.

For molecules that do not dissociate upon adsorption it is still possible for adsorption to be activated, since electrons within the molecule must rearrange before bonding to the surface can occur. Thus, on certain metals carbon monoxide is adsorbed in the form

and in this case curve 2 in the potential energy diagram would correspond to carbon monoxide in the form $>C=O$ and curve 1 to the normal hybridization in the gas phase molecule.

In many instances *Figure 35* is probably an oversimplification of the adsorption process since other intermediate states besides physical adsorption are thought to occur, namely, weak chemisorption either as atoms or molecules[79].

## PRECURSOR STATES

The simplest kind of chemisorption is one where molecules or atoms colliding with the surface are either chemisorbed directly or reflected back into the gas phase. However, the existence of intermediate binding states complicates this picture, since atoms or molecules may remain in these states for an appreciable time and migrate over the surface before being either chemisorbed or desorbed.

In *Figure 35b* physically adsorbed molecules are unlikely to pass over to the chemisorbed state. Provided the vibrational modes leading to desorption and to the chemisorbed state are similar, they will tend to desorb before gaining enough vibrational energy to surmount the necessary potential barrier. A physically adsorbed molecule can become chemisorbed only if it can make a single vibrational energy transition greater than the activation energy, $E$, or if there is a low probability factor for desorption so that vibrations with energy in excess of $q_p$, the heat of physical adsorption, are allowed. Generally $E$ is greatly in excess of the vibrational quanta, and the probability factor for desorption of physically held molecules is unity. That is, molecules can only enter the chemisorbed state directly from the gas phase.

In *Figure 35a* the situation is reversed and physically adsorbed molecules can desorb only if the probability factor for chemisorption is low. Hence, in non-activated processes physical adsorption may be very important as a precursor to chemisorption. As a result, collisions with occupied sites are not necessarily unsuccessful because physically adsorbed molecules may migrate to vacant sites and be chemisorbed.

If the precursor is a weak chemisorption, the probability factor for desorption may be low and in this case the precursor state may play an important part even in activated processes.

## GENERAL TYPES OF ADSORPTION

The kinetics of adsorption can be classified roughly into three different categories:

(*1*) Activated adsorption without the participation of a precursor. The characteristics of this type of adsorption are:

(a) Exponential increase in rate with increasing temperature.
(b) Continuous fall in rate with increasing coverage.
(c) Rate directly proportional to the ambient pressure.
(2) Non-activated adsorption. This is characterized by:
(a) Zero or negative temperature coefficient of velocity.
(b) Initial rate independent of coverage.
(c) Rate proportional to pressure.
(3) Activated adsorption with participation of precursors. This is characterized by:
(a) Exponential increase in rate with increase in temperature.
(b) Continuous fall in rate with increasing coverage.
(c) No simple dependence of rate on pressure—proportionality to $\sqrt{p}$ is, for example, common.

## DIRECT ACTIVATED ADSORPTION

### FORMULATION OF THE RATE EQUATION

For a simple activated adsorption the sticking probability, $s$, may be written as

$$s = \sigma f(\theta) e^{-E/RT} \tag{3.2}$$

In this equation $\sigma$ is the condensation coefficient. It is the probability that a molecule is adsorbed, provided it possesses the necessary activation energy $E$ and collides with a vacant surface site, and is in fact equal to the 'probability factor' mentioned earlier. $f(\theta)$ is a function of the surface coverage $\theta$ and represents the probability that a collision will take place at an available site.

Combining equations (3.1) and (3.2) we obtain for the rate of adsorption

$$u = \frac{\sigma p}{\sqrt{(2\pi mkT)}} f(\theta) e^{-E/RT} \tag{3.3}$$

Often the rate of adsorption falls extremely rapidly with increasing coverage, and this can be explained only if the activation energy increases with $\theta$. Similarly $\sigma$ may vary with $\theta$. If these variations with coverage arise from interactions on a uniform surface it is sufficient to indicate that $E$ and $\sigma$ are functions of $\theta$. For example, equation (3.3) becomes

$$u = \frac{\sigma(\theta)p}{\sqrt{(2\pi mkT)}} f(\theta) e^{-E(\theta)/RT} \tag{3.4}$$

However, if the variations arise from surface heterogeneity and different sites possess different values of $\sigma$ and $E$, it is necessary to

91

divide the surface up into a number of small elements of area d$s$, each of which is uniform and to each of which equation (3.3) applies. The rate of adsorption is then obtained by integration, giving, for unit area of surface,

$$u = \frac{p}{\sqrt{(2\pi m k T)}} \int_0^1 \sigma_s \, \mathrm{f}(\theta_s) \mathrm{e}^{-E_s/RT} \, \mathrm{d}s \qquad (3.5)$$

This equation can be solved only if the relationship between $\sigma_s$, $E_s$ and $s$ is known, and in general it is not.

THE TERM $\mathrm{f}(\theta)$

It is assumed in this section that a gas molecule must collide directly with a vacant site in order to be adsorbed, the term $\mathrm{f}(\theta)$ representing the probability that this will occur.

The variation of velocity with coverage is located solely in the term $\mathrm{f}(\theta)$ only if $E$ and $\sigma$ are independent of $\theta$. However, $E$ usually seems to increase with $\theta$ and the main variation of velocity with $\theta$ may be due to this.

Two separate types of adsorption are treated. In the first the molecule is adsorbed on a single site; in the second the molecule dissociates on adsorption into two radicals each of which occupies one site.

*Molecule occupying a single surface site*

When the coverage is $\theta$, the fractional number of uncovered single sites is $(1-\theta)$. The chance that a colliding molecule strikes a vacant site is for mobile and immobile layers alike

$$\mathrm{f}(\theta) = 1 - \theta \qquad (3.6)$$

*Molecule occupying two sites on dissociation*

(*a*) *Immobile layers*—It is assumed here that the two parts of the dissociated molecule remain on adjacent sites. $\mathrm{f}(\theta)$ might appear to be equal to $(1-\theta)^2$ and for small values of $\theta$ this is true, but at high coverages the probability of adsorption is greater than that indicated by this term. The chance of any site being vacant is $(1-\theta)$: the chance that a site next to an unoccupied site is itself unoccupied proves to be[80]

$$\frac{z}{z-\theta} \cdot (1-\theta) \qquad (3.7)$$

where $z$ is the number of nearest neighbours surrounding a site. Hence

$$f(\theta) = \frac{z}{z-\theta} \cdot (1-\theta)^2 \qquad (3.8)$$

At low $\theta$ values, $f(\theta) \rightarrow (1-\theta)^2$: at high $\theta$ values

$$f(\theta) \rightarrow z(1-\theta)^2/(z-1).$$

However, recent electron diffraction work[81, 82] shows that immobile layers do not necessarily build up in the way assumed in this calculation. It is found that many adsorbed layers have a two-dimensional structure, the adatoms being arranged according to a definite pattern. This will be dealt with in greater detail when non-activated adsorptions are discussed.

(b) *Mobile layers*—In mobile layers the atoms tend to spread out through the forces of repulsion which exist between them[83]. By this, vacant sites are also spread out, and although the chance of any one site being vacant is $(1-\theta)$, the chance of a site next to an unoccupied site being unoccupied is less than $(1-\theta)$.

However, the treatment of adsorption by statistical mechanics[84] shows that, although the number of vacant dual sites is diminished by interaction within a mobile layer, their reactivity is increased by a proportionate amount. Thus, the two effects tend to cancel out and $f(\theta)$ is effectively equal to $(1-\theta)^2$.

### THE ELOVICH EQUATION

For a wide variety of activated adsorptions the variation of velocity with amount adsorbed, $q$, obeys the equation[85]

$$\frac{dq}{dt} = ae^{-bq} \qquad (3.9)$$

where $a$ and $b$ are constants. This is commonly known as the Elovich equation. It can be derived for a uniform or a non-uniform surface on the basis of a variation of activation energy with $q$[86]. In both cases we consider, for simplicity, a single site adsorption, with $f(\theta)$ equal to $(1-\theta)$.

(1) *Uniform Surface*

If $E$ varies linearly with $\theta$ according to the relationship

$$E = E_0 + a\theta \qquad (3.10)$$

where $E_0$ and $a$ are constants, an Elovich equation may be derived. Substituting in equation (3.3), with $f(\theta) = (1 - \theta)$, we obtain

$$u = \frac{\sigma p}{\sqrt{(2\pi m k T)}}(1 - \theta)e^{-(E_0 + a\theta)/RT} \qquad (3.11)$$

Assuming $\sigma$ does not vary greatly with $\theta$, this gives

$$u \propto (1 - \theta)e^{-a\theta/RT} \qquad (3.12)$$

Provided $\theta$ is not close to unity, we may neglect the variation of $(1 - \theta)$ in comparison with the variation in $e^{-a\theta/RT}$. Thus

$$u \propto e^{-a\theta/RT} \qquad (3.13)$$

which is a form of the Elovich equation.

(2) *Non-uniform surface*

The surface is divided into a number of elements of area $ds$, each of which constitutes a uniform surface, and the activation energy for adsorption is assumed to increase linearly with $s$ so that

$$E_s = E_0 + as \qquad (3.14)$$

Substituting in equation (3.5), treating $\sigma$ as a constant and putting $f(\theta_s) = (1 - \theta_s)$ we obtain

$$u = \frac{\sigma p}{\sqrt{(2\pi m k T)}} \int_0^1 (1 - \theta_s)e^{-(E_0 + as)/RT}\, ds \qquad (3.15)$$

The integral in this equation cannot easily be evaluated and an approximation is therefore made. If the variation of $E$ is significant, the sites on the surface with the lower $E$ values will be covered far more quickly than the parts of the surface on which $E$ is high. Therefore, at a given moment, the surface will consist of two parts—an almost covered part (low $E$), and an almost bare part (high $E$). In this case, the integral of equation (3.15) may be replaced by an integral carried out simply over that part of the surface which is bare, for which $1 - \theta_s = 1$. The limits of integration are $s = \theta$, the fraction of the surface covered at the moment of consideration, and $s = 1$.

Then
$$u = \frac{\sigma p}{\sqrt{(2\pi m k T)}} \int_\theta^1 e^{-(E_0 + as)/RT}\, ds \qquad (3.16)$$

On integration,

$$u = \frac{\sigma p}{\sqrt{(2\pi m k T)}} \cdot \frac{RT}{a} \cdot e^{-E_0/RT}(e^{-a\theta/RT} - e^{-a/RT}) \qquad (3.17)$$

If $\theta$ does not approach unity, $e^{-\alpha\theta/RT} \gg e^{-\alpha/RT}$. Under these conditions, the velocity is again of the form

$$u \propto e^{-\alpha\theta/RT} \tag{3.18}$$

The velocity equation is, therefore,

$$\frac{\mathrm{d}\theta}{\mathrm{d}t} = ae^{-\alpha\theta/RT} \tag{3.19}$$

and on integration this gives

$$\theta = \frac{RT}{a} \ln \frac{(t+t_0)}{t_0}. \tag{3.20}$$

where

$$t_0 = \frac{RT}{a\alpha}.$$

The above derivation of the Elovich equation is based on a variation of activation energy with coverage. The equation may also be derived[87, 88] if the total number of surface sites is not constant but is a function of both the quantity of gas adsorbed and the temperature. It must also be assumed that the rate of adsorption is governed by the number of available sites. For the Elovich equation to apply, this number must diminish exponentially as the amount adsorbed increases, implying that chemisorbed molecules deactivate sites in excess of actual occupancy. That is, the simple relation $f(\theta) = (1-\theta)$ does not apply.

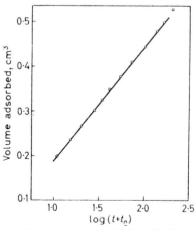

Figure 37. Hydrogen adsorption on 2MnO.Cr$_2$O$_3$ at 100°C
By courtesy of Taylor, H. A. and Thon, N. J. Amer. Chem. Soc. **74**, 4169, 1952

*Application to Experiment*

Many slow adsorptions obey either equation (3.18) or equation (3.20). In particular, Taylor and Thon[87] have shown that, for a large number of systems, plotting the volume adsorbed against $\ln(t+t_0)$, where $t_0$ is an adjustable constant, gives a straight line. An example, the adsorption of hydrogen on the mixed oxide $2MnO.Cr_2O_3$, is shown in *Figure 37*.

In some cases the initial velocity at $\theta=0$, namely the constant $a$ of equation (3.19) calculated from the intercept and slope of the $q-\ln(t+t_0)$ line, is far less than the experimental value. This indicates that on part of the surface there is a rapid chemisorption which does not obey the exponential velocity law.

In other cases, notably hydrogen chemisorption on ZnO, the slope of the $q-\ln(t+t_0)$ line changes slope abruptly, as shown in *Figure 38*. This suggests that two different sets of surface sites operate, each with its own values of the constants $E_0$ and $a$. Essentially the same conclusion had previously been reached from the form of the adsorption isobar, shown in *Figure 30*.

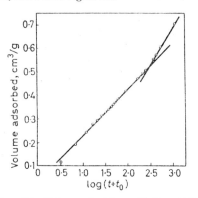

*Figure 38. Hydrogen adsorption on ZnO at 184° C*
By courtesy of Taylor, H. A. and Thon, N. *J. Amer. Chem. Soc.* **74**, 4169, 1952

Often, the constants $a$ and $\alpha$ of equation (3.19) show the expected temperature and pressure dependence. The constant $a$ is proportional to $1/\sqrt{(T)}.e^{-E_0/RT}$—equation (3.11)—or to $\sqrt{(T)}.e^{-E_0/RT}$—equation (3.17). It should therefore show a roughly exponential dependence on temperature, and in fact often does so. The activation energy obtained from this is the quantity $E_0$. By contrast, $\alpha$ tends to be temperature independent, as would be expected. The constant $a$ is in theory and often in practice proportional to the pressure—$a$ in practice is normally pressure independent, as theory suggests. Anomalous temperature and pressure dependence of $a$ and $\alpha$ is, however, found, and this Taylor and Thon attribute to different sets of sites operating in different temperature ranges.

## DETERMINATION OF $\sigma$ BY ABSOLUTE REACTION RATE THEORY[89]

The equilibrium between two reactants $A$ and $B$,

$$A \rightleftharpoons B \tag{3.21}$$

is determined by the ratio of concentrations, $c_A$ and $c_B$. This ratio is equal to the ratio of probabilities of the molecules existing as $A$ or $B$, that is, to the ratio of partition functions, $f_A$ and $f_B$. Thus

$$k_e = \frac{c_B}{c_A} = \frac{f_B}{f_A} \tag{3.22}$$

These equations assume that the energy levels of $A$ and $B$ are expressed in terms of the same zero. It is more practical to measure the energies relative to the energy of the molecules at the absolute zero. If this is done, and if $E$ is the difference between the energies $E_A$ and $E_B$ of $A$ and $B$ at the absolute zero, the equilibrium constant then becomes

$$k_e = \frac{c_B}{c_A} = \frac{f_B}{f_A}\,e^{-E/RT} \tag{3.23}$$

This result arises because $e^{-E_B/RT}$ and $e^{-E_A/RT}$ factorize out of each term comprising $f_B$ and $f_A$.

Partition functions can be written as products of the separate functions for individual modes of motion. Thus, for a molecule which is translating, rotating and vibrating

$$f = f_T f_R f_V \tag{3.24}$$

For translational motion with one degree of freedom, that is, along one co-ordinate

$$f_{T_1} = \frac{\sqrt{(2\pi m k T)}}{h} \cdot l_1 \tag{3.25}$$

where $m$ is the mass of the particle, $h$ is Planck's constant and $l_1$ is the distance along the co-ordinate through which the molecule may move. For three degrees of translational freedom in a rectangular container, the partition function is the product of three such terms, namely

$$f_T = \frac{(2\pi mk\,T)^{3/2}}{h^3} \cdot V \qquad (3.26)$$

where $V = l_1 \cdot l_2 \cdot l_3$ and is the volume of the container.

For linear molecules, the rotational partition function for two degrees of freedom is

$$f_R = \frac{8\pi^2 Ik\,T}{ah^2} \qquad (3.27)$$

where $I$ is the moment of inertia and $a$ is a symmetry factor. The latter is equal to 2 for a homonuclear, diatomic molecule.

For a vibration of frequency $\nu$

$$f_V = (1 - e^{-h\nu/kT})^{-1} \qquad (3.28)$$

This expression gives two important limiting values of $f_V$. If $\nu$ is small, so that $h\nu \ll kT$, $f_V$ approximates to $kT/h\nu$. If $\nu$ is large, so that $h\nu \gg kT$, $f_V$ approaches unity.

So far, equilibrium and not velocities have been considered. To derive a velocity of adsorption, we consider the potential energy of the reacting system as a function of the reaction co-ordinate, as shown in *Figure 5*. In moving from the gas phase to the adsorbed layer the molecule passes over a potential energy barrier, the height of which is the energy of activation. It is assumed that there are molecules at the top of the barrier in an activated or transition state, in statistical equilibrium with molecules in the gas phase and with vacant surface sites. Furthermore, in the transition state, the activated complexes are supposed to vibrate along the reaction co-ordinate (i.e. perpendicular to the surface) with frequency $\nu$. This vibration has the unusual feature that as the molecule moves either away from or towards the surface, its energy falls and it enters a more stable state. Contrary to the normal vibration, there is no restoring force, and each vibration therefore results in adsorption or desorption. $\nu$ is therefore the frequency of decomposition of the complexes, and if $c^{\ddagger}$ is their concentration per cm² of surface the velocity of adsorption per unit area is

$$u = \nu c^{\ddagger} \qquad (3.29)$$

We now derive expressions for $\nu c^{\ddagger}$ in terms of partition functions.

*I. Immobile Transition Complex*

If $N_g$ is the number of molecules in the gas phase, which is of volume $V$ cm³, and $N_s$ and $N^{\ddagger}$ are the numbers of bare sites and transition complexes on a surface of area $S$ cm², the following concentrations may be defined:

$$c_g = N_g/V \text{ gas molecules per cm}^3$$
$$c_s = N_s/S \text{ bare sites per cm}^2$$
$$c^{\ddagger} = N^{\ddagger}/S \text{ transition complexes per cm}^2.$$

The constant for equilibrium on a uniform surface between complexes, gas molecules and bare sites is then

$$k^{\ddagger} = \frac{c^{\ddagger}}{c_g c_s} = \frac{N^{\ddagger}}{(N_g/V)N_s} = \frac{f^{\ddagger}}{(f_g/V)f_s} \tag{3.30}$$

where the $f$'s are the complete partition functions for the species. Representing the partition function of the gas per unit volume $(f_g/V)$ as $F_g$, and separating the zero point energies from the partition functions, equation (3.30) becomes

$$\frac{c^{\ddagger}}{c_g c_s} = \frac{f^{\ddagger}}{F_g \cdot f_s} \cdot e^{-E/RT} \tag{3.31}$$

where $E$ is the activation energy of adsorption.

In $f^{\ddagger}$, there is a term due to the vibration perpendicular to the surface. Since there is no restoring force, the frequency of this vibration will be low, and its partition function is $kT/h\nu$. Separating this term from $f^{\ddagger}$,

$$\frac{c^{\ddagger}}{c_g c_s} = \frac{kT}{h\nu} \cdot \frac{f_{\ddagger}}{F_g \cdot f_s} \cdot e^{-E/RT} \tag{3.32}$$

where $f_{\ddagger}$ no longer incorporates this vibration. The velocity of chemisorption is then

$$u = \nu c^{\ddagger} = c_g c_s \cdot \frac{kT}{h} \cdot \frac{f_{\ddagger}}{F_g \cdot f_s} \cdot e^{-E/RT} \tag{3.33}$$

The following simplications of this equation are possible:

(a) For an ideal gas $c_g = p/kT$.

(b) For the solid there is only vibrational motion of high frequency and therefore $f_s = 1$.

(c) Since the transition complex is immobile, $f_{\ddagger}$ contains no translational or rotational terms and the remainder, due to vibration, may be represented by $b_{\ddagger}$.

(d) Separating from $F_g$ the translational partition function per unit volume we have

$$F_g = \frac{(2\pi mk T)^{3/2}}{h^3} \cdot b_g \qquad (3.34)$$

where $b_g$ is the partition function due to rotation and vibration.

(e) If the total number of surface sites per cm$^2$ is $n_s$, and a fraction $f(\theta)$ is available for chemisorption, $c_s = n_s \cdot f(\theta)$.

Inserting (a)-(e) in equation (3.33) we have

$$u = \frac{n_s h^2 b_{\ddagger}}{2\pi mk T b_g} \cdot \frac{p}{\sqrt{(2\pi mk T)}} \cdot f(\theta) \cdot e^{-E/RT} \qquad (3.35)$$

This equation is then compared with the velocity equation for a uniform surface

$$u = \frac{\sigma p}{\sqrt{(2\pi mk T)}} \cdot f(\theta) \cdot e^{-E/RT} \qquad (3.36)$$

giving

$$\sigma = \frac{n_s h^2 b_{\ddagger}}{2\pi mk T b_g} \qquad (3.37)$$

## II. Mobile Transition Complex

If the molecules are not localized in the activated state, the adsorption sites need not be regarded as reactants. The equilibrium between the gaseous and activated states then becomes

$$k^{\ddagger} = \frac{c^{\ddagger}}{c_g} = \frac{N^{\ddagger}/S}{N_g/V} = \frac{F^{\ddagger}}{F_g} \qquad (3.38)$$

where $F_g$ and $F^{\ddagger}$ are the partition functions for unit volume of gas and per cm$^2$ of activated complex respectively.

The equivalent of equation (3.33) is now

$$u = v c^{\ddagger} = c_g \cdot \frac{kT}{h} \cdot \frac{F_{\ddagger}}{F_g} \cdot e^{-E/RT} \qquad (3.39)$$

where $F_{\ddagger}$ no longer incorporates the weak vibration leading to adsorption, and the zero-point energy contribution has been extracted from the partition functions.

If the activated complex has complete rotational freedom it differs from the reacting gas simply in having lost a translational degree of freedom. We assume that complexes only form above vacant sites, a fraction $f(\theta)$ of the surface being unoccupied. Putting $c_g = p/kT$ as before, we find

$$u = \frac{p}{\sqrt{(2\pi mkT)}} \cdot f(\theta) \cdot e^{-E/RT} \tag{3.40}$$

and comparing (3.36) and (3.40) we see that $\sigma = 1$. If, however, rotation at right angles to the surface is not allowed in the transition complex[90], one degree of rotational freedom will also be lost. In this case, for diatomic molecules,

$$u = \frac{p}{\sqrt{(2\pi mkT)}} \cdot f(\theta) \cdot \left(\frac{h^2 a}{8\pi^2 IkT}\right)^{1/2} \cdot e^{-E/RT} \tag{3.41}$$

and

$$\sigma = \left(\frac{h^2 a}{8\pi^2 IkT}\right)^{1/2} \simeq \frac{1}{\sqrt{b_g}} \tag{3.42}$$

*Adsorption with dissociation*

So far it has been assumed that the adsorbate molecule does not dissociate during chemisorption. Such behaviour is uncommon, and it is pertinent to enquire whether dissociation alters the velocity equation (3.33) and the derived $\sigma$ values.

If a molecule $R_2$ is adsorbed on two sites $S$ as two radicals $R$, adsorption may be represented by the equation

$$R_2 + S_2 \rightarrow R_2 S_2^{\ddagger} \rightarrow 2RS$$

with formation of activated complexes $R_2 S_2^{\ddagger}$ again the slow step. This leads to a velocity of adsorption

$$u = c_g c_{s_2} \frac{kT}{h} \cdot \frac{f_{\ddagger}}{F_g f_{s_2}} e^{-E/RT} \tag{3.43}$$

where $c_{s_2}$ is the concentration of vacant dual sites. This equation is formally identical with equation (3.33) but leads to a somewhat different value of $\sigma$ because $c_s$ is equal to $n_s f(\theta)$ whereas $c_{s_2}$ is equal to $\frac{1}{2} s n_s f(\theta)$, $s$ being the number of sites adjacent to any single site. Putting $s = 4$, the most common value for a lattice plane, equation (3.37) becomes

$$\sigma = \frac{n_s h^2 b_{\ddagger}}{\pi mkT b_g} \tag{3.44}$$

When the transition complex is mobile the velocity equation is unaltered because the concentration of surface sites is not involved.

101

H

*Calculated Values of σ for Different Gases*

Values of σ may be calculated using equations (3.37), (3.42) and (3.44).

For chemisorption of single atoms there is no rotational or vibrational energy in the gas phase and $b_s=1$. In an immobile surface complex the two degrees of translational motion lost on adsorption will be replaced by two vibrations parallel to the surface. Thus $b_{\ddagger}$ contains two vibrational terms and will be equal to unity only if these are of high frequency.

For the adsorption of diatomic molecules $b_g$ will contain two rotational terms and a vibrational term. The last, however, will be equal to unity as the frequency will be high. For an immobile complex two degrees of translational freedom and two degrees of rotational freedom are lost. The former are replaced by two vibrations as before, and the latter by two torsional oscillations. Since at least one of these motions will be of high frequency $b_{\ddagger}$ is considered to contain 3 vibrational terms rather than 4.

Calculated values of σ are given in Table 10. For the immobile complex the value depends on whether the vibration of the complex is strong or weak. The upper limit of $b_{\ddagger}$ assumes weak vibrations with frequencies of $4 \times 10^{12} \sec^{-1}$ for hydrogen and $10^{12} \sec^{-1}$ for the other adsorbates.

TABLE 10

Values of σ Calculated from Transition State Theory

($T=300°K$ and $n_s=10^{15}$ sites $cm^{-2}$)

| Adsorbate | $h^2/2\pi mkT$ | $b_g$ | Range of values for $b_{\ddagger}$ | Values of σ | | |
|---|---|---|---|---|---|---|
| | | | | | Mobile Complex | |
| | | | | Immobile complex | Loss of one rotation | No loss of rotation |
| H atoms | $10^{-16}$ | 1 | 1–4 | 0·1–0·4 | — | 1 |
| H$_2$ molecules | $5 \times 10^{-17}$ | 3·5 | 1–8 | $3 \times 10^{-2}$–0·2 | 0·52 | 1 |
| O$_2$, N$_2$ | $3·5 \times 10^{-18}$ | 70 | 1–300 | $10^{-4}$–$3 \times 10^{-2}$ | 0·12 | 1 |
| CO | $3·5 \times 10^{-18}$ | 110 | 1–300 | $7 \times 10^{-5}$–$2 \times 10^{-2}$ | 0·1 | 1 |
| Cs | $7·5 \times 10^{-19}$ | 1 | 1–50 | $7·5 \times 10^{-4}$–$3·7 \times 10^{-2}$ | — | 1 |

QUANTUM MECHANICAL TREATMENT OF σ

Values of σ have been calculated by LENNARD-JONES and his co-workers[91] using quantum mechanics.

102

In considering the velocity of adsorption, the wave functions of the separated solid and gas molecule are first written down, and then the probability is calculated for transfer of a quantum of energy from the molecule to the solid. By this transfer, the system changes from a state where the energy is in a continuum (non-adsorbed state) to one where it is in a set of discrete levels (adsorbed state).

It is only possible to calculate probabilities for transfer of a single quantum of energy, and since chemisorption in general requires the transfer of several quanta, the method is strictly speaking limited to physical adsorption. However, in adsorption, it is likely that every molecule possessing the necessary activation energy changes from a physically to a chemically adsorbed state, and in this case the Lennard-Jones coefficients will apply to chemisorption.

Numerical values of $\sigma$ for adsorption of hydrogen are shown in Table 11. These vary somewhat with the temperature of adsorption, and also with the Debye characteristic temperature ($\Theta$) of the solid.

TABLE 11

Condensation Coefficients of Hydrogen

| $\Theta °K$ \ $T °K$ | 50 | 100 | 300 |
|---|---|---|---|
| 300 | 0·279 | 0·293 | 0·309 |
| 350 | 0·226 | 0·236 | 0·246 |
| 400 | 0·163 | 0·170 | 0·189 |

For the substances commonly used in hydrogen adsorption, $\Theta$ varies between about 225 and 420 °K, and therefore at room temperatures or below $\sigma$ will lie between 0·2 and 0·3.

EXPERIMENTAL KINETICS

The kinetics of a number of systems have been studied in detail. Some will be discussed here and the results compared with those of the previous sections.

*Adsorption of oxygen on cuprous oxide*[72, 75]

Oxygen is readily taken up by cuprous oxide at room temperature and adsorption proceeds beyond the monolayer stage, showing that some incorporation into the lattice occurs. Different kinetics are observed for premonolayer and postmonolayer adsorption.

103

For the initial stages of adsorption

$$\frac{d\theta}{dt} = Kp(1-\theta)^2 e^{-E/RT} \tag{3.45}$$

the activation energy, $E$, being constant at 7 kcal/mole. This corresponds to the simple theoretical equation for dissociative adsorption if

$$K = \sigma/\sqrt{(2\pi mkT)} \tag{3.46}$$

Normally the temperature dependence of this term is completely masked by the exponential, $e^{-E/RT}$, and $K$ can therefore be treated as a constant.

For the postmonolayer uptake

$$u = Kp e^{-E_0/RT} e^{-\alpha\theta/RT} \tag{3.47}$$

This equation can be compared with equation (3.17) and arises if the activation energy is of the form

$$E = E_0 + \alpha\theta \tag{3.48}$$

$E_0$ was of the same order of magnitude as the activation energy for the premonolayer adsorption, showing that the second process commences immediately after the first is completed.

*Adsorption of nitrogen on iron*[90]

*Figure 39* shows the variation of the activation energy and the heat of chemisorption with coverage for the adsorption of nitrogen on an

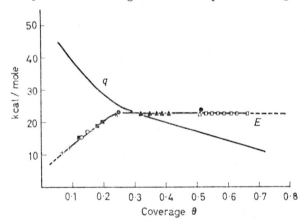

*Figure 39. Variation of activation energy and heat of chemisorption with coverage for nitrogen on an iron catalyst. E=activation energy of adsorption, q=heat of chemisorption*
By courtesy of Scholten, J. J. F. et. al. Trans. Faraday Soc. **55**, 2166, 1959

iron catalyst. There is a break in both plots at about $\theta = 0 \cdot 25$, which causes a change in the kinetics at this point. This is confirmed when the factor $A$ in the expression

$$\frac{d\theta}{dt} = Ap e^{-E/RT} \qquad (3.49)$$

is plotted against coverage (see *Figure 40*), $p$ being the pressure of nitrogen in cms.

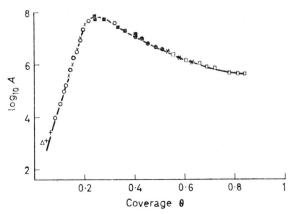

*Figure 40. The temperature-and-pressure-independent factor of the adsorption rate of nitrogen on iron, plotted against coverage*

By courtesy of Scholten, J. J. F. *et al. Trans. Faraday Soc.* **55**, 2166, 1959

In the range $\theta = 0 \cdot 07$ to $0 \cdot 22$ the rate expression is

$$\frac{d\theta}{dt} = 21 \cdot 9p e^{132 \cdot 4\theta/R} e^{(-5250-77500\theta)/RT} \text{ min}^{-1} \qquad (3.50)$$

whereas, in the range $\theta = 0 \cdot 25$ to $0 \cdot 70$

$$\frac{d\theta}{dt} = 2 \cdot 51 \times 10^6 p(1-\theta)^2 \cdot \theta^{-3} e^{-23000/RT} \text{ min}^{-1} \qquad (3.51)$$

Equation (3.50) may still contain the factor $(1-\theta)^2$ since to a good approximation this is equal to $\exp(-2 \cdot 22\theta)$ when $\theta < 0 \cdot 25$. It is essentially an Elovich equation, having an activation energy increasing linearly with $\theta$. The variation of the term $A$ with $\theta$ is interesting, and proves to be mainly due to a change in $\sigma$. Thus, remembering that $A$ is proportional to $\sigma f(\theta)$, and putting $f(\theta)$ equal to $(1-\theta)^2$, calculation gives

$$\sigma \simeq 5 \times 10^{-6} \quad \text{at} \quad \theta = 0 \cdot 07$$

$$\sigma \simeq 0 \cdot 5 \qquad \text{at} \quad \theta = 0 \cdot 25$$

Comparison of these values with those in Table 10 suggests that there is a transition from an immobile to a mobile transition complex.

Possibly the $\theta^{-3}$ term in equation (3.51) is also connected with a variation in the mobility of the activated complex.

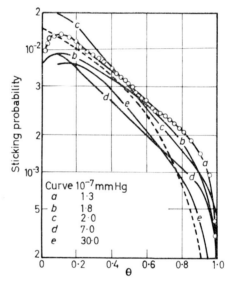

*Figure 41. The sticking probability of oxygen on silicon as a function of the fractional coverage $\theta$. The curves were obtained with different oxygen pressures*
By courtesy of Eisinger, J., and Law, J. T. *J. Chem. Phys.* **30**, 410, 1959

*The Adsorption of Oxygen on Silicon and Germanium*

It is not definitely established that these adsorptions are activated, but there is some evidence that they may be. The activation energy at $\theta = 0$ must, however, be very small.

EISINGER and LAW[92] have investigated the variation of sticking probability with coverage for the adsorption of oxygen on a silicon filament. Their results are shown in *Figure 41*. The dotted line is a plot of the function

$$s = 0.015 \cdot \frac{4}{4-\theta} \cdot (1-\theta)^2 \qquad (3.52)$$

which employs equation (3.8)

$$f(\theta) = \frac{z}{z-\theta} \cdot (1-\theta)^2 \qquad (3.53)$$

with $z$, the number of nearest neighbour sites, equal to 4. Agreement with experiment is seen to be fair. However, the fall in $s$ with increasing coverage may be due largely to an increasing activation energy and not to $f(\theta)$. Thus, over the middle range of coverage, $s$ appears to fall exponentially with increasing $\theta$, suggesting a linearly increasing activation energy. Again, the sticking probability at $\theta = 0$ is $\simeq 1.5 \times 10^{-2}$. Provided the activation energy at this coverage is very small $s$ should be equal to $\sigma$, and the value agrees well with the upper value given in Table 10 for an immobile complex—namely $3 \times 10^{-2}$.

SCHLIER and FARNSWORTH[93] have obtained approximate values for the sticking probabilities of oxygen on single crystal faces of germanium and silicon by following the change in the electron diffraction patterns of the surfaces during adsorption. Their maximum values are given in Table 12.

TABLE 12

Sticking Probabilities on Single Crystal Faces of Germanium and Silicon

| System | Sticking probability | |
|---|---|---|
| | (111) face | (100) face |
| $O_2$/Ge | $\sim 10^{-4}$ | $\sim 2 \times 10^{-3}$ |
| $O_2$/Si | $\sim 0.2$ | $\sim 3 \times 10^{-2}$ |

There is seen to be a considerable variation with crystal face for silicon. Whether this arises because of an activation energy term or because of a difference in the mobility of the activated complex is not certain.

107

The rate of adsorption on both elements is directly proportional to the pressure[93]. However, at high coverages a proportionality to $\sqrt{p}$ has been found[94-96], the adsorption obeying the Elovich equation. This will be discussed in more detail in a later section.

*Adsorption of nitrogen on barium*

WAGENER[41], has studied the kinetics of the adsorption of nitrogen on evaporated barium films, and has found an activation energy between 2 and 4 kcal/mole. An initial sticking probability of $3 \times 10^{-4}$ was computed for room temperature on the basis of adsorption on the geometric area of the film only. However, it would seem more correct to use the real area, and this gives for $s$ a value of about $2 \times 10^{-5}$. At $\theta = 0$, $\sigma$ is equal to $s \cdot e^{E/RT}$. Putting $E = 3$ kcal/mole this gives $\sigma \simeq 3 \times 10^{-3}$. Again, this is within the range of values given in Table 10 for an immobile transition complex.

### CALCULATION OF THE ACTIVATION ENERGY OF CHEMISORPTION

For simple assemblies of atoms at known distances apart, the total energy may be calculated from the forces between the atoms. Consequently, for a simple chemical reaction, it is possible to calculate the change in energy as the molecules approach one another from infinity and react. The maximum extent to which intermediate configurations possess a greater energy than that of the separated reactants is the activation energy.

In this way the activation energy for hydrogen chemisorption on carbon has been calculated by SHERMAN and EYRING[97], and on nickel by SHERMAN, SUN and EYRING[98], and by OKAMOTO, HORIUTI and HIROTA[99].

With carbon, the system was reduced to an assembly of four atoms, and chemisorption was represented as

$$\begin{matrix} H\text{------}H \\ \\ C\text{------}C \end{matrix} \quad \rightarrow \quad \begin{matrix} H & H \\ | & | \\ C\text{------}C \end{matrix}$$

The usual assumption of covalent bonds was made, namely that 10 per cent of the total energy of the system is, in all configurations, electrostatic in origin. Also the C—H bond was assumed to have a strength of 92 kcal/mole, and in chemisorption a C–C bond of strength 39 kcal/mole was supposed to be broken. Then since the molar heat of dissociation of hydrogen is 103 kcal/mole the heat of chemisorption is

$$2 \times 92 - 103 - 39 = 42 \text{ kcal/mole}$$

in fair agreement with Barrer's experimental value[59], 50 kcal/mole.

An interesting feature of the work is that activation energies were calculated for various distances between the carbon atoms. *Figure 42* shows that the energy varies markedly with spacing, and is a minimum for spacings of 3·5 Å. The reason for this behaviour is as follows. At very high separations of the carbon atoms the hydrogen

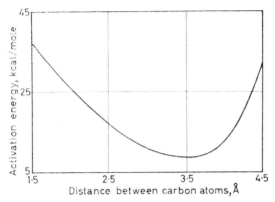

*Figure 42. The activation energy of hydrogen chemisorption by carbon*
By courtesy of Sherman, A. and Eyring, H. *J. Amer. Chem. Soc.* **54**, 2661, 1932

molecule must effectively be dissociated prior to adsorption. The activation energy is therefore high and approaches the heat of dissociation of the hydrogen molecule. At very low separations, the activation energy is again high because adsorption is hindered by repulsion forces. That is, representing chemisorption as

$$C^1C^2 + H^1H^2 \rightarrow C^1H^1 + C^2H^2$$

repulsions between $C^1$ and $H^2$ and between $C^2$ and $H^1$ are appreciable and raise the activation energy.

Now the spacings of adjacent carbon atoms in diamond and graphite are respectively 1·54 and 1·42 Å, on both of which the activation energies are very high. It seems likely that chemisorption will not, as is usually assumed, take place on pairs of adjacent atoms. With graphite, where the atoms in the surface are disposed in hexagonal rings, a far more favourable spacing is that between opposite atoms in a hexagon, 2·84 Å. The calculated activation energy, 14 kcal/mole, then agrees moderately well with Barrer's experimental value at low coverages, 22 kcal/mole[60]. On diamond, the most favourable spacing is about 2·8 Å, and the calculated energy, 15 kcal/mole, is in excellent agreement with the experimental value, namely 14 kcal/mole.

The calculations for hydrogen chemisorption on nickel[98] give less satisfactory results. Here the proportion of electrostatic energy was assumed to be 14 per cent in the H—H bond, 20 per cent in the Ni—H bond and 30 per cent in the Ni—Ni bond. The activation energy for adsorption on a 2·38 Å spacing was calculated to be 24 kcal/mole, and the heat of adsorption 4·6 kcal/mole.

However, the adsorption of hydrogen on nickel does not seem to require an activation energy, being rapid even at liquid helium temperature[100], and the experimental heat of adsorption is about 30 kcal/mole[35].

The failure of this calculation is probably due to the assumption that the hydrogen adatoms form simple covalent bonds with the surface nickel atoms. Metals have such a high density of electron levels that bonding is probably never really localized and this is in agreement with the small activation energies required for surface migration of adatoms (see Chapter IX).

## NON-ACTIVATED ADSORPTION

The adsorption of many gases on clean, transition metal films has been shown to be very fast and to remain so right down to 78 °K. Very rapid adsorption has also been observed in the field emission microscope at temperatures as low as 4 °K[101]. Any activation energy required for this kind of adsorption must clearly be extremely small.

For some systems, a constant sticking probability is found over wide ranges of temperature, indicating that adsorption is completely non-activated, while in none of the fast adsorptions so far studied has a sticking probability with a definite, positive temperature coefficient been found.

It might seem that non-activated adsorption could be treated by equating $E$ to zero in the equations derived for direct activated adsorption. However, precursor states are important when adsorption is non-activated and the kinetics of chemisorption cannot be described adequately in terms of collisions with vacant sites, as in the last section.

Since there is no firmly established theory that can account for the kinetics of non-activated adsorption in detail, we shall commence by discussing the experimental data and then attempt to develop the broad outlines of a theory.

### THE NATURE OF FILAMENT SURFACES

The majority of sticking probability determinations have been carried out on tungsten wires or ribbons and it is important to understand the nature of their surfaces, especially as there is evidence that sticking probabilities are sensitive to surface structure.

In drawing tungsten wires or rolling tungsten ribbons, the crystallites tend to become oriented with the (110) crystal direction along the axis. The wires, however, being of circular cross section, should expose a variety of stable crystal faces in the surface, whereas ribbons may expose one particular crystal face preferentially, particularly if the surface is strictly planar on an atomic scale.

The surfaces of tungsten ribbons have been examined by x-ray and electron diffraction and by optical and electron microscopy. Diffraction patterns have shown that the (311) and (411) crystal directions are most commonly perpendicular to the surface of ribbons[102, 103], and the (100) direction occasionally so[104]. However, these results only prove that particular planes are exposed in the surface if it is also shown that the surface is atomically smooth. EISINGER[105] found that the surfaces of his ribbons were smooth, at least within the 100 Å resolution of the electron microscope which he used, and concluded that the (311) plane was preferentially exposed in the surface. This is surprising since such a high index plane might be considered somewhat unstable.

PASTERNAK and WIESENDANGER[28], using a molybdenum ribbon with the (411) and (311) directions normal to the surface, found that grain growth occurred during their experiments and obtained a surface roughness factor of 1·2 from electron micrographs. This suggests that while ribbon surfaces may initially consist predominantly of one plane they may produce various facets as time passes and expose a number of planes.

The wires and ribbons used in kinetic measurements are usually polycrystalline. Before use they are heated to 2,300–2,800 °K for a number of hours, either in vacuo or, if it is necessary to remove traces of carbon, in a small pressure of oxygen. At these temperatures the crystallite size increases but the original orientation is usually preserved. The final number of crystallites depends on the ageing temperature and may vary from five[103] to one thousand[102]. EISINGER[105], however, has made single crystals of tungsten and molybdenum by slowly withdrawing ribbons from a mercury reservoir while passing a heavy current through them.

EARLY WORK

The first measurements of the velocity of a non-activated adsorption were made by TAYLOR and LANGMUIR[106] for the adsorption of caesium vapour on a tungsten wire. They found that the sticking probability was unity up to coverages as high as 0·98 of a monolayer, conditions under which a majority of the atoms colliding with the surface must strike occupied sites. They concluded that the caesium was initially adsorbed into a mobile, second layer in which it could migrate over the surface until a vacant site was found. A second layer was observed after completion of the first layer and identified with the precursor state.

Later, MORRISON and ROBERTS[107] measured the rate of condensation of oxygen on a tungsten wire by following the change in the neon accommodation coefficient on the introduction of a small partial pressure of oxygen into the circulating neon. A typical curve, obtained with an oxygen pressure of $2·3 \times 10^{-9}$ mm, is shown in *Figure 43*. The accommodation coefficient, $a$, increases almost

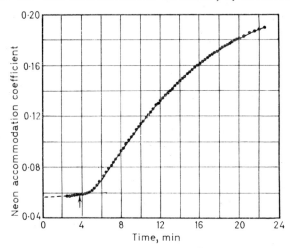

*Figure 43. Oxygen adsorption on a tungsten filament. The arrow indicates the moment at which oxygen was admitted*

By courtesy of Morrison, J. L. and Roberts, J. K. *Proc. Roy. Soc.* A**173**, 1, 1939

linearly with time between 6 and 10 minutes. If $a$ is a linear function of the adsorbed amount, this implies that the rate of adsorption is independent of coverage.

An initial sticking probability of unity can in fact be calculated from these results, but a number of assumptions enter the calculation and modern work suggests a rather lower value of $s$.

MODERN STUDIES USING METAL FILAMENTS

*The Adsorption of Nitrogen on Tungsten*

The kinetics of fast chemisorption have been largely elucidated by use of the flash filament technique described in Chapter II. This was first applied to the adsorption of nitrogen on tungsten, and more work has been done on this system than on any other. However, it is exceptional in that many workers have found a decrease in sticking probability as the temperature is raised. This has not been found with any other system so far studied.

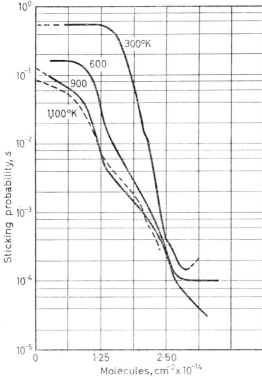

*Figure 44. Nitrogen adsorption on a tungsten ribbon*
By courtesy of Becker, J. A. and Hartman, C. D. *J. Phys. Chem.* **57**, 153, 1953

The original results for nitrogen on tungsten, due to BECKER and HARTMAN[108], are shown in *Figure 44*. The decrease in $s$ with increasing temperature is difficult to account for on the basis of the kinetic treatment given previously. Thus, if $E=0$, the decrease in $s$ would have to be attributed to a decrease in $\sigma$. However, since $s$ is high at room temperature, the transition complex must be mobile and $\sigma$ should vary as $T^{-1/2}$ (see equation (3.42)). This, though, is insufficient to explain the observed decrease in $s$.

Both the constancy of $s$ during the initial stages of adsorption and its dependence on temperature can be qualitatively accounted for in terms of a precursor state, possibly consisting of physically adsorbed molecules. These may either desorb or pass over to the final chemisorbed state, and the decrease in sticking probability with increasing temperature arises because desorption becomes more likely at higher temperatures. Also, the fact that molecules may migrate over the surface to vacant sites explains the initial constancy of $s$.

In the experiments of Becker and Hartman the temperature of the tungsten alone was varied, the incoming gas and the walls of the reaction vessel being at room temperature. Under these conditions the initial sticking probability undoubtedly decreases with increasing temperature. However, conflicting results have been obtained when the temperature of the whole system is varied. KISLIUK[102] found that the initial sticking probability, $s_0$, was constant between 196 and 473 °K under these conditions, but that $s_0$ was proportional to $1/T^2$ at higher temperatures when only the filament was heated. A similar constancy of $s_0$ has been reported between 90 and 480 °K[109]. EHRLICH[110], however, found a decrease in $s_0$ with increasing temperature under apparently identical circumstances.

It is not easy to resolve these differences. Possibly the sticking probability decreases only at high temperatures, although this conclusion still conflicts with Ehrlich's work. Whatever the explanation, the constant value of $s$ sometimes observed in the lower temperature range is probably genuine, because a spurious constancy could arise only by a fortuitous cancellation of opposing factors. If this is so, the desorption of molecules from the precursor state must be negligible under these conditions, otherwise $s$ would vary with temperature.

Sticking probabilities for nitrogen on tungsten at 300 °K, obtained by various workers, are summarized in Table 13.

The scatter of the results may in part be due to experimental errors and artefacts. In addition, the sticking probability may be sensitive to surface structure. Thus EHRLICH[110] has recorded average sticking probabilities of 0·11, 0·13 and 0·28 for three different wires although values for any one wire were reproducible to within 5 per cent.

The most striking variation in the initial sticking probability, however, is between the value of about 0·03 found by JONES and PETHICA[104] and by SAINI et al.[114] and the values found by other workers. This may be evidence that $s$ varies with crystal face since

TABLE 13

Sticking Probability Data for Nitrogen on Tungsten at 300°K

| $s_0$ | $n_c \times 10^{-14}$ | $n_{max} \times 10^{-14}$ | $n_c/n_{max}$ | Adsorbent surface | Reference |
|---|---|---|---|---|---|
| 0·55 | 1·0 | 3·0 | 0·33 | Ribbon, (411) plane? | Becker[103] |
| 0·30 | 1·8 | 5·5 | 0·33 | Single crystal ribbon, (311) plane? | Eisinger[111] |
| 0·42 | 0·5 | 1·8 | 0·28 | Ribbon | Schlier[112] |
| 0·30 ⎫<br>0·25 ⎭ | 1·5 | 3·0 | 0·50 | Ribbons, (311) plane? | Kisliuk[113] |
| 0·11 ⎫<br>0·13 ⎬<br>0·28 ⎭ | 0·75–0·40 | 2·8 | 0·27– ⎫<br>0·14 ⎭ | Wires | Ehrlich[110] |
| 0·035 | 1·2 | 2·9 | 0·42 | Ribbon, (100) plane? | Jones and Pethica[104] |
| 0·03 | 1·0 | 3·0 | 0·33 | Thin sheet | Saini, Ricca and Nasini[114] |

$n_c$ = number of molecules adsorbed per $cm^2$ when $s$ begins to fall.
$n_{max}$ = maximum number of molecules adsorbed per $cm^2$

Jones and Pethica claim that the (100) face predominated in the surface of their ribbon in contrast to the (311) and (411) faces claimed by other workers. Again, the latter give higher values than those obtained by Ehrlich for wires which must expose several planes.

Nitrogen is adsorbed on tungsten in three different states, designated $\alpha$, $\beta$ and $\gamma$. Of these $\beta$ is the normal strong chemisorption[115]. The population of the three states on the surface can be found at any time by flashing the filament (see Chapter IV) and, hence, sticking probability *versus* coverage curves can be constructed for the different binding states[110]. Such curves are shown in *Figure 45*. At low temperatures the region of constant sticking probability is seen to be considerably extended and this is associated with a large increase in the population of the weak, molecularly held $\gamma$ state. This may therefore be the precursor to strong chemisorption.

*The adsorption of carbon monoxide on tungsten*

Sticking probabilities between 315 and 580°K have been obtained for this system by REDHEAD[116], and are shown in *Figure 46*. Within the limits of experimental error $s_0$ is independent of temperature. Similar behaviour has been found by NASINI, SAINI and RICCA[109] between 90 and 481°K.

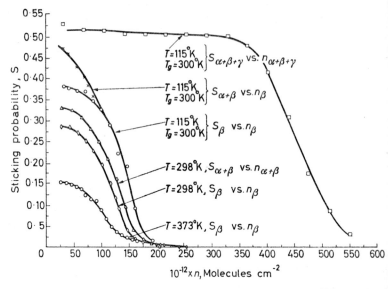

*Figure 45. Sticking probability for adsorption of nitrogen on a tungsten filament.* T= *surface temperature,* $T_g$ =*gas temperature*
By courtesy of Ehrlich, G. *J. Chem. Phys.* **34**, 29, 1961

Results obtained by other workers have usually been at room temperature only and are summarized in Table 14, together with those mentioned above.

TABLE 14

Sticking Probability Data for Carbon Monoxide on Tungsten at 300°K

| $s_0$ | $n_c \times 10^{-14}$ | $n_{max} \times 10^{-14}$ | $n_c/n_{max}$ | Adsorbent surface | Reference |
|---|---|---|---|---|---|
| 0·36 | 3·5 | 6·5 | 0·54 | Ribbon, (411) plane? | Becker[103] |
| 0·18 | 3·5 | 5·3 | 0·66 | Single crystal ribbon, (311) plane? | Eisinger[117] |
| 0·62 | 1·5 | 5·0 | 0·30 | Ribbon | Schlier[112] |
| 0·3⎫ 0·5⎭ | 2·2 | 4·5 | 0·49 | Wires | Ehrlich[118] |
| 0·50 | 4·0 | 9·5 | 0·40 | Wire | Redhead[116] |
| — | 4·6 | 9·3 | 0·50 | Thin sheet | Nasini *et al*[109] |

$n_c$ =number of molecules adsorbed per cm² when $s$ begins to fall
$n_{max}$ =maximum number of molecules adsorbed per cm²

116

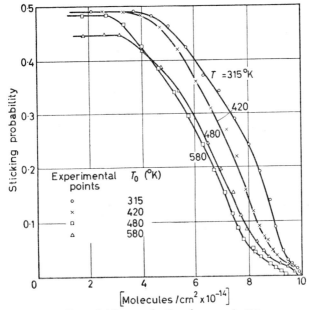

*Figure 46. Sticking probability as a function of coverage for* CO *on tungsten*
By courtesy of Redhead, P. A. *Trans. Faraday Soc.* **57**, 641, 1961

Again there is scatter among the various results but there seems to be no trend towards lower values of $s_0$ for wires, as in the case of nitrogen.

### The adsorption of hydrogen on tungsten

The results of EISINGER[105] for a single crystal tungsten ribbon, supposedly exposing the (311) plane, are shown in *Figure 47*. The initial sticking probability was not completely reproducible, varying between 0·15 and 0·30, but was independent of temperature, as shown in the figure.

At much higher temperatures the equilibrium surface concentration of hydrogen atoms becomes so low that it is not possible to carry out straightforward adsorption experiments. At sufficiently high temperatures, however, every hydrogen molecule entering the chemisorbed state is finally desorbed as two atoms, and it is possible to find $s_0$ from the rate of atomization. The value obtained in this way is 0·30 on a wire at 1,830°K[119], and also on a tungsten strip at 2,500°K[120]. Thus the sticking probability appears to be constant over a wide temperature range.

117

I

HICKMOTT[121], using a wire, has obtained rather lower values of $s_0$, but these too show little variation with temperature. Thus, $s_0$ was found to be 0·1 between 77 and 194 °K using the flash filament technique, and 0·05 between 1,450 and 2,000 °K, using the rate of atomization. Hickmott has also calculated the sticking probability

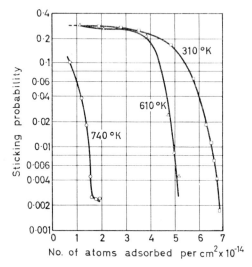

*Figure 47. The sticking probability of hydrogen on tungsten as a function of coverage for three different temperatures*
By courtesy of Eisinger, J. *J. Chem. Phys.* **29**, 1154, 1958

of hydrogen atoms from his results, finding it to be less than unity (0·16) and independent of temperature between 1,200 and 1,600 °K.

SMITH and FITE[120] have studied the atomization of hydrogen at high temperatures by impinging a beam of hydrogen molecules on to a tungsten target. A limiting value for the sticking probability of 0·3 was calculated and has been referred to earlier.

*Figure 48* shows that the angular distribution of hydrogen atoms evaporating from the tungsten surface at 2,500 °K is typical of random scattering, obeying the cosine law. For hydrogen molecules, on the other hand, there is a shift towards specular reflection, and this would probably be even more pronounced if the surface were atomically smooth. The maximum intensity, however, occurs at less than the specular angle, suggesting that the hydrogen molecules leave the hot surface with an increased normal component of momentum.

At 300 °K, however, the angular distribution of hydrogen molecules obeys the cosine law and is therefore random. Every incident molecule must, therefore, be adsorbed for a short time before evaporating and since the primary chemisorbed layer should be almost complete at 300 °K, this process must involve a weakly held second layer for which the sticking probability is close to unity.

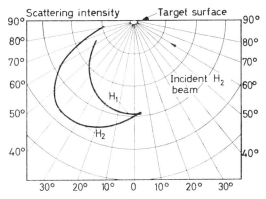

Figure 48. Angular distribution of hydrogen atoms ($H_1$) and molecules ($H_2$) evaporating from a tungsten surface at 2,500° K. The $H_2$ signals are shown on a reduced scale for clarity
By courtesy of Smith, J. N. and Fite, W. L. J. Chem. Phys. **37**, 898, 1962

*The adsorption of hydrogen on molybdenum*
Sticking probabilities of hydrogen on a molybdenum ribbon have been measured by Pasternak and Wiesendanger[28], and are shown in *Figure 49*. $s_0$ is seen to be constant over the temperature range employed.

Layers formed above 320 °K desorbed in one burst on flashing the filament, whereas layers formed below this temperature came off in two bursts, suggesting the presence of two different binding states. A maximum of about $3.5 \times 10^{14}$ molecules per $cm^2$ could be adsorbed in each of these. The weakly held hydrogen did not appear until the strongly held layer was almost complete, and this suggests that the former may be a precursor for the latter. On the other hand, the saturation coverage decreased continuously as the temperature was raised, indicating that there was only a small difference in binding energy between the end of the first adsorption and the beginning of the second.

At temperatures above 1,450 °K the rate of atomization gave

sticking probabilities varying between 0·12 and 0·15. The difference between these values and the value of 0·35 found in the adsorption experiments is probably not significant and $s_0$ would therefore appear to be fairly constant over the whole temperature range concerned.

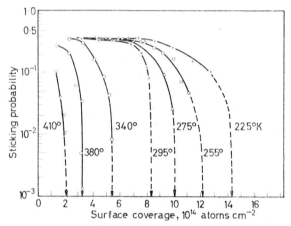

*Figure 49. Sticking probability versus coverage for hydrogen on molybdenum*
By courtesy of Pasternak, R. A. and Wiesendanger, H. U. D. *J. Chem. Phys.* **34**, 2062, 1961

## The adsorption of oxygen on tungsten

Oxygen reacts with hot tungsten filaments to form tungstic oxide, while carbon monoxide is formed when filaments containing traces of carbon are used. However, it is possible to allow for the first of these effects when using flash filament techniques, while the second can be eliminated by using carbon free filaments. Nevertheless results obtained for oxygen should be treated with caution.

BECKER[103] has observed two regions of constant sticking probability for oxygen on tungsten; one at $s_0 = 0·13$ and the other at $s = 0·04$. EISINGER[122] has found similar behaviour although the two regions are not so well defined and the sticking probabilities are roughly twice those found by Becker, $s_0$ being 0·24. SCHLIER[112] has also obtained sticking probabilities of oxygen as a function of coverage. His results show only one region where $s$ is constant, although there is a slight kink in the $s–\theta$ curve.

It is possible that these results are complicated by the presence of hot filament ionization gauges in the systems used. Similar results have been obtained with methane and ethylene[103], both of which interact with hot tungsten filaments. However, it is difficult to see in what way these interactions could give rise to the type of behaviour observed.

The sticking probability has not been determined as a function of temperature, but some idea of the values at elevated temperatures can be obtained from the rate of formation of oxide. Unfortunately, the experimental data is conflicting. Thus, it has been claimed[112, 123] that nearly every molecule of oxygen which collides with a hot filament is removed from the system as oxide in the temperature range 1,980–2,450 °K, suggesting a sticking probability of unity. Eisinger[122], however, finds that the fraction of the number of molecules colliding with the surface which forms oxide reaches a maximum of 0·03 at 1,800 °K with an oxygen pressure of about $10^{-5}$ mm. BECKER et al.[124] have found similar behaviour. The low rates of oxide formation were measured on ribbons allegedly exposing (311) and (411) faces, whereas the results giving sticking probabilities of unity were measured on surfaces which probably exposed a variety of faces: possibly the discrepancies are connected with differences in surface structure.

*The nickel–chlorine reaction*

McKINLEY and SHULER[125] have studied the high temperature reaction of chlorine with nickel wires. The nickel chloride formed is sufficiently volatile at the temperatures employed for the reaction to proceed on a virtually clean metal surface. Between 20 and 50 per cent of the chlorine molecules striking the wire form nickel chloride and this percentage is independent of temperature in the range 1,200–1,700 °K. Since the reaction is apparently non-activated, the rate of adsorption of chlorine must be rate-determining, and the sticking probability is presumably between 0·2 and 0·5. During the reaction a characteristic pattern consisting of 3-sided pyramids develops on the wire surface, indicating a preferential attack at certain crystal faces.

More recent experiments[126] using a molecular beam of chlorine show that 20 to 40 per cent of the chlorine molecules react between 1,100 and 1,600 °K, the remainder being specularly reflected without a measurable change in translational energy. These results are similar to those found for beams of hydrogen impinging on tungsten[120].

FROMMER and POLANYI[127] have found a collision yield of about 0·3 for the copper/chlorine reaction, which is independent of temperature between 670 and 970 °K. They also report similar results for many different metals and alloys.

DEDUCTIONS FROM FILAMENT WORK

The average value for the initial sticking probability does not seem to vary significantly from one system to another and appears to be centred on a value near 0·3. Thus, average values are: $N_2/W$, 0·29 (300°K); $CO/W$, 0·41; $H_2/W$, 0·24; $H_2/Mo$, 0·35; $O_2/W$, 0·34; $Cl_2/Ni$, 0·2–0·4. The sticking probability of hydrogen atoms on tungsten also seems to come within this range. The only exception is the case of caesium on tungsten where the sticking probability is unity. This would suggest that $s_0$ is not normally affected greatly either by the nature of the adsorbate, or by the particular metal used. However, for any particular system, there is often considerable variation in the reported values of the sticking probability, probably due mainly to variations in the structure of the surfaces. In this way, the nature of the metal surface does have an influence.

Using the case of hydrogen on tungsten, the argument may be taken further. In the molecular beam experiments of SMITH and FITE[120] the hydrogen molecules striking the hot tungsten surface were either atomized or reflected unchanged. Under these circumstances the fate of any particular hydrogen molecule is entirely determined during its initial impact with the surface and only a limited number of factors can be involved in determining this. They are:

(a) The amount of translational, vibrational and rotational energy possessed by the incoming molecule.

(b) The orientation of the molecule at the moment of impact.

(c) The angle of approach of the molecule.

(d) The point at which the molecule strikes the surface.

(e) The moment at which impact occurs.

(c) can immediately be ruled out because all the molecules approached the surface at the same angle in the beam experiments.

Now the factor which determines whether or not a hydrogen molecule is reflected at 2,500 °K presumably determines the sticking probability at low temperatures since, within experimental error, the fraction of the total number of molecules arriving at the surface that reacts is the same in both cases. This being so, we can eliminate two more possibilities by reference to flash filament work. HICK-MOTT's[121] result, namely that there is no variation of $s$ with the temperature of the hydrogen, eliminates (a). (b) also can be ruled out since the sticking probability of a hydrogen atom would appear to be less than one at high temperatures and of roughly the same magnitude as that of a hydrogen molecule, whereas it should be unity if the orientation of an atom or molecule were the deciding factor.

At low temperatures hydrogen molecules are held in a weakly bound second layer, and those molecules which do not enter the chemisorbed state may remain on the surface for some time before evaporating. Under these circumstances $(e)$ becomes irrelevant as a factor in determining the sticking probability.

Thus $(d)$ remains as the only possibility. A variation of sticking probability with the point of impact on the surface can arise either through isolated atoms having high activity, or through patches or groups of active sites. The first possibility can probably be eliminated for the same reason as $(e)$: if hydrogen molecules migrate across the surface for a short distance in a weakly held second layer, it becomes meaningless to define a sticking probability for any particular site.

It thus appears that for certain regions of a tungsten surface the sticking probability for hydrogen is close to unity, whereas for other regions the value is much smaller. If these areas are associated with different crystallographic planes, a difficulty arises in that the sticking probability on Eisinger's single crystal ribbons, allegedly exposing the (311) face, should be either very low or unity, whereas it is not significantly different from other values. However, doubt remains as to whether or not his ribbons actually expose a single face in the surface.

These conclusions can, presumably, be extended to the other systems where the sticking probability is independent of temperature. If all molecules striking active patches are chemisorbed and nearly all molecules striking patches of low activity are finally desorbed, $s_0$ should be equal to the active fraction of the surface. Thus it would appear that with tungsten, molybdenum and nickel approximately one third of the surface is, on average, active.

*The variation of sticking probability with coverage*

The constancy of the sticking probability during the initial stages of adsorption is explicable if the probability of molecules desorbing from the mobile, second layer approaches zero on the active regions. It would then be anticipated that the sticking probability would begin to fall once the active regions were covered. Thus there should be some correlation between $s_0$ and $n_c/n_{max}$, the fractional coverage at which $s$ begins to decrease. At $300\,^{\circ}\mathrm{K}$ average values for $n_c/n_{max}$ are: $N_2/W$, 0·34; $CO/W$, 0·48; $H_2/W$, 0·50; $H_2/Mo$, 0·50; $O_2/W$ (BECKER[103]), 0·26; $Cs/W$, 0·98. Thus for $N_2$, $CO$, $O_2$ and $Cs$ on tungsten $s_0 \simeq n_c/n_{max}$. However this does not apply to the hydrogen adsorptions, while for nitrogen on tungsten EHRLICH[110] found that the region of constant sticking probability is smaller for a filament with a high value of $s_0$ than for one with a low value, which hardly suggests a correlation between $n_c/n_{max}$ and $s_0$.

Once the active regions are covered, the sticking probability might be expected to fall abruptly to a value corresponding to that for the regions of low activity. However, such behaviour is observed only in the case of oxygen on tungsten. This may mean that molecules striking active regions that are fully occupied, migrate in the second layer to regions of low activity, where they are chemisorbed. As adsorption proceeds, these molecules must travel longer distances before finding vacant sites, and desorption from this second layer will increase. In this way, $s$ will begin to fall once the active regions are covered, but only slowly.

*The nitrogen–tungsten system*

This system differs from the others in a number of respects and some of the conclusions drawn above are not strictly applicable here.

The salient features of the kinetics[108] are:

(*a*) A continuous decrease in $s_0$ with increasing temperature.

(*b*) A constant $s$ during the initial stages of adsorption for temperatures below 900 °K.

EHRLICH[128] has concluded that these results can be explained only in terms of a surface with areas of high and low activity as described above, the active patches being tentatively identified in this case with the areas surrounding lattice steps. However, unlike the other systems discussed, $s_0$ cannot be equal simply to the active fraction of the surface, because of its dependence on temperature.

However, if molecules in the weakly held, second layer can migrate from inactive to active regions and then be chemisorbed, the effective area of the active patches is increased. It also becomes temperature dependent—an increase in temperature decreases the mean distance over which a molecule may migrate before desorbing. As a result $s$ also decreases. Again, provided no molecules escape from the active regions, $s$ will be independent of coverage until these regions are fully occupied. This latter circumstance would seem to apply to nitrogen on tungsten below 900 °K, although above this temperature, where there is no region of constant sticking probability, some of the molecules in the second layer are presumably able to desorb from the active regions.

124

KISLIUK[129] has attempted to explain the dependence of sticking probability on coverage assuming a uniform surface. However, the theoretical $s-\theta$ curves do not fit the experimental data well. On this model, $s$ is strictly independent of coverage only when desorption of molecules from the second layer is negligible, and in this case $s$ should remain constant up to full coverage. Again, the experimental $s-\theta$ curves seem to involve a discontinuity where $s$ first begins to decrease, suggesting a qualitative change in the adsorption process at this point.

KINETICS INVOLVING PRECURSOR STATES

In the adsorption of hydrogen on tungsten the molecular beam work suggests that every incoming molecule is initially weakly adsorbed at 300°K. This may also apply to other systems at this temperature. On a partially covered surface molecules may either desorb from this layer or enter the primary chemisorbed state, and the overall sticking probability will be determined by the relative rates of the two processes. For non-activated chemisorption the potential energy diagram is shown in *Figure 50*.

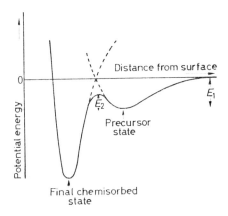

*Figure 50. Potential energy diagram for non-activated adsorption with precursor state*

We must now consider possible reasons why $s$ should be high on certain regions of the surface, and low on others. If the probability factor, $\sigma$, for the transition to the primary chemisorbed layer is close to unity, then, according to the argument advanced on page 90, molecules will be unable to desorb from the precursor state, and $s$ will be unity. If, however, the activated complex leading to the primary chemisorbed state has fewer degrees of freedom than a molecule in the second layer, $\sigma$ will be much less than one, and there will be competition between desorption and chemisorption.

This problem has been treated quantitatively for a uniform surface by EHRLICH[128, 130]. For a single vibration the probability $P_1$, of a molecule desorbing from the second layer is simply $e^{-E_1/RT}$, provided molecules possessing the necessary activation energy always desorb. Similarly, the probability, $P_2$, of a molecule entering the primary chemisorbed state is given by

$$P_2 = f(\theta) \cdot \sigma \cdot e^{-E_2/RT} \qquad (3.54)$$

where $f(\theta)$ represents the fraction of the total surface area available for the formation of the primary state at coverage $\theta$, and $E_2$ is the activation energy necessary to enter the primary layer. Then if the vibrational modes leading to desorption and to the primary chemisorbed state are the same

$$s = \frac{P_2}{P_1+P_2} = \frac{1}{1 + \dfrac{e^{(E_2-E_1)/RT}}{f(\theta) \cdot \sigma}} \qquad (3.55)$$

For diatomic molecules forming an immobile transition complex we can put $\sigma = 10^{-3}$, the mean of the ranges of values given in Table 10. This sort of value may also apply even when the primary chemisorbed layer is mobile, since mobility normally consists of activated hops and not true translation. For a clean metal surface $f(\theta) = 1$ and

$$s_0 = (1 + 10^3 \, e^{(E_2-E_1)/RT})^{-1} \qquad (3.56)$$

$s_0$ will be close to unity only if $e^{(E_2-E_1)/RT} \ll 10^{-3}$, i.e. if $(E_1-E_2)$ is greater than about 4 kcal/mole at $300\,°K$. $E_2$ is unknown, although it must be less than $E_1$. For the purposes of a rough calculation we put $E_2 = 1/2 \cdot E_1$, and in this case the second layer must have a heat considerably in excess of 8 kcal/mole to give a sticking probability near to unity. This value is well outside the normal limits for heats of physical adsorption. However, it is not impossible that an intermediate chemisorbed layer of appreciable

126

binding energy is formed on certain crystallographic regions of the metal surface. Intermediate atomic states have been postulated for the adsorption of hydrogen on both nickel[45] and platinum[131] as well as for other systems[79].

For $E_1 = 4$ kcal/mole, an upper limit for most physical adsorptions, and again putting $E_2 = 1/2 \cdot E_1$, the sticking probability for a diatomic molecule is about $3 \times 10^{-2}$ at 300 °K, and unity at 78 °K. Thus every molecule should be chemisorbed at sufficiently low temperatures, even with a physically adsorbed precursor. Thus, the regions of high and low sticking probability, discussed previously may arise because of differences, either in the value of $\sigma$, or in the binding energy of the second layer.

For the adsorption of caesium on tungsten, the sticking probability is unity over the whole surface, and this may be attributed to a high heat of adsorption in the second layer.

ADSORPTION STUDIES USING THE FIELD EMISSION MICROSCOPE

In the field emission microscope, electrons emitted from a small metal tip (usually tungsten) on application of a very high electrical field travel radially outwards to a fluorescent screen, producing a highly magnified work function 'map' of the metal surface. By observing the changes in work function on adsorbing gases on the tip, relative rates of adsorption can be obtained on different crystallographic regions of the surface.

On adsorbing nitrogen[132], carbon monoxide[132] or hydrogen[133] on a tungsten tip at sufficiently low temperatures, the work function changes uniformly over the whole emitting area, indicating that the rate of adsorption is the same on all regions of the surface. Oxygen appears to behave differently[134], but since the computed sticking probability at 20 °K is unity the rate of adsorption must, again, be the same over the whole surface.

At room temperature, however, certain regions of the tip darken more rapidly than others during the initial adsorption, indicating that the work function is increasing at a greater rate than on the rest of the surface. This is a widely observed phenomenon and has been reported in detail for oxygen[123, 135–137], carbon monoxide[132] and hydrogen[137, 138] on tungsten. In each case the triangular areas centred on the (111) planes, darken somewhat more rapidly than the rest of the tip as illustrated in *Figure 51*, while the bridges connecting the (110) and (211) groups of planes darken most rapidly of all.

The adsorption of nitrogen at room temperature appears to be more complicated than that of other gases but the regions surrounding the (111) planes still behave differently from the rest of the surface[132]. Thus the work function of these regions appears to increase slightly on adsorption of nitrogen, whereas there is a decrease in work function around the (100) faces.

The rapid change in work function of the (111) regions could be due to:

(*a*) differences in sticking probability

(*b*) differences in work function increment for a given amount of adsorption, or

(*c*) migration of adsorbed atoms or molecules to the (111) regions.

(*c*) can be ruled out for oxygen, nitrogen and carbon monoxide since these gases form immobile layers at room temperature[101, 132], while (*b*) cannot easily account for the more uniform emission observed when adsorption is carried out at low temperatures. Thus, the effect must be due to a higher sticking probability on the (111) regions of the tip than elsewhere on the surface. These regions can in fact be identified with the 'active patches' discussed previously.

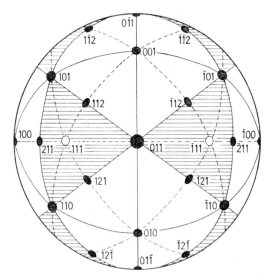

*Figure 51. Crystallographic projection diagram of a tungsten single crystal hemisphere. The hatched areas represent the regions of a field emission tip that darken first on adsorption of gas*

The various regions of the tip probably behave differently because of differences in the electron orbitals exposed in the surface. Clearly the surface orbitals will tend to rehybridize in order to lower the surface energy but the nature of this rehybridization and the type of orbital exposed will vary with crystallographic orientation. This may well cause differences in chemisorbing properties. Unfortunately not enough is known about metal surfaces to predict the behaviour of any particular crystal face.

At very low temperatures, where adsorption appears to occur uniformly over the whole surface, the sticking probability is presumably close to unity, in agreement with the theory outlined in the last section.

### ELECTRON DIFFRACTION WORK

From changes in electron diffraction patterns during adsorption on a metal it is possible to determine the way in which the adsorbed layer is built up, and to make estimates of the sticking probabilities on the different crystal faces.

Up to now nickel is the only transition metal which has been studied in any detail. In adsorption of oxygen marked differences are found between the (111) and (100) faces on the one hand, and the (110) face on the other[81, 139–141]. On the (100) face the oxygen initially forms a two-dimensional crystalline layer with the same arrangement of atoms as the substrate but with twice the spacing (*Figure 52b*). This structure is formed at room temperature but is developed more perfectly at elevated temperatures, when the adsorbed layer is probably mobile. From the time taken for the structure to appear at a known pressure of oxygen, a sticking probability of about 0·01 can be calculated.

On further exposure to oxygen a second structure is formed, shown in *Figure 52c*. Later still, the diffraction beams produced by this structure become weaker and finally disappear, while new beams appear due to the formation of oxide.

Similar structures are formed on the (111) face, the initial sticking probability again being about 0·01[142].

On the (110) face[141] oxygen adsorption induces rearrangement of the surface nickel atoms to form a succession of new structures and it is these, rather than the oxygen atoms, which give rise to additional diffraction beams. Thus, the position of the oxygen atoms on the surface cannot be ascertained directly but can only be inferred from the positions of the surface nickel atoms. The sticking probability is approximately unity up to the completion of the first structure, which probably corresponds to about half coverage, and then falls as successive structures are formed. In any case, the adsorption of oxygen on nickel appears to be another system showing marked differences in rate on different crystal planes.

Adsorbed hydrogen cannot be observed directly because it has a very small scattering cross section for low energy electrons. However, hydrogen has recently been detected on the (111) face of nickel[143],

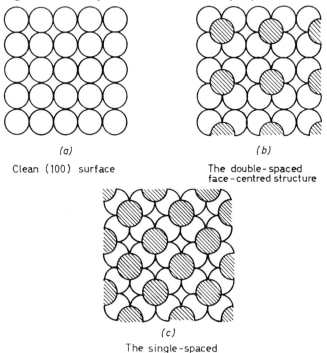

(a)

Clean (100) surface

(b)

The double-spaced
face-centred structure

(c)

The single-spaced
simple-square structure

*Figure 52. Schematic diagrams of the oxygen structures formed on a (100) nickel surface. The shaded circles give the positions taken up by the oxygen atoms*

because, like oxygen, it causes a rearrangement of the surface nickel atoms. A lower limit for the sticking probability of 0·1 was estimated for completion of the first structure.

Since surface sites are not filled in a completely random way, even when the surface layer is immobile, the $(1-\theta)^2$ term used to represent the fraction of vacant pairs of sites at coverage, $\theta$, may be incorrect. For the case shown in *Figure 52* there are no more vacant dual sites available after $\theta=0·5$. However, such sites are apparently not necessary for dissociative adsorption of oxygen, otherwise adsorption would cease at this stage.

## QUANTITATIVE MEASUREMENTS ON EVAPORATED METAL FILMS

The results discussed so far have been largely confined to tungsten. Sticking probabilities have, however, been obtained for other transition metals using evaporated films, and initial values are given in Table 15. Results are due to WAGENER[41] unless otherwise indicated.

TABLE 15

Initial Sticking Probabilities at 300°K on Evaporated Metal Films

| Metal | Gas | | | | |
|---|---|---|---|---|---|
| | CO | $N_2$ | $CO_2$ | $H_2$ | $D_2$ |
| Ba | 0·29 | activated | $\sim$0·6 | $\sim 10^{-3}$ | |
| Ti | 1·0 | 0·25 | 0·49 | | |
| Mo | 0·29 | 0·23 | | 0·30* | 0·30* |
| Ni | 0·38 | | | | |

* Reference 144.

With the exception of those for CO/Ti and $H_2$/Ba, the probabilities again appear to be near 0·3, suggesting that, as for tungsten, approximately one third of the metal surfaces are highly active in chemisorption, and possess a sticking probability of unity. The sticking probability for CO/Ti was presumably independent of temperature since Wagener was unable to detect any activation energy.

It was impossible to determine whether $s$ was initially constant in many of these experiments since the outer surfaces of the films were quickly saturated, and various processes could have been rate determining while the inner recesses of the film were being covered.

## CONDENSATION OF METAL VAPOURS

Sticking probabilities of metal vapours have been measured on various target materials. Unfortunately, much of the work has been carried out under indifferent vacuum conditions, and reproducibility between different workers is often poor. However, a recent review by WEXLER[145] suggests that the sticking probability of a vapour on its own metal is unity provided the surface is maintained in a clean condition. Otherwise it is difficult to make generalizations. Of some 72 values of $s$ tabulated by Wexler, 19 are lower than 0·01,

17 are between 0·2 and 0·4, and 20 are over 0·9. Thus, the probabilities are not randomly distributed but appear to have preferred values of unity, about 0·3, and some quantity approaching zero.

This conclusion is supported by the work of BAKER and BRINK[146] who have studied the adsorption of potassium beams on a variety of surfaces. *Figure 53* shows the amount of potassium deposited on a gold plate as a function of time for a constant beam flux. After about 40 minutes, when the deposit was probably between 30 and 40 Å thick, there is a fairly abrupt change, the rate of deposition increasing roughly by a factor of three. Taking the sticking probability for the higher rate as unity (i.e. for the deposition of potassium on potassium) the value for the initial stage must be between 0·3 and 0·4.

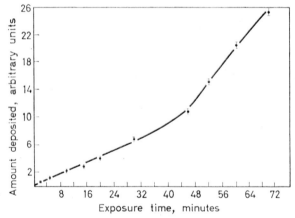

*Figure 53. The rate of deposition of potassium vapour on gold plate*
By courtesy of Baker, F. S. and Brink, G. O. *J. Chem. Phys.* **37**, 1012, 1962

Using gold as a standard, initial probabilities were then determined on twenty other surfaces. These lay between 0·17 and 0·53 with a mean value of 0·36.

It is difficult to decide whether the change from a lower to a higher sticking probability occurs when the deposit is sufficiently thick to mask any effect due to the substrate, or when the gettering action of the potassium already deposited has reduced the partial pressure of contaminants sufficiently for a clean surface to be maintained. By analogy with the adsorption of gases on metals the major part of the initial deposition may well be occurring on only a fraction of the exposed surface.

ACTIVATED PROCESSES INVOLVING PRECURSOR STATES

Rapid chemisorption on evaporated metal and semi-conductor films is usually followed by a slow uptake of gas whose kinetics normally obey the equation

$$\text{rate} = kp^x \exp\left(-\,av/RT\right) \qquad (3.57)$$

where $v$ is the volume of gas adsorbed and $k$, $x$ and $a$ are constants, depending on the particular system concerned. The form of the exponential term implies that the activation energy increases linearly with the amount of gas adsorbed.

$x$ is approximately 0·5 for oxygen on W, Mo and Rh[48], Si[94] and Ge[95, 96], for hydrogen on Fe[44] and Ni[45], and for nitrogen on Ta, Cr and Fe[50]. For the adsorption of nitrogen on iron there is almost no fast chemisorption, and the slow uptake therefore occurs on a virtually bare surface. In addition, the dependence of the rate on $\sqrt{p}$ is at variance with the direct proportionality to pressure observed with a promoted iron catalyst[90].

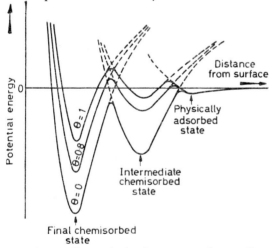

Figure 54. *Potential energy diagram showing the appearance of an overall activation energy between the intermediate and final chemisorbed states at high coverage*
(After Gundry and Tompkins[45], and Bond[132])

The value of $x$ for slow uptakes of carbon monoxide is a little uncertain. Originally[44], $x$ was reported to be close to unity for CO on iron, but a re-examination of the results[45] indicates that a better value is 0·85. In addition[45] $x$ is equal to 0·65 for CO on nickel, confirming that a non-integral value of $x$ must be accepted for carbon monoxide.

133

K

Direct irreversible adsorption clearly cannot be rate-determining with any of the gases mentioned, otherwise $x$ would be unity. A value less than unity can be explained only by an equilibrium between the gas phase and a precursor state, from which molecules or atoms irreversibly enter the primary chemisorbed state.

For hydrogen, oxygen and nitrogen a $\sqrt{p}$ dependence would arise if the molecules are dissociated into atoms in the precursor state[45, 79]. Such a precursor has already been postulated in connection with the kinetics of non-activated adsorption, though desorption from it was negligible and consequently there was no equilibrium with the gas phase. However, as the surface coverage increases, the heat of chemisorption nearly always falls and the activation energy necessary to pass from the precursor to the primary chemisorbed state may become greater than the activation energy for desorption from this state, as shown in *Figure 54*. In these circumstances, chemisorption becomes activated and equilibrium can be established between the gas phase and the precursor state, since the rate of desorption is much greater than the rate of chemisorption.

Labelling the physically adsorbed state '$P$', and the intermediate and final chemisorbed states '$A$' and '$B$' respectively, the mechanism of adsorption for a diatomic molecule $X_2$ may be represented as

$$p_{X_2} \overset{K_1}{\rightleftharpoons} [X_2]_P \overset{K_2}{\rightleftharpoons} 2[X_A] \overset{k_3}{\rightarrow} 2[X_B]$$

where $K_1$ and $K_2$ are equilibrium constants and $k_3$ is a velocity constant.

The coverage in the physically adsorbed layer will normally be small and proportional to the gas pressure. Thus

$$[X_2]_P = K_1 p_{X_2} \qquad (3.58)$$

Then, assuming that equilibrium between $(X_2)_P$ and $(X_A)$ is achieved very quickly in comparison with formation of $B$ from $A$, the equilibrium between the physically adsorbed state and state $A$ is given by

$$[X_A]^2 = K_2[X_2]_P = K_1 K_2 p_{X_2} \qquad (3.59)$$

If the transition from $A$ to $B$ is rate determining, then the rate of

$$\text{chemisorption} = k_3[X_A] \qquad (3.60)$$

$$= k_3 \sqrt{(K_1 K_2)} p_{X_2}^{\frac{1}{2}} \qquad (3.61)$$

$$= k p_{X_2}^{\frac{1}{2}} e^{-E/RT} \qquad (3.62)$$

134

where $k$ is independent of pressure and temperature, and $E$ is the activation energy for chemisorption.

If $E$ varies linearly with the volume of gas adsorbed,

$$E = a(v-v_0) \tag{3.63}$$

where $a$ is a constant and $v_0$ is the volume adsorbed when the activation energy first appears. Thus

$$\text{rate} = kp_{X_2}^{\frac{1}{2}} e^{-\alpha(v-v_0)/RT} \tag{3.64}$$

$$= k'p_{X_2}^{\frac{1}{2}} e^{-\alpha v/RT} \tag{3.65}$$

which is the rate equation observed experimentally.

For carbon monoxide we assume that the concentration in the physical layer obeys the Freundlich isotherm[45]

$$[CO]_P = K_1'p_{CO}^x \tag{3.66}$$

where $x$ is less than one. This then leads to the observed kinetic equation.

The interpretation assumes that the slow process is a surface phenomenon. However, slow oxygen uptakes are undoubtedly often due to the start of bulk oxidation. In this case the final state must lie somewhat below the metal surface, although otherwise the picture remains unchanged. For the initiation of oxidation LANYON and TRAPNELL[48] have suggested the following sequence

$$
\begin{array}{ccccccccccccc}
 & & & & & & & & & \text{O} & \text{O} & & \\
\text{O} & \text{O} & \text{O} & \text{O} & & \text{O} & \text{O} & \text{M} & \text{O} & {}_{+O_2} & \text{O} & \text{M} & \text{M} & \text{O} \\
\text{M} & \text{M} & \text{M} & \text{M} & \longrightarrow & \text{M} & \text{M} & \text{O} & \text{M} & \longrightarrow & \text{M} & \text{O} & \text{O} & \text{M} \\
\text{M} & \text{M} & \text{M} & \text{M} & & \text{M} & \text{M} & \text{M} & \text{M} & & \text{M} & \text{M} & \text{M} & \text{M} \\
 & & \text{I} & & & & & \text{II} & & & & & \text{III} &
\end{array}
$$

where the oxygen molecule is chemisorbed only when a metal and an oxygen atom have interchanged. The replenishment of the metal surface implied by I→II is known to occur in vacuo at room temperature and below.

Now oxygen chemisorption causes a surface dipole which is negative outwards and increases the work function: a mechanism such as I→II would tend to offset the increase, and this has recently been found to be the case with nickel[147] and iron[148].

# REFERENCES

[1] Dewar, J. *Proc. Roy. Soc.* A**74**, 122, 1904
[2] Keyes, F. G. and Marshall, M. J. *J. Amer. Chem. Soc.* **49**, 156, 1927
[3] Bull, H. I., Hall, M. H. and Garner, W. E. *J. Chem. Soc.* 837, 1931
[4] Langmuir, I. *J. Amer. Chem. Soc.* **40**, 1361, 1918
[5] Taylor, H. S. *J. Amer. Chem. Soc.* **53**, 578, 1931
[6] Taylor, H. S. and Williamson, A. T. *J. Amer. Chem. Soc.* **53**, 2168, 1931
[7] Schwab, G. M. *Catalysis.* London; Macmillan, 1937
[8] Taylor, H. S. and Strother, C. O. *J. Amer. Chem. Soc.* **56**. 586, 1934
[9] Emmett, P. H. and Harkness, R. W. *J. Amer. Chem. Soc.* **57**, 1631, 1935
[10] Smith, E. A. and Taylor, H. S. *J. Amer. Chem. Soc.* **60**, 362, 1938
[11] Kummer, J. T. and Emmett, P. H. *J. Phys. Chem.* **56**, 258, 1952
[12] Ward, A. F. H. *Proc. Roy. Soc.* A**133**, 522, 1931
[13] Allmand, A. J. and Chaplin, R. *Trans. Faraday Soc.* **28**, 223, 1932
[14] Schuit, G. C. A. and de Boer, N. H. *Nature, Lond.* **168**, 1040, 1951
[15] Roberts, J. K. *Proc. Roy. Soc.* A**152**, 445, 1935
[16] Beeck, O., Smith, A. E. and Wheeler, A. *Proc. Roy. Soc.* A**177**, 62, 1940
[17] Trapnell, B. M. W. *Proc. Roy. Soc.* A**218**, 566, 1953
[18] Beebe, R. A. and Dowden, D. A. *J. Amer. Chem. Soc.* **60**, 2912, 1938
[19] Gould, A. J., Bleakney, W. and Taylor, H. S. *J. Chem. Phys.* **2**, 362, 1934
[20] Dowden, D. A., Mackenzie, N. and Trapnell, B. M. W. *Proc. Roy. Soc.* A**237**, 245, 1956
[21] Frankenburger, W. and Hodler, A. *Trans. Faraday Soc.* **28**, 229, 1932
[22] Frankenburger, W. and Messner, G. *Z. phys. Chem.* (*Bodenstein Festband*) 593, 1931
[23] Johnson, R. P. *Phys. Rev.* **54**, 459, 1938
[24] Taylor, J. B. and Langmuir, I. *Phys. Rev.* **44**, 423, 1933
[25] Roberts, J. K. *Proc. Roy. Soc.* A**152**, 464, 1935
[26] Roberts, J. K. *Nature, Lond.* **137**, 659, 1936
[27] Hickmott, T. W. and Ehrlich, G. *J. Chem. Phys.* **24**, 1263, 1956
[28] Pasternak, R. A. and Wiesendanger, H. U. D. *J. Chem. Phys.* **34**, 2062, 1961
[29] Allen, J. A. and Mitchell, J. W. *Disc. Faraday Soc.* **8**, 309, 1950
[30] Beeck, O, and Wheeler, A. *J. Chem. Phys.* **7**, 631, 1939
[31] Beeck, O. *Adv. in Catalysis* **2**, 151, 1950
[32] Bennett, M. J. and Tompkins, F. C. *Trans. Faraday Soc.* **58**, 816, 1962
[33] Eley, D. D. and Wilkinson, P. R. *Proc. Roy. Soc.* A**254**, 327, 1960
[34] Kemball, C. *Proc. Roy. Soc.* A**207**, 539, 1951
[35] Wahba, M. and Kemball, C. *Trans. Faraday Soc.* **49**, 1351, 1953
[36] Wright, P. G., Ashmore, P. G. and Kemball, C. *Trans. Faraday Soc.* **54**, 1692, 1958
[37] Saleh, J. M., Kemball, C. and Roberts, M. W. *Trans. Faraday Soc.* **57**, 1771, 1961
[38] Trapnell, B. M. W. *Trans. Faraday Soc.* **52**, 1618, 1956
[39] Collins, A. C. and Trapnell, B. M. W. *Trans. Faraday Soc.* **53**, 1476, 1957

[40] Greenhalgh, E., Hayward, D. O. and Trapnell, B. M. W. *J. Phys. Chem.* **61**, 1254, 1957

[41] Wagener, S. *J. Phys. Chem.* **60**, 567, 1956; **61**, 267, 1957

[42] Pritchard, J. and Tompkins, F. C. *Trans. Faraday Soc.* **56**, 540, 1960

[43] Trapnell, B. M. W. *Proc. Roy. Soc.* A**206**, 39, 1951

[44] Porter, A. S. and Tompkins, F. C. *Proc. Roy. Soc.* A**217**, 529, 544, 1953

[45] Gundry, P. M. and Tompkins, F. C. *Trans. Faraday Soc.* **52**, 1609, 1956; **53**, 218, 1957

[46] Beeck, O., Ritchie, A. W. and Wheeler, A. *J. Colloid Sci.* **3**, 505, 1948

[47] Matsuda, A. and Nakata, T. *J. Res. Inst. Catalysis, Hokkaido Univ.* **6**, 88, 1958

[48] Lanyon, M. A. H. and Trapnell, B. M. W. *Proc. Roy. Soc.* A**227**, 387, 1955

[49] Rideal, E. K. and Trapnell, B. M. W. *Proc. Roy. Soc.* A**205**, 409, 1951

[50] Greenhalgh, E., Slack, N. and Trapnell, B. M. W. *Trans. Faraday Soc.* **52**, 865, 1956

[51] Trapnell, B. M. W. *Trans. Faraday Soc.* **48**, 160, 1952

[52] Brennan, D., Hayward, D. O. and Trapnell, B. M. W. *Proc. Roy. Soc.* A**256**, 81, 1960

[53] Burdon, R. S. *Proc. Phys. Soc.* **47**, 460, 1935

[54] Cook, S. G. *Phys. Rev.* **34**, 513, 1929

[55] Kemball, C. *Trans. Faraday Soc.* **42**, 526, 1946

[56] Kemball, C. and Rideal, E. K. *Proc. Roy. Soc.* A**187**, 53, 1946
Kemball, C. *Proc. Roy. Soc.* A**190**, 117, 1947

[57] Kemball, C. *Proc. Roy. Soc.* A**201**, 377, 1950

[58] Schwab, G. M. *Catalysis.* London; Macmillan, 1937, p. 213

[59] Barrer, R. M. *J. Chem. Soc.* 1261, 1936

[60] Barrer, R. M. and Rideal, E. K. *Proc. Roy. Soc.* A**149**, 231, 1935
Barrer, R. M. *Proc. Roy. Soc.* A**149**, 253, 1935
Barrer, R. M. *J. Chem. Soc.* 1256, 1936

[61] Rideal, E. K. and Trapnell, B. M. W. *J. chim. Phys.* **47**, 126, 1950

[62] Hindin, S. G. and Weller, S. W. *Adv. in Catalysis* **9**, 70, 1957

[63] Barry, T. I. and Stone, F. S. *Proc. Roy. Soc.* A**255**, 124, 1960

[64] Winter, E. R. S. *Adv. in Catalysis* **10**, 196, 1958

[65] Garner, W. E. *J. Chem. Soc.* 1239, 1947

[66] Winter, E. R. S. *J. Chem. Soc.* 1522, 1954

[67] Kubokawa, Y., Matsura, I. and Toyama, O. *Bull. Univ. Osaka* A**9**, 45, 1961

[68] Kubokawa, Y. and Toyama, O. *J. Phys. Chem.* **60**, 833, 1956

[69] Cimino, A., Molinari, E. and Cipollini, E. *Proc. 2nd International Congress on Catalysis (Editions Technip, Paris)* **1**, 263, 1961

[70] Garner, W. E. and Kingman, F. E. T. *Trans. Faraday Soc.* **27**, 322, 1931

[71] Winter, E. R. S. in *Chemisorption* (ed. W. E. Garner). London; Butterworths, 1957, p. 189

[72] Rudham, R. and Stone, F. S. in *Chemisorption* (ed. W. E. Garner). London; Butterworths, 1957, p. 205

[73] Winter, E. R. S. *J. Chem. Soc.* 3824, 1955

[74] Garner, W. E. and Veal, F. J. *J. Chem. Soc.* 1487, 1935
Dowden, D. A. and Garner, W. E. *J. Chem. Soc.* 893, 1939
Garner, W. E. and Ward, T. *J. Chem. Soc.* 857, 1939
Ward, T. *J. Chem. Soc.* 1244, 1947
Garner, W. E., Gray, T. J. and Stone, F. S. *Proc. Roy. Soc.* A**197**, 294, 1949
Garner, W. E., Stone, F. S. and Tiley, P. F. *Proc. Roy. Soc.* A**211**, 472, 1952

[75] Jennings, T. J. and Stone, F. S. *Adv. in Catalysis* **9**, 441, 1957

[76] Stone, F. S., Rudham, R. and Gale, R. L. *Z. Elektrochem.* **63**, 129, 1959

[77] Stone, F. S. *Adv. in Catalysis* **13**, 1, 1962

[78] Houghton, G. and Winter, E. R. S. *J. Chem. Soc.* 1509, 1954

[79] Bond, G. C. *Catalysis by Metals.* London and New York; Academic Press, 1962, Chapters 5 and 6

[80] Miller, A. R. *Proc. Camb. Phil. Soc.* **43**, 232, 1947

[81] Schlier, R. E. and Farnsworth, H. E. *Adv. in Catalysis* **9**, 434, 1957

[82] Germer, L. H. *Adv. in Catalysis* **13**, 191, 1962

[83] Peierls, R. E. *Proc. Camb. Phil. Soc.* **32**, 471, 1936

[84] Laidler, K. J. *J. Phys. Chem.* **57**, 318, 1953

[85] Tamman, G. and Koster, W. *Z. anorg. Chem.* **123**, 196, 1922
Roginsky, S. and Zeldovich, Ya. *Acta Physicochim.* **1**, 554, 595, 1934
Elovich, S. Yu. and Zhabrova, G. M. *Zh. fiz. Khim.* **13**, 1761, 1939

[86] Brunauer, S., Love, K. S. and Keenan, R. G. *J. Amer. Chem. Soc.* **64**, 751, 1942

[87] Taylor, H. A. and Thon, N. *J. Amer. Chem. Soc.* **74**, 4169, 1952

[88] Low, M. J. D. *Chem. Rev.* **60**, 267, 1960

[89] Glasstone, S., Laidler, K. J. and Eyring, H. *The Theory of Rate Processes.* New York; McGraw-Hill, 1941.
Laidler, K. J. *J. Phys. Chem.* **53**, 712, 1949

[90] Scholten, J. J. F., Zwietering, P., Konvalinka, J. A. and de Boer, J. H. *Trans. Faraday Soc.* **55**, 2166, 1959

[91] Lennard-Jones, J. E. and Devonshire, A. F. *Proc. Roy. Soc.* A**156**, 6, 1936

[92] Eisinger, J. and Law, J. T. *J. Chem. Phys.* **30**, 410, 1959

[93] Schlier, R. E. and Farnsworth, H. E. *J. Chem. Phys.* **30**, 917, 1959

[94] Law, J. T. *J. Phys. Chem. Solids* **4**, 91, 1958

[95] Green, M., Kafalas, J. A. and Robinson, P. H. In *Semiconductor Surface Physics* (ed. R. H. Kingston). University of Pennsylvania Press, Philadelphia, 1957, p. 349

[96] Bennett, M. J. and Tompkins, F. C. *Proc. Roy. Soc.* A**259**, 28, 1960

[97] Sherman, A. and Eyring, H. *J. Amer. Chem. Soc.* **54**, 2661, 1932

[98] Sherman, A., Sun, C. E. and Eyring, H. *J. Chem. Phys.* **3**, 49, 1935

[99] Okamoto, G., Horiuti, J. and Hirota, K. *Sci. Papers Inst. phys. chem. Res. Tokyo* **29**, 223, 1936

[100] Wortman, R., Gomer, R. and Lundy, R. *J. Chem. Phys.* **27**, 1099, 1957

[101] Gomer, R. *Field Emission and Field Ionization.* Harvard University Press, Cambridge, U.S.A., 1961

102 Kisliuk, P. *J. Chem. Phys.* **30**, 174, 1959
103 Becker, J. A. in *Solid State Physics* (eds. F. Seitz and D. Turnbull), **7**, 379, New York; Academic Press, 1958,
104 Jones, P. L. and Pethica, B. A. *Proc. Roy. Soc.* A**256**, 454, 1960
105 Eisinger, J. *J. Chem. Phys.* **29**, 1154, 1958
106 Taylor, J. B. and Langmuir, I. *Phys. Rev.* **44**, 423, 1933
107 Morrison, J. L. and Roberts, J. K. *Proc. Roy. Soc.* A**173**, 1, 1939
108 Becker, J. A. and Hartman, C. D. *J. Phys. Chem.* **57**, 153, 1953
109 Nasini, A. G., Saini, G. and Ricca, F. *Proc. 2nd International Congress on Catalysis (Editions Technip, Paris)* **1**, 241, 1961
110 Ehrlich, G. *J. Chem. Phys.* **34**, 29, 1961
111 Eisinger, J. *J. Chem. Phys.* **28**, 165, 1958
112 Schlier, R. E. *J. Appl. Phys.* **29**, 1162, 1958
113 Kisliuk, P. *J. Chem. Phys.* **31**, 1605, 1959
114 Saini, G., Ricca, F. and Nasini, A. G. *Ric. Sci.* **29**, 1523, 1959
115 Hickmott, T. W. and Ehrlich, G. *J. Phys. Chem. Solids* **5**, 47, 1958
116 Redhead, P. A. *Trans. Faraday Soc.* **57**, 641, 1961
117 Eisinger, J. *J. Chem. Phys.* **27**, 1206, 1957
118 Ehrlich, G. *J. Chem. Phys.* **34**, 39, 1961
119 Brennan, D. and Fletcher, P. C. *Proc. Roy. Soc.* A**250**, 389, 1959
Brennan, D. and Fletcher, P. C. *Trans. Faraday Soc.* **56**, 1662, 1960
120 Smith, J. N. and Fite, W. L. *J. Chem. Phys.* **37**, 898, 1962
121 Hickmott, T. W. *J. Chem. Phys.* **32**, 810, 1960
122 Eisinger, J. *J. Chem. Phys.* **30**, 412, 1959
123 Muller, E. W. *Z. Elektrochem.* **59**, 372, 1955
124 Becker, J. A., Becker, E. J. and Brandes, R. G. *J. Appl. Phys.* **32**, 411, 1961
125 McKinley, J. D. and Shuler, K. E. *J. Chem. Phys.* **28**, 1207, 1958
126 McKinley, J. D. *J. Phys. Chem.* **66**, 554, 1962
127 Frommer, L. and Polanyi, M. *Z. physik. Chem.* **137**A, 201, 1928
128 Ehrlich, G. *J. Phys. Chem. Solids* **1**, 3, 1956
129 Kisliuk, P. *J. Phys. Chem. Solids* **3**, 95, 1957; **5**, 78, 1958
130 Ehrlich, G. *J. Phys. Chem.* **59**, 473, 1955
131 Pliskin, W. A. and Eischens, R. P. *Z. Phys. Chem. (Frankfurt)* **24**, 11, 1960
132 Ehrlich, G. and Hudda, F. G. *J. Chem. Phys.* **35**, 1421, 1961
133 Rootsaert, W. J. M., van Reijen, L. L. and Sachtler, W. M. H. *J. Catalysis* **1**, 416, 1962
134 George, T. H. and Stier, P. M. *J. Chem. Phys.* **37**, 1935, 1962
135 Becker, J. A. and Brandes, R. G. *J. Chem. Phys.* **23**, 1323, 1955
136 Becker, J. A. *Adv. in Catalysis* **7**, 135, 1955
137 Lodge, G. W. *Ph.D. Thesis.* Imperial College, London, 1957
138 Becker, J. A. *Proceedings 2nd International Congress on Catalysis (Editions Technip., Paris)* **2**, 1777, 1961
139 Farnsworth, H. E. and Tuul, J. *J. Phys. Chem. Solids* **9**, 48, 1959
140 Germer, L. H., Scheibner, E. J. and Hartman, C. D. *Phil. Mag.* **5**, 222, 1960
141 Germer, L. H. and MacRae, A. U. *J. Appl. Phys.* **33**, 2923, 1962

[142] Germer, L. H. and MacRae, A. U. *J. Chem. Phys.* **36**, 1555, 1962
[143] Germer, L. H. and MacRae, A. U. *J. Chem. Phys.* **37**, 1382, 1962
[144] Hunt, A. L., Damm, C. C. and Popp, E. C. *J. Appl. Phys.* **32**, 1937, 1961
[145] Wexler, S. *Rev. mod. Phys.* **30**, 402, 1958
[146] Baker, F. S. and Brink, G. O. *J. Chem. Phys.* **37**, 1012, 1962
[147] Delchar, T. A. and Tompkins, F. C.—Unpublished results
[148] Quinn, C. M. and Roberts, M. W. *Proc. Chem. Soc.*, 246, 1962

# IV

# VELOCITIES OF DESORPTION

IF it is assumed that desorption may take place from occupied sites, provided the adsorbed particle possesses the necessary activation energy, the velocity of desorption, $u'$, becomes

$$u' = K \cdot f'(\theta) e^{-E'/RT} \qquad (4.1)$$

where $K$ and $E'$ are the velocity constant and activation energy of desorption, and $f'(\theta)$ is the fraction of sites available for desorption at coverage $\theta$. $E'$ is related to the heat $q$ and activation energy $E$ of adsorption by the equation

$$E' = q + E \qquad (4.2)$$

Since adsorption is always exothermic, $E'$ is appreciable even in the limiting case where $E = 0$. That is, desorption, unlike adsorption, is bound to be activated.

As in the case of adsorption, an equation such as (4.1) is probably too simple to be obeyed by many systems. Thus $E'$ is very likely to vary with $\theta$, if only because $q$ varies with $\theta$, while $K$ may likewise do so if the frequency of vibration of the surface bond varies with $\theta$. So far as $f'(\theta)$ is concerned, simple statistical terms are normally assumed to be correct, as very little is known about the mechanism of desorption.

If the variation of $K$ and $E'$ with $\theta$ is due to surface interactions rather than heterogeneity, and the surface is regarded as uniform,

141

it is sufficient to indicate the dependence of $K$ and $E$ on $\theta$, and write equation (4.1) as

$$u' = K(\theta) \cdot f'(\theta) \cdot e^{-E'(\theta)/RT} \tag{4.3}$$

As in the case of adsorption (see Chapter III), if the variation arises from heterogeneity, it is necessary to divide the surface into a number of elements of area $ds$, each constituting a uniform surface to which equation (4.1) can be applied. Integrating over unit area of surface, so that $ds = 1$, we obtain $u'$ as

$$u' = \int_0^1 K_s \cdot f'(\theta_s) \cdot e^{-E_s/RT} \, ds \tag{4.4}$$

In general, of course, the variations of $\theta_s$, $K_s$ and $E'_s$ with $s$ are not known.

### THE ACTIVATION ENERGY OF DESORPTION

VARIATION WITH $\theta$

With the non-activated chemisorptions the variation of $E'$ with $\theta$ is due solely to the variation of $q$ with $\theta$, and since $q$ falls as $\theta$ increases, so does $E'$. As a result desorption is faster from concentrated layers, and the change with $\theta$ can be very large indeed. For example, if $q$ falls from 40 to 10 kcal/mole as $\theta$ increases, the resulting change in $u'$ at 250 °C is a factor

$$e^{(40,000-10,000)/2 \times 523} \simeq 10^{13}$$

With activated chemisorptions the effect is likely to be smaller because $E$ seems to increase with $\theta$ and this, to some extent, offsets the fall in $q$. Nevertheless, it is likely that $E'$ will increase as $\theta$ falls. The effect may be treated quite simply if the increase is due to surface interactions on a uniform surface and the variation of $E'$ with $\theta$ is linear:

$$E' = E'_0 - \beta\theta \tag{4.5}$$

The treatment is similar to that given in Chapter III for adsorption. Thus, $K$ is assumed to be independent of $\theta$, and the value of $E'$ from equation (4.5) is inserted in equation (4.3). For the case of an atom or molecule desorbing as such $f'(\theta) = \theta$ and the desorption velocity becomes

$$u' = K \cdot \theta \cdot e^{-(E_0' - \beta\theta)/RT} \tag{4.6}$$

Provided $\theta$ does not approach zero we may neglect the variation of $\theta$ as compared with the variation in $e^{\beta\theta/RT}$ and the dependence of $u'$ upon coverage is of the form

$$u' \propto e^{\beta\theta/RT} \tag{4.7}$$

This equation can also be derived for a non-uniform surface[1], provided the variation of $E_s'$ over the surface is of the form

$$E_s' = E_0' - \beta s \tag{4.8}$$

where $s$ is the fraction of the total surface area for which the activation energy is greater than $E_s'$.

Inserting this value of $E_s'$ in equation (4.4) and putting $f'(\theta_s) = \theta_s$ and $K_s = K$ we obtain

$$u' = K \int_0^1 \theta_s e^{-(E_0' - \beta s)/RT} \, ds \tag{4.9}$$

If the variation in $E'$ is significant, desorption will take place far more rapidly from sites of low activation energy. The surface will then consist at any moment of an almost bare part (low $E_s'$) and an almost covered part (high $E_s'$). In this case the integral of equation (4.9) may be replaced by one carried out simply over the covered part of the surface, for which $\theta_s = 1$, with the integration limits $s = 0$ and $s = \theta$. Thus

$$u' = K \int_0^\theta e^{-(E_0' - \beta s)/RT} \, ds \tag{4.10}$$

which gives

$$u' = K \frac{RT}{\beta} e^{-E_0'/RT} (e^{\beta\theta/RT} - 1) \tag{4.11}$$

This is again of the form

$$u' \propto e^{\beta\theta/RT}$$

Putting $u' = -\dfrac{d\theta}{dt}$ and integrating this gives

$$\theta = \frac{RT}{\beta} \ln \frac{t_0}{t + t_0} \tag{4.12}$$

where $t_0$ is a constant.

Desorption data are rather few, but LANGMUIR[2] has found that the velocity of thorium evaporation from tungsten increases exponentially with increase in adsorbed amount. The desorption of nitrogen from iron has been investigated by SCHOLTEN and his co-workers[3], who found a linear dependence of activation energy on adsorbed amount. Two different iron samples gave

$$E' = 64 \cdot 5 - 20\theta \text{ kcal/mole}$$

and $$E' = 55 - 29 \cdot 2\theta \text{ kcal/mole}.$$

## EXPERIMENTAL STUDIES

In order to measure true desorption velocities and hence activation energies, the desorbed molecule must not be allowed to strike the surface again before being removed from the system. If it does, it may be readsorbed. With powders and evaporated films this condition is not easily fulfilled, and in addition it is difficult to raise these adsorbents to the high temperatures often necessary in desorption studies. Hence, quantitative measurements of $E'$ have mainly been made using metal filaments. The most interesting application of such measurements is to the case of non-activated chemisorptions. Here $E'=q$, so that the temperature coefficient of desorption velocity gives a heat of chemisorption. However, two points must be made in this connection.

(1) The mechanisms of adsorption and desorption may be different. Thus some gases, such as oxygen, are dissociated in chemisorption and may be desorbed as atoms, not as molecules. In this case the heat of desorption will differ from the calorimetric heat of adsorption, the two in fact being related by the equation

$$q_{ads} = 2q_{des} - D \qquad (4.13)$$

where $q_{ads}$ is the heat of adsorption per gram molecule, $q_{des}$ the heat of desorption per gram atom, and $D$ the dissociation energy per gram molecule.

(2) At the high temperatures required for desorption the adsorbed layer will probably be mobile. As a result there will be an equilibrium distribution over the various surface sites. On the other hand, the layer formed during adsorption may be immobile and far from equilibrium. The average binding energies in the two types of layer can differ, and for this reason the two heats need not be comparable.

Activation energies of desorption have been measured for the following systems. With all these adsorption is non-activated.

### (1) Nitrogen on tungsten

This system has been studied by EHRLICH[4] and by HICKMOTT and EHRLICH[5], using the method of flash desorption described in Chapter

144

II, in which the transient pressure rise is measured when a covered filament is rapidly heated. The results of a typical experiment are shown in *Figure 55*. Desorption is seen to proceed in three distinct steps, suggesting the existence of three states of adsorption, designated $\alpha$, $\beta$ and $\gamma$. Of these, the $\alpha$ and $\gamma$ states are rather weakly

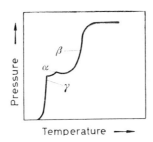

*Figuree 55. The desorption of nitrogen from tungsten commencing at 115° K*
By courtesy of Ehrlich, G. *J. Chem. Phys.* **34**, 29, 1961

bound, and are not normally formed at temperatures much above 300°K. Detailed study of the desorption has yielded the following additional results.

(*a*) Desorption from the $\beta$ state is a second order process, showing that the gas is held on the surface as atoms and desorbed as molecules. The activation energy of desorption is 80 kcal/mole and is independent of coverage. This value is rather less than the calorimetric heat of adsorption, namely 95 kcal/mole[6].

(*b*) Desorption from the $\gamma$ state is first order with respect to the surface concentration. This, together with a heat of desorption of 9 kcal/mole, suggests a weak molecular chemisorption.

(*c*) The $\alpha$ state is probably a molecular chemisorption too. A value of 20 kcal/mole was obtained for the heat of desorption.

(*d*) The relative populations of the various states tends to vary with surface conditions. Also at low temperatures adsorption into the $\beta$ state is hindered by competitive growth of the $\gamma$ state.

*(2) Hydrogen on tungsten*
This system has been studied by HICKMOTT[7], again using the flash desorption method. If hydrogen was allowed to adsorb on the filament at 194°K or at room temperature before flashing, the pressure versus time curve showed a single peak. If, however, the filament was covered at 77°K and then flashed desorption occurred in two stages, suggesting the existence of two states of binding,

145

designated $\alpha$ and $\beta$. A small amount of the $\alpha$ state was observed before completion of the $\beta$ state, but the majority was formed after the $\beta$ state was almost fully occupied.

The rate of desorption of the $\beta$ state was proportional to the second power of the surface coverage, suggesting an atomic layer evaporating as molecules. At low coverage the activation energy was 31 kcal/mole and at half coverage 20 kcal/mole. These values agree with heats obtained from isotherms using the Clausius–Clapeyron equation. On the other hand the values are less than the corresponding calorimetric heats for an evaporated film[6] (45 and 33 kcal/mole).

The concentration of the $\alpha$ state was found to be proportional to the ambient pressure of hydrogen, suggesting a molecular adsorption on top or in the gaps of the primary atomically chemisorbed layer.

### (3) Carbon monoxide on tungsten

Flash desorption studies by EHRLICH[8] and by REDHEAD[9] show different binding states for CO adsorbed on tungsten. A typical experiment by Ehrlich is shown in *Figure 56*, while Redhead's results are shown in *Figure 78* (Chapter VII). The following points arise from this work.

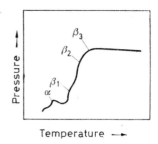

*Figure 56. The desorption of CO from tungsten, commencing at 298° K*
By courtesy of Ehrlich, G. *J. Chem. Phys.* **34**, 39, 1961

(a) There are two basic mechanisms, $\alpha$ and $\beta$, the former probably being single point and the latter two point chemisorption (see Chapter VII).

(b) The $\beta$ state shows three subphases, $\beta_1$, $\beta_2$, and $\beta_3$, possibly arising from adsorption on different lattice spacings.

(c) Table 36 summarizes the heats of desorption from the various binding states. According to Redhead the value for each state is

independent of population. Together with a similar result for the
β-state of nitrogen on tungsten, this result offers the only example of
a constant desorption heat.

## (4) Oxygen on tungsten

Flash desorption studies with this system have been largely
unsuccessful for two reasons. Firstly, desorption may take place as
oxide at high coverages[10, 11], and this complicates the interpretation
of pressure rises. Secondly, oxygen interacts with traces of carbon
found in tungsten filaments to form carbon monoxide[11] and this
gas may be the main constituent of peaks observed in the pressure
versus time curve[5]. However, several activation energies of desorption have been determined for this system, none of them involving
measurement of a pressure rise on desorption. The method of
LANGMUIR and VILLARS[12] depends on the fact that the electron
emission from a tungsten filament in the presence of a small pressure
of caesium vapour varies with the amount of oxygen on the filament
surface. These workers measured the length of time for which an
oxygenated tungsten filament had to be heated in vacuo before the
emission reached an ordained value, the emission current being
measured after bringing the filament to some fixed low temperature
and introducing caesium to a constant pressure. The times
necessary for a given amount of evaporation to take place at various
temperatures are shown in Table 16. A plot of log $t$ against $1/T$
gives an activation energy for desorption of 162 kcal/g atom.

TABLE 16

Desorption of Oxygen from Tungsten

| Temperature (°K) | 1,856 | 1,978 | 2,070 |
|---|---|---|---|
| Time for given amount of evaporation (mins) | 27 | 2 | 0·3 |

This energy might appear to be an average for coverages between
the initial $\theta = 1$, and the final $\theta$ value corresponding to the ordained
emission current. However, the desorption times will have been
used mainly in desorbing the last, most strongly adsorbed gas, and
therefore the energy will be the value for the coverage at the end
of desorption. Langmuir and Villars showed this coverage to be
very low.

In the method of JOHNSON and VICK[13], the change in thermionic
emission from an oxygenated filament is measured as desorption

147

proceeds. If it is assumed that $\theta$ varies linearly with the work function it is possible to measure $\theta$ as a function of time as evaporation proceeds. From such measurements the energy of desorption was found to be 147 kcal/g atom.

In the work of BOSWORTH and RIDEAL[14] the change in contact potential of an oxygenated surface with respect to a clean surface was measured at different temperatures. Assuming that contact potential is proportional to $\theta$, activation energies were calculated at different $\theta$ values. Since oxygen desorption may take place as oxide at high coverages, results at low coverages are more trustworthy, and here the value was 150 kcal/g atom, in good agreement with the previous values.

In the work both of Langmuir and Villars, and of Johnson and Vick, the rate of desorption was proportional to the first power of the surface coverage, suggesting that desorption is taking place as atoms. In this case the desorption heats will refer to one gram atom, and using a mean value of 153 kcal/g atom, the normal heat of adsorption of molecular oxygen as atoms using equation (4.13) becomes

$$q_{\text{ads}} = 2 \times 153 - 117$$
$$= 189 \text{ kcal/g mole}$$

This figure is in fair agreement with the calorimetric heat of chemisorption on an evaporated film, 194 kcal/mole, recorded by BRENNAN, HAYWARD and TRAPNELL[15].

### (5) Thorium on tungsten

Values of 204 and 177 kcal/g atom have been obtained for dilute layers using the electron emission method[2,16]. These large values approach the sublimation energy of tungsten, namely 221 kcal/g atom.

### (6) Sodium on tungsten

The desorption of sodium from tungsten has been studied by BOSWORTH[17] using the contact potential method. Evaporation curves are shown in *Figure 57*, and these give the activation energies shown in Table 17.

### (7) Caesium on tungsten

The desorption of caesium from tungsten is more complex than that of other metal vapours because it takes place both as ions and as neutral atoms. The relative amounts of the two species which are desorbed varies with both $T$ and $\theta$.

The rate of desorption of ions is measured by the ion current passing to a negative electrode. The rate of desorption of atoms is measured by allowing a known fraction of these atoms to strike a nearby incandescent filament. These are ionized, and from the increase in ion current, the rate of desorption of atoms from the first filament may be obtained.

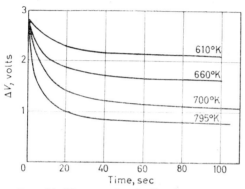

*Figure 57. The evaporation of sodium from tungsten*
By courtesy of Bosworth, R. C. L. *Proc. Roy. Soc.* **A162**, 32, 1937

TABLE 17

Desorption of Sodium from Tungsten

| $\theta$ | 0 | 0·13 | 0·27 | 0·40 | 0·54 | 0·67 |
|---|---|---|---|---|---|---|
| $E'$ (kcal/g atom) | 32 | 28·5 | 27 | 23 | 20 | 17 |

While ions and atoms are evaporating, the electron emission is measured. From this, the evaporation rates may be expressed in terms of the change in the work function. Lastly, the work function may be related to $\theta$ by an independent series of experiments. In this way, Taylor and Langmuir[18] measured the emissions of atoms, ions and electrons as functions of temperature, for various values of $\theta$. The rate of desorption of atoms, $u'$, per unit area was expressed at each value of $\theta$ by an equation

$$\ln u' = a' - E'/RT \qquad (4.14)$$

where $a'$ is independent of $T$, and $E'$ is the activation energy. Values of $a'$ and $E'$ are given in Table 18 as functions of $\theta$.

149

L

TABLE 18

The Desorption of Neutral Atoms from WCs Surfaces

| $\theta$ | $a'$ | $E'$ (kcal/g atom) |
|---|---|---|
| 0·00 | — | 65 |
| 0·01 | 57·3 | 64 |
| 0·10 | 60·3 | 60 |
| 0·20 | 61·6 | 57 |
| 0·30 | 62·7 | 53 |
| 0·40 | 63·7 | 50 |
| 0·50 | 64·7 | 48 |
| 0·60 | 65·9 | 45 |
| 0·70 | 67·3 | 43 |
| 0·80 | 69·6 | 42 |
| 0·90 | 75·5 | 41 |
| 1·00 | — | 40 |

These figures show the normal decrease in $E'$ as $\theta$ increases. In addition they show a marked increase in $a'$. Using the simple desorption equation

$$u' = K\theta e^{-E'/RT} \tag{4.15}$$

we see that $a' = \ln K\theta$ and it may then readily be shown that the increase in $a'$ is mainly due to an increase in $K$, a result which will be mentioned later.

### THE VELOCITY CONSTANT OF DESORPTION

THEORETICAL TREATMENTS

*(1) The Polanyi–Wigner equation*

A simple velocity equation for atoms or molecules desorbing without association is obtained[19] by assuming that any particle possessing the requisite activation energy desorbs within the period of one vibration perpendicular to the surface. If the frequency of this vibration is $\nu$,

$$u' = \nu . n_s\theta . e^{-E'/RT} \tag{4.16}$$

and comparison of this equation with (4.15) shows that

$$K = \nu n_s \tag{4.17}$$

For a chemical bond, $\nu$ is likely to be about $10^{13}$ sec$^{-1}$, and with $n_s = 10^{15}$ sites/cm$^2$, $K = 10^{28}$ cm$^{-2}$ sec$^{-1}$.

## (2) The Langmuir equation

Using an empiric vapour pressure equation, LANGMUIR[20] has derived for the lifetime of an adsorbed particle on the surface, $\tau$, the expression

$$\tau = 4 \cdot 7 \times 10^{-27} \frac{n_s M^{1/2}}{T} e^{E'/RT} \qquad (4.18)$$

where $M$ is the molecular weight of the adsorbed particle.

Now if we consider an atom or molecule adsorbed and desorbed as such, the rate of evaporation, $u'$, divided by the number of adsorbed radicals per sq. cm, $n_s\theta$, where $n_s$ is the number of sites per sq. cm, gives the average probability per second for desorption. The reciprocal of this is $\tau$. Thus

$$\tau = \frac{n_s\theta}{u'} \qquad (4.19)$$

Combining this equation with equation (4.15) we find

$$\tau = \frac{n_s e^{E'/RT}}{K} \qquad (4.20)$$

and combining equations (4.20) and (4.18) we obtain

$$K = 2 \cdot 1 \times 10^{26} \frac{T}{M^{1/2}} \qquad (4.21)$$

At room temperatures, and for particles of molecular weight between 30 and 40, this gives $K \simeq 10^{28}$ cm$^{-2}$ sec$^{-1}$.

## (3) Quantum mechanical treatment

LENNARD-JONES and his co-workers[21] have calculated $\tau$ by quantum mechanics, using the same assumptions as those used in calculating $\sigma$ (see Chapter III). Since the method amounts to calculating the probability of transfer of a single quantum of energy from the solid to the adsorbed molecule, it may be valid only for physical adsorption. At any rate for physical adsorption of hydrogen at room temperature, the method gives $\tau \simeq 10^{-11}$ sec. $E'$ is equal to the heat of adsorption, normally about 1,500 cal/mole, and inserting these values in equation (4.20), we find $K = 1 \cdot 37 \times 10^{27}$ cm$^{-2}$ sec$^{-1}$ if $n_s = 10^{15}$ sites/cm$^2$.

## (4) Calculation by statistical mechanics

### (a) Simple desorption

It may readily be shown[22, 23] that the velocity of desorption is given by

$$u' = \nu c^{\ddagger} \qquad (4.22)$$

where $\nu$ is the frequency of vibration of the activated complexes perpendicular to the surface and $c^{\ddagger}$ is their concentration. $\nu$ is also the frequency of decomposition of the complexes, which are assumed to be in statistical equilibrium with adsorbed molecules. The formation of activated complexes from the chemisorbed layer is assumed to be the rate determining step in desorption.

In this equilibrium, surface sites play no part, and in the case where there is no association, the equilibrium constant is given by

$$k^{\ddagger} = \frac{c^{\ddagger}}{c_a} = \frac{f^{\ddagger}}{f_a} \tag{4.23}$$

where $f^{\ddagger}$ and $f_a$ are the complete partition functions of the complexes and adsorbed molecules respectively, and the $c$'s their concentrations. Separating the zero-point energies from the partition functions, and from $f^{\ddagger}$ the term $kT/h\nu$ due to the vibration perpendicular to the surface, we have

$$\frac{c^{\ddagger}}{c_a} = \frac{kT}{h\nu} \cdot \frac{f_{\ddagger}}{f_a} \cdot e^{-E'/RT} \tag{4.24}$$

where $E'$ is the activation energy of desorption. The velocity of desorption, $u'$, is then

$$u' = \nu c^{\ddagger} = c_a \cdot \frac{kT}{h} \cdot \frac{f_{\ddagger}}{f_a} \cdot e^{-E'/RT} \tag{4.25}$$

Now if the fraction of sites available for desorption is $f'(\theta)$, and the total number is $n_s$ per cm$^2$, $c_a = n_s \cdot f'(\theta)$. Inserting this in equation (4.25), and comparing the resulting equation with the desorption equation for a uniform surface,

$$u' = K \cdot f'(\theta) \cdot e^{-E'/RT} \tag{4.26}$$

we have

$$K = n_s \cdot \frac{kT}{h} \cdot \frac{f_{\ddagger}}{f_a} \tag{4.27}$$

Two types of behaviour may be considered.

(1) If the complexes and adsorbed molecules possess identical degrees of freedom, and the frequency of vibration of the adsorbed molecule perpendicular to the surface is high so that the vibrational partition function for this mode is unity, $f_{\ddagger} = f_a$ and

$$K = n_s \cdot \frac{kT}{h} \tag{4.28}$$

152

$K$ is thus proportional to $T$, and with $n_s = 10^{15}$ per cm$^2$, is equal to $6.24 \times 10^{27}$ cm$^{-2}$ sec$^{-1}$ at room temperature and $2.08 \times 10^{28}$ at $1,000 \,^\circ$K.

(2) Since the activated complex is less strongly bound to the surface than is the adsorbed molecule, it may possess greater freedom of movement. In this case $f_{\ddagger}/f_a$ becomes greater than unity. In the extreme case, where the complex has translational and rotational freedom and the adsorbed molecule has not, $f_{\ddagger}/f_a$ might amount to $10^3$ or $10^4$. The values of $K$ then become greater than the previous value by this factor.

### (b) Desorption with association

Equation (4.27) does not apply if association takes place during desorption. Considering now the case where two radicals $R$ adsorbed on sites $S$ associate to form a molecule $R_2$, we have

$$2RS \rightarrow R_2S_2^{\ddagger} \rightarrow R_2 + S_2$$

This leads to a velocity of desorption

$$u' = \frac{kT}{h} \cdot c_a^2 \cdot \frac{f_{\ddagger}}{f_a^2} \cdot e^{-E'/RT} \qquad (4.29)$$

Remembering that $c_a^2 = n_s f'(\theta)$, equation (4.29) gives

$$K = n_s \cdot \frac{kT}{h} \cdot \frac{f_{\ddagger}}{f_a^2} \qquad (4.30)$$

Three types of behaviour may be considered.

(1) If the complexes and adsorbed radicals are both immobile, and only vibrations of high frequency occur $f_{\ddagger} = f_a = 1$. In this case $K = n_s kT/h$.

(2) Sometimes the complex may be mobile while the adsorbed radicals are immobile. In this case $f_a = 1$, but $f_{\ddagger}$ may considerably exceed unity. Desorption will then be faster than in the first case.

(3) Both radicals and complexes may be mobile—a possible example is the desorption of hydrogen chemisorbed on metal surfaces as atoms. In this case, two translational degrees of freedom are lost in forming the complex, tending to make $f_{\ddagger}/f_a^2$ less than unity. However, this will be to some extent offset by the rotational partition function being appreciable for the complex, but unity for the adsorbed atoms. The first effect may in general be larger than the second, tending to make desorption rather slower than in the first case.

The quantum mechanical treatment of desorption, and the Polanyi–Wigner and Langmuir equations all suggest that $K$ will lie in the region of $10^{28}$ cm$^{-2}$ sec$^{-1}$ at room temperatures. The statistical treatment suggests that this will only be the case if the term $f_{\ddagger}/f_a$ (or $f_{\ddagger}/f_a{}^2$ for associative desorption) is equal to unity.

Desorption velocities have been measured for oxygen[12], hydrogen[7], nitrogen[5], and caesium[18] on tungsten, for carbon monoxide on platinum[24], and for nitrogen on iron[3]. The velocity of desorption of oxygen from sparse layers on tungsten at 2,000 °K is

$$u' = 1 \cdot 34 \times 10^{31} \, e^{-162,000/RT} \tag{4.31}$$

For this desorption LANGMUIR and VILLARS[12] found a first order dependence on surface coverage. Hence the desorption velocity equation is

$$u' = K\theta \, e^{-E'/RT} \tag{4.32}$$

Assuming that $\theta$ was about 0·1 we obtain

$$K = 1 \cdot 34 \times 10^{32} \tag{4.33}$$

For this desorption, transition state theory gives

$$K = 4 \cdot 2 \times 10^{28} \, . f_{\ddagger}/f_a \tag{4.34}$$

Theory and experiment only agree if the complex is more mobile than the adsorbed atoms so that $f_{\ddagger}/f_a = 3 \times 10^3$.

For the desorption of CO from platinum[24] at 600 °K

$$u' = 2 \cdot 79 \times 10^{29} \, e^{-E'/RT} \tag{4.35}$$

In this case $\theta$ is unknown, but placing it equal to 0·5 and using equation (4.15), we find

$$K = 5 \cdot 6 \times 10^{29} \tag{4.36}$$

At 600 °K, transition state theory gives

$$K = 1 \cdot 2 \times 10^{28} f_{\ddagger}/f_a \tag{4.37}$$

Again, theory and experiment only agree if the complex is more mobile than the adsorbed molecule, so that $f_{\ddagger}/f_a \simeq 50$.

The desorption of hydrogen[7] and nitrogen[5] from tungsten are both bimolecular, the rate being proportional to $\theta^2$. For hydrogen at about 600°K, Hickmott's results give

$$K = 8 \cdot 5 \times 10^{27} \tag{4.38}$$

assuming $1 \cdot 3 \times 10^{15}$ adsorption sites per cm², compared with the value from transition state theory

$$K = 1 \cdot 2 \times 10^{28} f_{\ddagger}/f_a^2 \qquad (4 \cdot 39)$$

The two expressions agree if $f_{\ddagger}/f_a^2 = 0 \cdot 7$ and this is not improbable since both adsorbed atoms and transition complexes are likely to be mobile.

For nitrogen[5], Hickmott and Ehrlich find a considerable variation in $K$ with tungsten sample, a surprising result since all samples originated from the same spool of wire. For desorption at $1,600 \,^{\circ}\mathrm{K}$, values of $K$ varied between $8 \times 10^{25}$ and $2 \times 10^{29}$, compared with the value of $3 \cdot 2 \times 10^{29} f_{\ddagger}/f_a^2$ from transition state theory. This variation may be due to an experimental artefact, absolute determinations of wire temperatures at $1,600 \,^{\circ}\mathrm{K}$ being subject to significant errors.

The results for caesium desorption from tungsten have been given in Table 18 in which $a' = \ln (K\theta)$. Calculation then shows that $K$ increases progressively from $8 \times 10^{26}$ at $\theta = 0 \cdot 01$ to $7 \times 10^{32}$ at $\theta = 0 \cdot 9$. In this adsorption, the caesium atom covers four surface tungsten atoms, so $n_s = 2 \cdot 5 \times 10^{14}$. For desorption at $500 \,^{\circ}\mathrm{K}$, transition state theory then gives

$$K = 2 \cdot 5 \times 10^{27} \cdot f_{\ddagger}/f_a \qquad (4.40)$$

At low $\theta$ values, experiment and theory agree if complex and adsorbed molecule have about equal mobilities, but at high $\theta$'s the complex becomes more mobile than the adsorbed atom. This effect is probably due to the increase in repulsion forces which takes place as the layer becomes more densely packed.

For the bimolecular desorption of nitrogen from an iron powder at about $650 \,^{\circ}\mathrm{K}$, SCHOLTEN et al.[3] have obtained values of $K$ as a function of $\theta$. They find a continuous decrease as $\theta$ increases, according to the equation

$$\log K = 29 \cdot 68 - 4 \cdot 62\theta \qquad (4.41)$$

This compares with the value from transition state theory at $650 \,^{\circ}\mathrm{K}$

$$\log K = 28 \cdot 15 + \log (f_{\ddagger}/f_a^2) \qquad (4.42)$$

It is at first sight surprising that $K$ should decrease as $\theta$ increases. However, comparison of (4.41) and (4.42) shows that at low $\theta$, $f_{\ddagger}/f_a^2$ is greater than unity, whereas at higher $\theta$ it is less than unity. This implies that at low $\theta$ the complex is mobile but the adsorbed atoms are immobile, whereas at high $\theta$ both are mobile. The result is not unreasonable.

155

The overall conclusion is that $K$ does not show such simple behaviour as to allow it to be assigned a universal value, both because it varies from system to system, and also because it varies with $\theta$ within a single system.

## THE TERM $f'(\theta)$

The only cases where there are experimental data for $f'(\theta)$ are the desorption of nitrogen from iron[3] and of hydrogen[7], nitrogen[5], oxygen[12, 13] and carbon monoxide[8] from tungsten. In the first three cases the desorption velocity is roughly proportional to $\theta^2$, indicating a bimolecular desorption of two atoms as a molecule: for oxygen and CO the desorption is proportional to $\theta$ at low coverages, indicating unimolecular desorption, as atoms with oxygen, and molecules with CO.

However, statistical theory has yielded insight into the term $f'(\theta)$, and for the various types of layer discussed in Chapter III gives the following results.

### MOLECULE OCCUPYING A SINGLE SITE

Since desorption can proceed from any single occupied site

$$f'(\theta) = \theta \tag{4.43}$$

### MOLECULE OCCUPYING TWO SITES

(*1*) *Type I layers*—two atoms desorbing as a diatomic molecule.

(*a*) Immobile Layers—the value of $f'(\theta)$ might appear to be $\theta^2$. However, in such layers some single sites are left vacant when the monolayer is completed. As a result $f'(\theta)$ proves to be rather less than $\theta^2$ though for most practical purposes it is sufficient to equate $f'(\theta)$ with $\theta^2$. In fact[25]

$$f'(\theta) = \frac{(z-1)^2}{z(z-\theta)}\,\theta^2 \tag{4.44}$$

where $z$ is the number of nearest neighbours surrounding a site. In theory, some single atoms will remain on the surface, which do not desorb, because there are no atoms on nearest neighbour sites.

(*b*) Mobile Layers—where one might expect $f'(\theta)$ to be very much less than $\theta^2$, owing to the tendency of mobile layers to spread out through repulsive interactions. In treating this effect PEIERLS[26] derived the expression

$$f'(\theta) = \theta\,\frac{\eta\epsilon}{1+\eta\epsilon} \tag{4.45}$$

156

where $\dfrac{\theta}{1-\theta} = \dfrac{\epsilon(1+\eta\,\epsilon)}{1+\epsilon}$ and $\eta = \mathrm{e}^{-V/RT}$ (4.46)

Here $V$ is the interaction energy between nearest neighbours, and other interactions are neglected. However, statistical mechanics has shown that the velocity of desorption is proportional to $c_{a2}/f_{a_2}$ where $c_{a_2}$ is the concentration of occupied pairs and $f_{a_2}$ is their partition function. Now a pair has an energy lower than that of two separate sites by an amount $V$, and as a result the partition function, as well as the concentration, is altered by interactions. A treatment of the effect by LAIDLER[27] shows that the two effects exactly balance, and that the desorption velocity is in fact proportional to $\theta^2$.

(2) *Type II adsorption*—large molecule precluding adsorption on nearby sites.

As in this case there is no association during desorption.

$$\mathrm{f}'(\theta) = \theta$$

for immobile and mobile layers alike.

## REFERENCES

[1] Brunauer, S., Love, K. S. and Keenan, R. G. *J. Amer. Chem. Soc.* **64**, 751, 1942

[2] Langmuir, I. *Phys. Rev.* **22**, 357, 1923

[3] Scholten, J. J. F., Zwietering, P., Konvalinka, J. A. and de Boer, J. H. *Trans. Faraday Soc.* **55**, 2166, 1959

[4] Ehrlich, G. *J. Chem. Phys.* **34**, 29, 1961

[5] Hickmott, T. W. and Ehrlich, G. *J. Phys. Chem. Solids* **5**, 47, 1958

[6] Beeck, O. *Adv. in Catalysis* **2**, 151, 1950

[7] Hickmott, T. W. *J. Chem. Phys.* **32**, 810, 1960

[8] Ehrlich, G. *J. Chem. Phys.* **34**, 39, 1961

[9] Redhead, P. A. *Trans. Faraday Soc.* **57**, 641, 1961

[10] Eisinger, J. *J. Chem. Phys.* **30**, 412, 1959

[11] Sclier, R. E. *J. Appl. Phys.* **29**, 1162, 1958

[12] Langmuir, I. and Villars, D. S. *J. Amer. Chem. Soc.* **53**, 486, 1931

[13] Johnson, M. and Vick, F. A. *Proc. Roy. Soc.* **A151**, 308, 1935

[14] Bosworth, R. C. L. and Rideal, E. K. *Physica* **4**, 925, 1937

[15] Brennan, D., Hayward, D. O. and Trapnell, B. M. W. *Proc. Roy. Soc.* **A256**, 81, 1960

[16] Andrews, M. R. *Phys. Rev.* **33**, 454, 1929

[17] Bosworth, R. C. L. and Rideal, E. K. *Proc. Roy. Soc.* **A162**, 1, 1937
Bosworth, R. C. L. *Proc. Roy. Soc.* **A162**, 32, 1937

[18] Taylor, J. B. and Langmuir, I. *Phys. Rev.* **44**, 423, 1933

[19] See Garner, W. E. *J. Chem. Soc.* 1239, 1947

[20] Langmuir, I. *J. Amer. Chem. Soc.* **54**, 2798, 1932
[21] Lennard-Jones, J. E. and Devonshire, A. F. *Proc. Roy. Soc.* A**156**, 6, 1936
[22] Glasstone, S., Laidler, K. J. and Eyring, H. *The Theory of Rate Processes.* New York; McGraw-Hill, 1941
[23] Laidler, K. J. *J. Phys. Chem.* **53**, 712, 1949
[24] Langmuir, I. *Trans. Faraday Soc.* **17**, 621, 1922
[25] Miller, A. R. *Proc. Camb. Phil. Soc.* **43**, 232, 1947
[26] Peierls, R. E. *Proc. Camb. Phil. Soc.* **32**, 471, 1936
[27] Laidler, K. J. *J. Phys. Chem.* **57**, 318, 1953

# V

# ADSORPTION ISOTHERMS

ADSORPTION equilibrium can be expressed either as isotherms, isobars or isosteres. A set of curves of any one type may be converted to a set of either of the other two types, and therefore it is sufficient to consider simply one of the three types. The most convenient to consider is the adsorption isotherm.

An isotherm may have one of five general forms, shown in *Figure 58*. Some of these are associated with formation of multilayers, others with condensation of gas in capillaries to form a pseudo-liquid: only the first type is associated with formation of a simple monolayer. Since chemisorption usually comes within this latter category, Type I isotherms are normally found.

Some typical experimental isotherms, obtained by FRANKENBURG[1] for hydrogen chemisorption on a tungsten powder, are shown in *Figure 59*.

Most of this chapter is concerned with chemisorptions in which the gas phase equilibrium pressure is appreciable and easily measured. The majority of the very fast chemisorptions on clean metal surfaces, discussed in Chapter III, are associated with immeasurably small equilibrium pressures and, in general, isotherms for these adsorptions are only available for the high coverage regions where the pressure above the surface becomes detectable.

In deriving theoretical isotherms, three approaches are possible. First, in kinetic terms, the condition for equilibrium is that the velocities of adsorption and desorption are equal, and isotherms may be obtained by equating these velocities. Second, in statistical terms, the equilibrium constant is given by a ratio of partition functions of vacant sites, adsorbed molecules and gas phase molecules, and isotherms may be obtained by equating this ratio to the

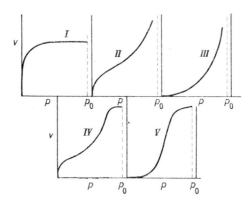

Figure 58. The five types of adsorption isotherm. $p_0 =$ saturation vapour pressure

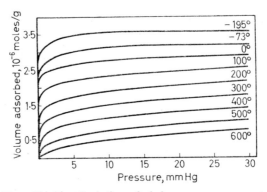

Figure 59. Adsorption isotherms for hydrogen on a tungsten powder
By courtesy of Frankenburg, W. G. J. Amer. Chem. Soc. 66, 1827, 1944

corresponding ratio of concentrations. The statistical approach is more powerful than the kinetic approach because it gives numerical values for constants which cannot be evaluated by the kinetic method. Third, equilibrium may be approached thermodynamically, either using the condition that the change in free energy on transferring an infinitesimal amount of gas from the gas phase to the surface at constant temperature is zero, or alternatively using the Gibbs adsorption equation.

Three theoretical isotherms, those of Langmuir, Freundlich and Temkin, are important. Each is characterized by certain assumptions, in particular as to the manner in which the differential heat of adsorption varies with adsorbed amount, and each is applicable to certain experimental systems.

## THE LANGMUIR ISOTHERM[2]

### (1) KINETIC DERIVATION

In the simplest case the velocities of adsorption and desorption, $u$ and $u'$, on a uniform surface are given by

$$u = \frac{\sigma p}{\sqrt{(2\pi m k T)}} \cdot f(\theta) \cdot e^{-E/RT} \tag{5.1}$$

$$u' = K \cdot f'(\theta) \cdot e^{-E'/RT} \tag{5.2}$$

At equilibrium $u = u'$. Equating (5.1) and (5.2), and remembering that

$$E' - E = q \tag{5.3}$$

the adsorption isotherm becomes, after transposing,

$$p = \frac{K}{\sigma} \cdot \sqrt{(2\pi m k T)} \cdot \frac{f'(\theta)}{f(\theta)} \cdot e^{-q/RT} \tag{5.4}$$

A Langmuir isotherm is obtained if it is assumed that the expression $K/\sigma \cdot e^{-q/RT}$ is independent of $\theta$. If we then place

$$\frac{1}{a} = \frac{K}{\sigma} \cdot \sqrt{(2\pi m k T)} \cdot e^{-q/RT} \tag{5.5}$$

where $a$ is dependent on temperature alone, the isotherm (5.4) reduces to

$$p = \frac{1}{a} \cdot \frac{f'(\theta)}{f(\theta)} \tag{5.6}$$

Specific isotherms for different kinds of adsorption may be obtained by inserting in (5.6) the appropriate expressions for $f(\theta)$ and $f'(\theta)$ obtained in Chapters III and IV. This leads to the following equations.

(*a*) *Molecule occupying a single site in adsorption*

In this case, for mobile and immobile layers alike,

$$f(\theta) = 1 - \theta \tag{5.7}$$

$$f'(\theta) = \theta \tag{5.8}$$

and the isotherm becomes

$$p = \frac{\theta}{a(1 - \theta)} \quad \text{or} \quad \theta = \frac{ap}{1 + ap} \tag{5.9}$$

(*b*) *Molecule occupying two sites in adsorption*

(i) *Type I layers*—If a molecule dissociates in adsorption to two atoms each occupying a single site, and the layer is immobile,

$$f(\theta) = \frac{z}{z - \theta} \cdot (1 - \theta)^2 \tag{5.10}$$

$$f'(\theta) = \frac{(z-1)^2}{z(z - \theta)} \cdot \theta^2 \tag{5.11}$$

where $z$ is the number of nearest neighbour sites, and the isotherm becomes

$$\theta = \frac{\dfrac{z}{z-1} \cdot \sqrt{(ap)}}{1 + \dfrac{z}{z-1} \cdot \sqrt{(ap)}} = \frac{\sqrt{(a'p)}}{1 + \sqrt{(a'p)}} \tag{5.12}$$

where

$$a' = \left(\frac{z}{z-1}\right)^2 a \tag{5.13}$$

If the layer is mobile, the total effect is such that

$$f(\theta) = (1 - \theta)^2 \tag{5.14}$$

$$f'(\theta) = \theta^2 \tag{5.15}$$

and this gives an isotherm

$$\theta = \frac{\sqrt{(ap)}}{1 + \sqrt{(ap)}} \tag{5.16}$$

(ii) *Type II layers*—If the molecule does not dissociate in adsorption but is sufficiently large to preclude adsorption on nearest neighbour sites, for immobile layers

162

$$f(\theta) = 1 - \tfrac{5}{2}\theta + \tfrac{3}{2}\theta^2 + \tfrac{3}{4}\theta^3 \quad \text{for } 0\cdot5 > \theta > 0 \tag{5.17}$$

$$f(\theta) = \tfrac{1}{2}[(1-\theta) - 3(1-\theta)^3 + 5(1-\theta)^4] \quad \text{for } 1\cdot0 > \theta > 0\cdot5 \tag{5.18}$$

and
$$f'(\theta) = \theta \tag{5.19}$$

These expressions lead to isotherms

$$\theta = ap(1 - \tfrac{5}{2}\theta + \tfrac{3}{2}\theta^2 + \tfrac{3}{4}\theta^3) \quad \text{for } 0\cdot5 > \theta > 1\cdot0 \tag{5.20}$$

$$\theta = \tfrac{1}{2}ap[(1-\theta) - 3(1-\theta)^3 + 5(1-\theta)^4] \quad \text{for } 1\cdot0 > \theta > 0\cdot5 \tag{5.21}$$

## (2) STATISTICAL DERIVATION

To obtain the adsorption isotherm statistically[3] it is necessary to define the quantities

$$c_g = N_g/V \text{ gas molecules/cm}^3$$
$$c_s = N_s/S \text{ unoccupied sites/cm}^2$$
$$c_a = N_a/S \text{ adsorbed molecules/cm}^2$$

The equilibrium equations for adsorption are then

$$\frac{c_a}{c_g c_s} = \frac{N_a}{(N_g/V)N_s} = \frac{f_a}{(f_g/V)f_s} \tag{5.22}$$

where the $f$'s are the complete partition functions for the species. Removing the zero point energies from these partition functions, and placing $f_g/V = F_g$ where $F_g$ is now the partition function of the gas phase per unit volume,

$$\frac{c_a}{c_g c_s} = \frac{f_a}{F_g \cdot f_s} \cdot e^{q/RT} \tag{5.23}$$

where $q$ is the heat of adsorption. Since $f_s$ is composed solely of vibrational terms of high frequency, it may be equated to unity, and remembering that for an ideal gas $c_g \cdot kT = p$, the isotherm becomes

$$\frac{c_a}{c_s} = \frac{p}{kT} \cdot \frac{f_a}{F_g} \cdot e^{q/RT} \tag{5.24}$$

Now
$$\frac{c_a}{c_s} = \frac{f'(\theta)}{f(\theta)} \tag{5.25}$$

and therefore

$$p = kT \cdot \frac{F_g}{f_a} \cdot e^{-q/RT} \cdot \frac{f'(\theta)}{f(\theta)} \tag{5.26}$$

This equation is identical with equation (5.6) if

$$\frac{1}{a} = kT \cdot \frac{F_g}{f_a} \cdot e^{-q/RT} \tag{5.27}$$

Thus, provided the heat of adsorption is known, the statistical method in principle enables the $a$ constant of the Langmuir isotherm to be calculated. One interesting point is that since $a \propto f_a$, it varies according as the adsorbed molecules are mobile or immobile.

Alternatively, on comparing equations (5.27) and (5.5) we see that the statistical method gives for the ratio of velocity constants $K/\sigma$,

$$\frac{K}{\sigma} = \sqrt{\left(\frac{kT}{2\pi m}\right)} \cdot \frac{F_g}{f_a} \tag{5.28}$$

A similar derivation of the Langmuir isotherm by statistical methods has been made by FOWLER[4].

## (3) THERMODYNAMIC DERIVATION

Without making any assumptions as to the nature of the adsorbed layer, it is possible to derive the following thermodynamic equation:

$$\frac{1}{A} = -\frac{p}{RT} \frac{d\gamma}{dp} \tag{5.29}$$

where $\gamma$ is the surface energy, $A$ is the area occupied by one mole of adsorbate on the surface, and $p$ is the equilibrium pressure exerted by the gas phase. This relationship is one form of the Gibbs' adsorption equation.

If the adsorbed layer is treated as a two-dimensional gas, the surface spreading pressure $F$ which it exerts is equal to the reduction in surface energy.

Hence
$$d\gamma = -dF \tag{5.30}$$

and equation (5.29) may be written as

$$\frac{1}{A} = \frac{p}{RT} \frac{dF}{dp} \tag{5.31}$$

VOLMER[5] has shown that a Langmuir isotherm may be derived from (5.31) if the adsorbed layer obeys the equation of state

$$F(A - A_0) = RT \tag{5.32}$$

where $A_0$ allows for the area occupied by the adsorbed molecules themselves and is analogous to the volume correction term '$b$' in the van der Waals equation of state for a three dimensional gas.

Provided that $A_0 \ll A$ equations (5.31) and (5.32) may be combined to give

$$\frac{1}{A} = \frac{k'p}{1 + 2A_0 k'p} \qquad (5.33)$$

where $k'$ is a constant of integration and is a function of temperature alone. At very high pressures this equation reduces to

$$A = 2A_0 \qquad (5.34)$$

and assuming that this corresponds to full coverage we may write

$$\theta = \frac{2A_0}{A} = \frac{2A_0 k'p}{1 + 2A_0 k'p} \qquad (5.35)$$

which corresponds to the Langmuir isotherm.

## FEATURES OF THE LANGMUIR ISOTHERM

### UNDERLYING ASSUMPTIONS

FOWLER has emphasized[4] that three important conditions are implied in the kinetic and statistical derivations of the Langmuir isotherm. These are the following:

(*a*) Adsorption is localized and takes place only through collision of gas molecules with vacant sites.

(*b*) Each site can accommodate one and only one adsorbed particle.

(*c*) The energy of an adsorbed particle is the same at any site on the surface, and is independent of the presence or absence of nearby adsorbed molecules.

The first two conditions are implied in the use of the probability terms $f(\theta)$ and $f'(\theta)$: the third condition is implied in the use of equations (5.1) and (5.2) and also when the quantity $a$ of equations (5.5) and (5.27) is assumed independent of $\theta$.

We have already seen in Chapter III that the second part of condition (*a*) is seldom obeyed during the initial stages of chemisorption on clean metal surfaces, the rate of adsorption being independent of the surface coverage. However, it probably applies to slower chemisorptions where a small activation energy is involved and, as mentioned earlier, it is for this type of system that experimental isotherms can normally be obtained. For many chemisorptions condition (*b*) may be obeyed. It is doubtful whether (*c*) is other than rarely obeyed, since this condition requires that the surface is perfectly uniform and that forces of attraction and repulsion between adsorbed molecules are negligible. Only if this is so is the expression $f_a \cdot e^{q/RT}$ independent of $\theta$, as is required by equation (5.27).

The assumptions underlying the thermodynamic derivation differ from those given above in that the adsorption is considered to be non-localized. Hence, although the two methods of approach yield the same mathematical form for the isotherm, they are not equivalent and it is not possible to equate the term $2A_0k'$ in equation (5.35) with the quantity $a$ of equations (5.9) and (5.27).

METHODS OF TESTING THE ISOTHERM

The isotherm (5.9) for single site adsorption may be arranged to the form

$$\frac{p}{\theta} = \frac{1}{a} + p \tag{5.36}$$

Plotting $p/\theta$ against $p$ should therefore give a straight line whose slope is unity at all temperatures, and whose intercept to a first approximation increases exponentially with temperature.

Sometimes, values of $\theta$ are unknown, and only volumes of gas adsorbed, $v$, are available. In such cases, if $v_m$ is the volume adsorbed which gives a complete monolayer, equation (5.9) becomes

$$\theta = \frac{v}{v_m} = \frac{ap}{1 + ap} \tag{5.37}$$

or

$$\frac{p}{v} = \frac{1}{av_m} + \frac{p}{v_m} \tag{5.38}$$

Thus, plotting $p/v$ against $p$ gives a straight line of slope $1/v_m$.

For an adsorption where the molecule dissociates to two radicals each occupying one site, equations (5.12) and (5.16) may be rearranged to

$$\frac{\sqrt{p}}{v} = \frac{1}{\sqrt{(a')} \cdot v_m} + \frac{\sqrt{p}}{v_m} \tag{5.39}$$

and

$$\frac{\sqrt{p}}{v} = \frac{1}{\sqrt{(a)} \cdot v_m} + \frac{\sqrt{p}}{v_m} \tag{5.40}$$

Plotting $\sqrt{(p)}/v$ against $\sqrt{p}$ thus gives straight lines of slope $1/v_m$.

An alternative method[6] of testing the simple isotherm (5.9) is to express it as

$$\theta = ap(1 - \theta) \tag{5.41}$$

Taking logarithms and transposing,

$$\ln \frac{\theta}{p} = \ln a + \ln(1 - \theta) \tag{5.42}$$

Since $(1-\theta) < 1$

$$\ln (1 - \theta) = - (\theta + 1/2 . \theta^2 + 1/3 . \theta^3 + \ldots) \tag{5.43}$$

and except when $\theta \rightarrow 1$, this may be simplified to $\ln(1-\theta) = -\theta$. In this case, (5.42) approximates to

$$\ln \frac{\theta}{p} = \ln a - \theta \tag{5.44}$$

A test of the Langmuir equation is therefore to plot $\ln \theta/p$ against $\theta$, and to see whether a straight line of slope $-1$ results. If $\theta$ is unknown, equation (5.44) may be written

$$\ln \frac{v}{p} = \ln av_m - \frac{v}{v_m} \tag{5.45}$$

If adsorption involves dissociation, the analogue of equation (5.45) is

$$\ln \frac{v}{\sqrt{p}} = \ln \left( \sqrt{(a)} . v_m \right) - \frac{v}{v_m} \tag{5.46}$$

### THE VARIATION OF $\theta$ WITH $p$ AND THE ORDER OF CATALYTIC REACTIONS

The simple Langmuir isotherm

$$\theta = \frac{ap}{1+ap} \tag{5.47}$$

gives two limiting types of behaviour. At very low pressures, where $ap \ll 1$, the isotherm reduces to

$$\theta = ap \tag{5.48}$$

while at very high pressures, where $ap \gg 1$

$$\theta \rightarrow 1 \tag{5.49}$$

and is, to a first approximation, independent of the pressure. At intermediate pressures, we may write

$$\theta = ap^m \tag{5.50}$$

where $m$ diminishes progressively from unity to zero as the pressure increases. A further result of some importance is that at high pressures, where $\theta \to 1$, the transposed form of equation (5.47),

$$ap(1 - \theta) = \theta \tag{5.51}$$

reduces to

$$ap(1 - \theta) = 1 \tag{5.52}$$

or

$$1 - \theta = \frac{1}{ap} \tag{5.53}$$

Thus, the amount of vacant space on the surface is inversely proportional to the pressure.

Although the isotherm (5.47) is unlikely to be obeyed exactly by many systems, it has proved useful in interpreting the orders of catalytic reactions. The principle underlying the method is that the velocity of reaction will be proportional to the $\theta$ values of the adsorbed particles which are reaction intermediates. Detailed expositions of this topic have been made by HINSHELWOOD[7], and by SCHWAB[8].

First, if a single reactant is involved, and this is weakly adsorbed, so that $\theta$ is low, equation (5.48) shows that a first order reaction may be expected. The decomposition of formic acid on a variety of surfaces is an example of such behaviour[9]. If, however, the reactant is very strongly adsorbed, so that most of the surface is covered, equation (5.49) shows that a zero order reaction may be found: an example is the decomposition of ammonia on a tungsten filament[10]. For intermediate strengths of adsorption, equation (5.50) indicates a fractional order.

Sometimes, a reaction product will be more strongly adsorbed than the reactant itself. The product will then tend to cover much of the surface, leaving only a small part for adsorption of reactants. It will therefore exert a retarding action. Equation (5.53) shows, in an extreme case, that the amount of surface available for adsorption of reactant is inversely proportional to the pressure of product. Since on this free space reactant is relatively weakly adsorbed, its coverage is proportional to its pressure, and the velocity equation will be

$$\frac{dx}{dt} = \frac{k(b - x)}{x} \tag{5.54}$$

where $x$ is the amount of product formed after time $t$ from an initial concentration of reactant $b$. The decomposition of ammonia on a platinum filament[10] follows such a law:

$$\frac{-d[NH_3]}{dt} = k \cdot \frac{p_{NH_3}}{p_{H_2}} \qquad (5.55)$$

In other cases, retardation is not so strong and the velocity equation is more nearly

$$\frac{dx}{dt} = \frac{k(b-x)}{x^m} \qquad (5.56)$$

where $1 > m > 0$.

When two reactants are involved, and both are weakly adsorbed, the rate of reaction will be proportional to the product of their pressures. However, if reactant $A$ is much more strongly adsorbed than reactant $B$, it will exert an inhibiting effect, and the kinetic law will be similar to either equation (5.54) or (5.56). An example is the combination of CO and $O_2$, the rate of which on certain quartz surfaces[11] is proportional to

$$p_{O_2}/p_{CO}$$

Retardation by product can also take place in reaction between two substances. A classic example is the reaction

$$2SO_2 + O_2 \rightarrow 2SO_3$$

at platinum surfaces. The rate of reaction is given[12] by

$$\frac{d[SO_3]}{dt} = k \frac{p_{O_2}}{\sqrt{(p_{SO_3})}} \qquad (5.57)$$

when $SO_2$ is in excess, and by

$$\frac{d[SO_3]}{dt} = k \frac{p_{SO_2}}{\sqrt{(p_{SO_3})}} \qquad (5.58)$$

when $O_2$ is in excess. The term $1/\sqrt{(p_{SO_3})}$ is a measure of the amount of space left free for adsorption of reactants, and this is mainly covered by whichever reactant is in excess.

## THE FREUNDLICH ISOTHERM

Early during the study of adsorption it became clear that many experimental data did not obey the Langmuir isotherm. An alternative isotherm, which was empiric at the time of its proposal, was suggested by FREUNDLICH[13]. This may be expressed in the form

$$v = cp^{1/n} \qquad (5.59)$$

where $c$ and $n$ are quantities dependent on $T$, and $c$ also depends on the units employed for measurement, the surface area of the adsorbent and so on. $n$, which is always greater than unity, is characteristic

TABLE 19

Adsorption of Carbon Monoxide on Charcoal

| $T(°C)$ | $c$ | $1/n$ |
|---|---|---|
| −78 | 14·29 | 0·13 |
| 0 | 2·96 | 0·33 |
| 35 | 1·24 | 0·46 |
| 61 | 0·72 | 0·48 |
| 100 | 0·32 | 0·52 |

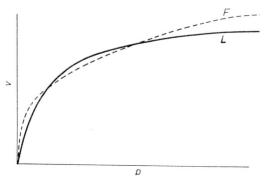

Figure 60. Langmuir and Freundlich isotherms.
L . . . Langmuir isotherm.   F . . . Freundlich isotherm

of the particular system which is studied. Usually both $c$ and $n$ decrease with increasing temperature, as shown in Table 19 for the physical adsorption of carbon monoxide on charcoal[14].

Since the amount adsorbed is proportional to a fractional power of the pressure, the Freundlich isotherm is similar to the Langmuir isotherm in the region of moderate coverage. Moreover, by suitable choice of constants, the two isotherms can be made almost coincident, as shown in *Figure 60*. However, the Freundlich isotherm is often obeyed over wide ranges of adsorbed amount, and also by systems which do not obey the Langmuir isotherm. For these reasons it should not be regarded simply as an approximate form of the Langmuir isotherm.

Since its promulgation, it has been shown that the Freundlich isotherm may be derived theoretically if certain assumptions are made concerning the nature of the surface and the mechanism of adsorption. Two such derivations have been made, one of which uses a thermodynamic approach, the other a kinetic approach.

### THERMODYNAMIC DERIVATION

RIDEAL[15] has shown that the Freundlich isotherm may be derived from the Gibbs' adsorption equation if it is assumed that the surface layer obeys an equation of state of the form

$$FA = nRT \qquad (5.60)$$

where $n$ is a constant correcting for the mutual interaction of the adsorbed molecules. The forces within the surface layer are attractive if $n$ is less than unity and repulsive if $n$ is greater than unity.

Differentiation of this equation gives

$$\frac{\mathrm{d}F}{\mathrm{d}A} = \frac{-nRT}{A^2} \qquad (5.61)$$

Inserting this in the Gibbs' adsorption equation

$$\frac{1}{A} = \frac{p}{RT} \cdot \frac{\mathrm{d}F}{\mathrm{d}p} = \frac{-np}{A^2} \cdot \frac{\mathrm{d}A}{\mathrm{d}p} \qquad (5.62)$$

and rearranging, we arrive at

$$\frac{1}{n} \frac{\mathrm{d}p}{p} = -\frac{\mathrm{d}A}{A} = \frac{\mathrm{d}v}{v} \qquad (5.63)$$

where $v$ is the volume of gas adsorbed and is proportional to $1/A$.

On integration this equation gives

$$v = cp^{1/n} \qquad (5.64)$$

where $c$ is a constant.

Experimental values of $n$ are usually greater than unity and this means, on the basis of the above derivation, that the forces between the adsorbed molecules are repulsive. Other evidence shows this to be the case for the chemisorption of gases on most solids.

STATISTICAL DERIVATION

Equation (5.27) showed that the simple Langmuir isotherm will only be obeyed if the quantity $a$, which is proportional to $f_a \cdot e^{q/RT}$, is independent of $\theta$. In general this will not be so.

This difficulty was anticipated by LANGMUIR[2], who suggested that if the quantity $a$ varied with $\theta$ because the surface was heterogeneous, the total coverage could be obtained by a process of summation. Thus, the surface could be divided into a number of groups of identical sites, designated $i$, each of which had a particular $a$ value. Then

$$\theta_i = \frac{a_i p}{1 + a_i p} \tag{5.65}$$

and the total coverage is

$$\theta = \Sigma n_i \theta_i \tag{5.66}$$

where $n_i$ is the fraction of the total number of sites which are of type $i$. If the $a$ values are sufficiently near to one another to form a continuous distribution, equation (5.66) reduces to

$$\theta = \int n_i \theta_i di \tag{5.67}$$

where $n_i di$ is the frequency of occurrence of $\theta_i$ between $i$ and $i + di$. In general this integration cannot be carried out because the distribution function $n_i$ is unknown. However, it is possible to show that a certain type of distribution function leads to a Freundlich isotherm.

In the simpler case we consider the variation of $a_i$ due simply to variation of $q$. Then equation (5.67) may be expressed as

$$\theta = \int n_q \theta_q dq \tag{5.68}$$

It may then be shown that if $n_q$ is exponentially dependent on $q$ according to an equation

$$n_q = n_0 e^{-q/q_m} \tag{5.69}$$

where $n_0$ and $q_m$ are constants, a Freundlich isotherm is obtained. The proof of this is due first to ZELDOWITSCH[16]. A more elegant method is due to TAYLOR and HALSEY[17, 18], and in this the isotherm is determined as

$$\theta = \int_0^\infty n_q \cdot \frac{a_q p}{1 + a_q p} \cdot dq \tag{5.70}$$

Placing $a_q = a_0 e^{q/RT}$, where $a_0$ is a constant since $f_a$ is assumed constant, and inserting the value of $n_q$ from equation (5.69), equation (5.70) becomes, after rearranging,

$$\theta = \int_0^\infty \frac{n_0 e^{-q/q_m} \cdot dq}{1 + e^{-q/RT}/a_0 p} \qquad (5.71)$$

Provided $q \gg \pi RT$, i.e. the heat of adsorption considerably exceeds about three times the thermal energy, the integration is possible and gives

$$\theta = (a_0 p)^{RT/q_m} \cdot n_0 q_m \qquad (5.72)$$

This is a Freundlich isotherm. From it, the heat of adsorption is obtained by applying the Clausius–Clapeyron equation

$$q = R \left( \frac{d \ln p}{d(1/T)} \right)_\theta \qquad (5.73)$$

giving

$$q = - q_m \ln \theta + q_m \ln (n_0 q_m) \qquad (5.74)$$

A certain simplification of the isotherm (5.72) may be achieved. First, equation (5.72) shows that when $p = 1/a_0$, $\theta = n_0 q_m$ at all temperatures. Under these conditions, equation (5.74) shows that $q = 0$. At pressures greater than $1/a_0$, equation (5.72) suggests that $\theta$ is greater than $n_0 q_m$. However, equation (5.74) shows that $q$ is then negative, so that adsorption is endothermic, and this is forbidden on thermodynamic grounds. Therefore $\theta = n_0 q_m$ is the maximum adsorption, and the $\theta$ scale may be rearranged so that this state corresponds to $\theta = 1$. Equation (5.72) then becomes

$$\theta = (a_0 p)^{RT/q_m} \qquad (5.75)$$

and equation (5.74) becomes

$$q = - q_m \ln \theta \qquad (5.76)$$

A later treatment by HALSEY[18] takes into account the possible variation of $f_a$ with $\theta$ as well as of $q$ with $\theta$, and gives

$$\theta = (a_0 p)^{RT/q_m(1-rT)} \qquad (5.77)$$

where $r$ is a further constant. The isotherm is still of the Freundlich type, and application of the Clausius–Clapeyron equation to it gives,

$$q = - q_m \ln \theta \qquad (5.78)$$

173

## FEATURES OF THE FREUNDLICH ISOTHERM

### UNDERLYING ASSUMPTIONS

The Langmuir isotherm assumes the product $f_a$ . $e^{q/RT}$ to be constant at all $\theta$ values, and since the separate quantities $f_a$ and $e^{q/RT}$ are not likely to change to equal but opposite extents with $\theta$, this implies that both $f_a$ and $q$ must be constant. The Freundlich isotherm, however, implies that $q$ falls logarithmically as $\theta$ increases.

In deriving the Freundlich isotherm it has been assumed that this heat fall is due to surface heterogeneity. It is, however, pertinent to enquire whether obedience to the Freundlich isotherm necessarily indicates heterogeneity, or whether the alternative cause of a falling heat, namely increasing surface repulsions, might not account for the result.

Differentiating equation (5.76) gives

$$\frac{dq}{d\theta} = -\frac{q_m}{\theta} \tag{5.79}$$

and this shows that $q$ falls most rapidly at low $\theta$ values. Now such behaviour cannot be accounted for in terms of surface repulsions. The fall in heat due to repulsions may be calculated statistically for various types of adsorption, and the $q$–$\theta$ curves which are obtained are discussed in Chapter VI. The important point is that these, if anything, show a heat which falls least rapidly at low $\theta$ values, because in dilute layers the adsorbed particles tend to be too far apart for repulsions to be appreciable. Equation (5.76) is therefore only explicable in terms of heterogeneity.

It is to be noted, however, that the thermodynamic derivation of the Freundlich isotherm does involve surface repulsions.

### METHOD OF TESTING

In testing whether a set of experimental data obeys the Freundlich isotherm, it is invariable to plot log $\theta$ against log $p$. The simpler isotherm (5.75) gives

$$\log \theta = \frac{RT}{q_m} \log a_0 + \frac{RT}{q_m} \log p \tag{5.80}$$

while the isotherm (5.77) gives

$$\log \theta = \frac{RT}{q_m(1-rT)} \log a_0 + \frac{RT}{q_m(1-rT)} \log p \tag{5.81}$$

174

In both cases log $\theta$–log $p$ plots should give a family of straight lines. In equation (5.80) both the slopes and the intercepts are proportional to the absolute temperature and to $T/(1-rT)$ in equation (5.81). The lines in both cases converge and meet at the common point $p=1/a_0$, $\theta=1$.

If $\theta$ is unknown, it is necessary to use adsorbed volumes, $v$, and equating $\theta$ to $v/v_m$, where $v_m$ is the monolayer volume, equation (5.80) gives

$$\log v = \log v_m + \frac{RT}{q_m} \log a_0 + \frac{RT}{q_m} \log p \qquad (5.82)$$

and equation (5.81) a similar relation. From equation (5.82) it is in principle possible to obtain $v_m$ by measuring intercepts at different temperatures. An alternative method is to extrapolate log $v$–log $p$ plots to the point of common intersection, $p=1/a_0$, when $v=v_m$.

## HEAT OF ADSORPTION

The logarithmic $q$–$\theta$ relation may be obeyed by some systems over the main $\theta$ range, but it will not be obeyed at $\theta \to 0$, because $q$ never approaches $\infty$ at low coverages. That is, in terms of the distribution of energy among sites given by equation (5.69), there are no sites with infinite energy. In practice, one may expect an upper limit for the energy of a site, so that when the heat has reached the value corresponding to this energy, it will stay constant when $\theta$ decreases further.

## THE SATURATION STATE

The empiric form of the Freundlich isotherm, $v=cp^{1/n}$, suggests that $v$ increases indefinitely as $p$ increases. As experimental isotherms always seemed to approach saturation at high pressures, it was at one time thought that the Freundlich isotherm was invalid. However, in agreement with experiment, the non-empiric forms of the isotherm, equations (5.75) and (5.76), have been shown to imply that a saturated state is reached at $p=1/a_0$.

## THE ISOTHERM FOR DISSOCIATIVE ADSORPTION

If adsorption involves dissociation, and an exponential distribution of energy among sites is inserted in a Langmuir isotherm

$$\theta = \frac{\sqrt{(ap)}}{1+\sqrt{(ap)}} \qquad (5.83)$$

the isotherm

$$\theta = [\sqrt{(a_0 p)}]^{RT/q_m} \qquad (5.84)$$

is obtained, similar to the isotherm (5.75). The isotherm for dissociative adsorption corresponding to equation (5.77) is

$$\theta = [\sqrt{(a_0 p)}]^{RT/q_m(1-rT)} \tag{5.85}$$

### THE TEMKIN ISOTHERM

Of the two isotherms considered so far, the Freundlich isotherm is likely to be more widely obeyed than the Langmuir isotherm, because heats of chemisorption normally fall with increasing $\theta$, and such an effect is only allowed for in the Freundlich isotherm. However, relatively few experimental $q$–$\theta$ curves are logarithmic in form, and for this reason the Freundlich isotherm is unlikely to be more than an approximation to the truth with many adsorptions. Very often, the heat fall is more nearly linear than logarithmic, and it is with this type of behaviour that the Temkin isotherm[19] is concerned. The isotherm is in fact derived[20] by inserting in the Langmuir isotherm the condition that the heat of adsorption decreases linearly with $\theta$. Such a heat fall can arise either on a uniform surface from repulsive forces, or from surface heterogeneity.

#### DERIVATION OF THE ISOTHERM FOR A UNIFORM SURFACE

Since all sites are identical it is sufficient to insert in a Langmuir isotherm the condition that $q$ varies according to an equation

$$q = q_0(1 - \alpha\theta) \tag{5.86}$$

where $\alpha$ is a constant and $q_0$ is the heat of adsorption at $\theta=0$. Thus, for single site adsorption for which the Langmuir isotherm may be written

$$\frac{\theta}{1-\theta} = a_0 p e^{q/RT} \tag{5.87}$$

we have

$$\frac{\theta}{1-\theta} = a_0 p e^{q_0(1-\alpha\theta)/RT} \tag{5.88}$$

Taking logarithms and transposing

$$\ln p = -\ln A_0 + \frac{q_0\alpha\theta}{RT} + \ln \frac{\theta}{1-\theta} \tag{5.89}$$

where $A_0 = a_0 e^{q_0/RT}$ and is independent of $\theta$. Now for chemisorption $q_0\alpha \gg RT$, and in the middle range of coverage, where $\ln \theta/(1-\theta)$ varies very slowly with $\theta$, the main variation of $\ln p$ is due to variation of the term $q_0\alpha\theta/RT$. This will not apply if $\theta$ approaches zero or unity when $\ln \theta/(1-\theta)$ changes very rapidly with $\theta$, but in the middle region of coverage it is possible, without serious error, to neglect the variation of $\ln \theta/(1-\theta)$ and to equate it to zero, the value at $\theta = 0.5$. In this case equation (5.89) simplifies to

$$\theta = \frac{RT}{q_0 a} \ln A_0 p \qquad (5.90)$$

This isotherm, characterized by a linear variation of $\ln p$ with $\theta$, is a Temkin isotherm.

DERIVATION OF THE ISOTHERM FOR A NON-UNIFORM SURFACE

Here it is necessary to divide the surface into a number of uniform elements $ds$, on each of which the heat of adsorption is constant. Each of these elements is assumed to obey a Langmuir isotherm,

$$\theta_s = \frac{a_0 p e^{q/RT}}{1 + a_0 p e^{q/RT}} \qquad (5.91)$$

and the value of $\theta$ over the whole surface is obtained by integration as

$$\theta = \int \theta_s ds \qquad (5.92)$$

Since $q$ falls linearly with $s$

$$q = q_0(1 - as) \qquad (5.93)$$

Inserting (5.91) and (5.93) in (5.92), and assuming the total surface area $s$ is unity,

$$\theta = \int_0^1 \frac{A_0 p e^{-\alpha q_0 s/RT}}{1 + A_0 p e^{-\alpha q_0 s/RT}} \cdot ds \qquad (5.94)$$

where $A_0 = a_0 e^{q_0/RT}$ as before. This gives

$$\theta = \frac{RT}{q_0 a} \ln \left[ \frac{1 + A_0 p}{1 + A_0 p e^{-\alpha q_0/RT}} \right] \qquad (5.95)$$

In the middle range of surface coverage, it may be assumed that the pressure is sufficiently large for $A_0 p$ to be much greater than unity but still sufficiently low for $A_0 p e^{-\alpha q_0/RT}$ to be much less than unity. Equation (5.93) then simplifies to

$$\theta = \frac{RT}{q_0 a} \ln A_0 p \qquad (5.96)$$

This isotherm is identical with the isotherm (5.90).

## FEATURES OF THE TEMKIN ISOTHERM

### METHOD OF TESTING

Obedience to the Temkin isotherm is always tested by showing that in the middle region of coverage, plotting $\ln p$ against $\theta$, or against the volume adsorbed, gives a straight line with the slope proportional to the absolute temperature. At high and low coverages, when the isotherm (5.96) does not apply, deviations from linearity may however be expected, even if the adsorption has the necessary linear fall of $q$ with $\theta$.

### THE SATURATION STATE

The isotherm (5.96) seems to show that $\theta$ may be increased indefinitely by increasing $p$, suggesting that there is no saturation state. This is, of course, because equation (5.96) does not apply at high pressures and high coverages—when the exact isotherms (5.89) and (5.95) are used, $\theta$ is found to approach unity as $p$ approaches infinity, as expected.

### THE ISOTHERM FOR DISSOCIATIVE ADSORPTION

If adsorption involves dissociation, and the isotherm is derived by inserting a linear heat fall in a Langmuir isotherm

$$\frac{\theta}{1-\theta} = \sqrt{(a_0 p e^{q/RT})} \tag{5.97}$$

equations (5.90) and (5.96) are still obtained. The identical Temkin isotherm is thus applicable to dissociative and non-dissociative adsorption alike.

### THE APPLICATION OF ISOTHERMS TO EXPERIMENTAL DATA

There is no doubt that many sets of experimental data will appear to obey one, or even more than one, isotherm when further considerations show that such obedience is impossible. Spurious obedience to the Langmuir isotherm is very frequent—as an example we may consider the chemisorption of hydrogen by a mixed manganous-chromic oxide powder[21], data for which are given in Table 20.

The points at 444 °C, plotted as $p/v$ against $p$ or as $\sqrt{(p)}/v$ against $\sqrt{p}$ give a good straight line, suggesting that the Langmuir isotherm is obeyed, though leaving uncertainty as to whether or not the

TABLE 20

Chemisorption of $H_2$ on $MnO/Cr_2O_3$ at 305 and 444 °C

| $T=305\,°C$ | | $T=444\,°C$ | |
|---|---|---|---|
| Pressure (mm Hg) | Vol. adsorbed (cm³) | Pressure (mm Hg) | Vol. adsorbed (cm³) |
| 44 | 156·9 | 3 | 57·1 |
| 51 | 160·8 | 22 | 83·3 |
| 63 | 163·6 | 48 | 95·0 |
| 121 | 167·0 | 77 | 98·1 |
| 151 | 169·6 | 165 | 100·9 |
| 230 | 171·1 | | |
| 269 | 171·6 | | |

hydrogen molecule is fully dissociated in the act of chemisorption. The slope of either line should be $1/v_m$, and each gives a monolayer volume close to 100 cm³. The data at 305 °C show, however, that the volume chemisorbed can approach twice this quantity, and Langmuir plots at this temperature give a monolayer volume of about 175 cm³.

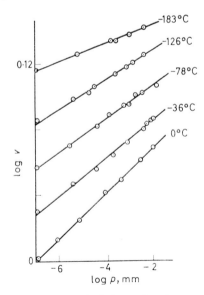

*Figure 61. Log-log isotherms for hydrogen adsorption on tungsten films*
By courtesy of Trapnell, B.M.W. *Proc. Roy Soc.* A**206**, 39, 1951

179

Such behaviour—apparent obedience to the Langmuir isotherm, yet with the monolayer volume varying considerably with temperature—is often found. It indicates that the apparent obedience is not significant, and probably arises because the data refer to a relatively limited range of $\theta$ values, within which deviations from the isotherm are too small to be detected.

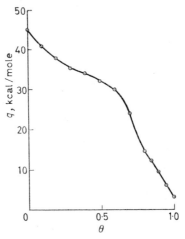

*Figure 62. Heat of chemisorption of hydrogen on tungsten*
By courtesy of Trapnell, B.M.W. *Proc. Roy. Soc.* **A206**, 39, 1951

TABLE 21

Slopes of Log-Log Isotherms in $H_2$ Chemisorption by W Films

| $T(°K)$ | *Inverse slope* | *Product* |
|---------|-----------------|-----------|
| 273 | 72 | $1.96 . 10^4$ |
| 237 | 83 | $1.97 . 10^4$ |
| 195 | 102 | $1.99 . 10^4$ |
| 147 | 125 | $1.84 . 10^4$ |
| 90 | 167 | $1.50 . 10^4$ |

Obedience to the Freundlich isotherm within a restricted range of coverage has been found by TRAPNELL[22] for hydrogen chemisorption on evaporated tungsten films. Isotherms were obtained for the region of coverage $\theta=75$ to 100 per cent: these did not obey the Langmuir isotherm, but *Figure 61* shows that there is good obedience to the Freundlich isotherm. Furthermore, Table 21 shows that, except at liquid air temperatures, the product of the inverse slopes of log-log plots and the temperature is constant, as required by equation (5.84). However, the heat fall does not obey the equation $q = -q_m \ln \theta$, at least, over the main $\theta$ range. *Figure 62* shows that the $q-\theta$ curve is more nearly linear than logarithmic, although for the restricted range of coverage over which the isotherms were obtained, it can be treated as roughly logarithmic.

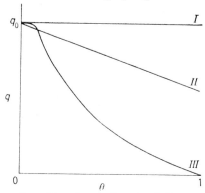

Figure 63. q–θ curves for various isotherms
*I Langmuir isotherm.   II Temkin isotherm.   III Freundlich isotherm.*

TABLE 22

Chemisorption of $H_2$ on Cu Powder at 25 °C

| Powder A | | Powder B | |
|---|---|---|---|
| Pressure (cm Hg) | Vol. adsorbed (cm³) | Pressure (cm Hg) | Vol. adsorbed (cm³) |
| 0·019 | 0·042 | 0·105 | 0·239 |
| 0·066 | 0·138 | 0·170 | 0·464 |
| 0·097 | 0·163 | 0·295 | 0·564 |
| 0·101 | 0·161 | 0·325 | 0·559 |
| 0·110 | 0·171 | 0·540 | 0·659 |
| 0·190 | 0·221 | 0·890 | 0·761 |
| 0·265 | 0·256 | 1·065 | 0·800 |
| 0·405 | 0·321 | 1·765 | 0·941 |
| 0·555 | 0·371 | 2·15 | 0·995 |
| 0·750 | 0·411 | 3·62 | 1·121 |
| 0·815 | 0·421 | 4·51 | 1·160 |
| 1·195 | 0·471 | 7·45 | 1·281 |
| 1·755 | 0·550 | 9·58 | 1·300 |
| | | 20·48 | 1·471 |

N

To be certain that a particular isotherm is truly obeyed, two conditions must be satisfied. The first is that the $q$–$\theta$ curve must be shown to be of the form implied by the isotherm in question. The forms for the three isotherms are shown in *Figure 63*. The second is that the experimental data must cover the appropriate $\theta$ range. In testing obedience to the Langmuir and Freundlich isotherms, the data must apply to the widest possible range of coverage: in testing the Temkin isotherm, coverages must lie between about 20 per cent and 80 per cent.

Examples of obedience to each of the three isotherms which satisfy these conditions may now be discussed.

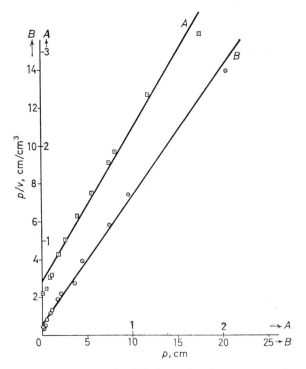

*Figure 64. Langmuir plots for hydrogen adsorption on copper powder*

A case where the Langmuir isotherm is probably applicable is to the chemisorption of hydrogen on a copper powder, studied by WARD[23]. Data from typical experiments are given in Table 22. Log-log plots show distinct deviations from linearity at low and at high adsorbed volumes, so that the Freundlich isotherm is not obeyed. The heat of adsorption is independent of surface coverage, and this suggests that the Langmuir isotherm might be applicable. In fact, both sets of data give good straight lines when plotted as $p/v$ against $p$, as shown in *Figure 64*. It is of interest, however, that plots of $\sqrt{(p)}/v$ against $\sqrt{p}$, characteristic of a dissociative adsorption, are not linear.

Two chemisorptions which obey the Freundlich isotherm over the main $\theta$ range are those of hydrogen and nitrogen on tungsten powder, studied by FRANKENBURG[1] and by DAVIS[24] respectively. The characteristics of these adsorptions on powders, as also of the adsorption of hydrogen on copper powder just discussed, are quite different from the characteristics of the same adsorptions on evaporated films, probably because the surfaces of the powders were not entirely pure. Frankenburg's measurements are the most extensive yet made, covering a wide range of temperature ($-194$ to $600\,^{\circ}\mathrm{C}$) and pressure ($10^{-5}$ to $30$ mm). The isotherms have been shown in *Figure 59*: when plotted as log-log isotherms, excellent straight lines are obtained, as shown in *Figure 65*. On slight extrapolation, the lines converge and meet at the point $S$, and measurement of the surface area of the powder by low temperature nitrogen adsorption showed that the volume of hydrogen adsorbed at $S$ corresponds to one atom per surface tungsten atom.

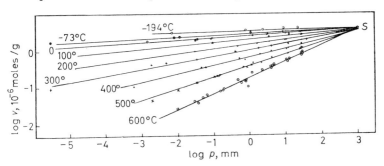

*Figure 65. Log-log isotherms for hydrogen adsorption on a tungsten powder*
By courtesy of Frankenburg, W. G. *J. Amer. Chem. Soc.* **66**, 1827, 1944

The slopes of the log-log isotherms increase regularly with temperature: values of the inverse slope are given in Table 23. The product of these and the temperature is not constant, but decreases continuously with rising temperature. The slopes are not therefore directly proportional to $T$, but when the product of inverse slope and temperature is plotted against temperature, an excellent straight line results[18].

This shows that the slopes are proportional to $T/(1-rT)$, where $r$ is a constant, and since the isotherms meet at a common point as

TABLE 23

Log-Log Isotherms for $H_2$ Chemisorption on W Powder

| Temperature (°K) | Inverse slope | Product |
|---|---|---|
| 79 | 67·4 | 5,325 |
| 200 | 24·1 | 4,820 |
| 273 | 16·63 | 4,540 |
| 373 | 10·82 | 4,036 |
| 473 | 7·58 | 3,586 |
| 573 | 5·60 | 3,209 |
| 673 | 4·17 | 2,806 |
| 773 | 3·06 | 2,366 |
| 873 | 2·31 | 2,017 |

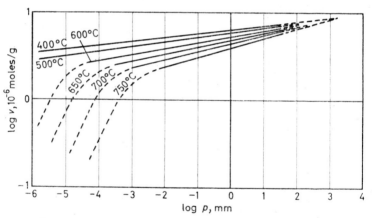

Figure 66. Log-log isotherms for nitrogen adsorption on a tungsten powder
By courtesy of Davis, R. T., J. Amer. Chem. Soc. 68, 1395, 1946

well, the adsorption obeys either equation (5.77) or (5.85). It is not possible to decide which is obeyed, but the latter is more likely since hydrogen chemisorption is normally dissociative. In this case the constants are found to be $1/a_0 = 3,150$ mm, $q_m = 5,700$ cal/mole, and $r = 0·75 \times 10^{-3}$ per degree.

These results do not however apply to coverages less than 0·8 per cent, where the slope of the log-log isotherms at all temperatures is equal to 2. This shows that $\theta$ is proportional to $\sqrt{p}$, the law at low coverages for a dissociative adsorption following a Langmuir isotherm. Moreover, below 0·8 per cent coverage the heat of adsorption is independent of $\theta$, as required by the Langmuir isotherm. These facts mean that the exponential distribution of energy among sites implied in the Freundlich isotherm, which would cause an infinite heat as $\theta \to 0$, breaks down, and is replaced by a constant site energy, which gives rise to a constant heat.

The results with nitrogen chemisorption are very similar, although owing to slower equilibrium, isotherms could not be obtained below 400°C. As a result, coverages between 70 and 100 per cent could not be observed. Over the main $\theta$ range, log-log plots are linear, as shown in *Figure 66*, and the lines converge to a common point, at which one nitrogen atom is present per two surface tungsten atoms. The slopes of the log-log isotherms increase continuously with temperature, and the product of the inverse slope and temperature again decreases continuously with temperature as shown in Table 24.

TABLE 24

Log-Log Isotherms for $N_2$ Chemisorption on W Powder

| Temperature (°K) | Inverse slope | Product |
|---|---|---|
| 673 | 22·55 | 15,180 |
| 773 | 18·25 | 14,110 |
| 873 | 14·37 | 12,540 |
| 923 | 12·48 | 11,520 |
| 973 | 10·79 | 10,530 |
| 1,023 | 9·28 | 9,490 |

However, the product does not fall linearly with temperature, and it is uncertain whether this is a real effect, in which case equation (5.85) is not obeyed, or whether it is due to the greater experimental inaccuracies encountered with this system.

As with hydrogen, the slope of the log-log isotherms below a certain coverage is equal to 2 at all temperatures, indicating obedience to the Langmuir isotherm. For nitrogen adsorption this coverage is probably about 30 per cent.

Close adherence to the Temkin isotherm has been found by HICKMOTT[25] for the adsorption of hydrogen on a tungsten filament.

Isotherms plotted as log $p$ against molecules adsorbed per sq. cm are shown in *Figure 67*. Taking Roberts figure for the number of sites per sq. cm of apparent surface as $1 \cdot 7 \times 10^{15}$, the $\theta$ values in Hickmott's experiments lie between about $0 \cdot 4$ and $0 \cdot 7$, a suitable range for obedience to the Temkin isotherm. Not only is each isotherm in *Figure 67* linear over a two hundredfold range of pressure, but

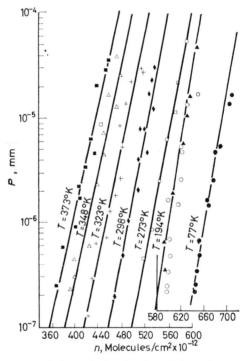

Figure 67. *Isotherms for the adsorption of hydrogen by tungsten*
By courtesy of Hickmott, T. W. *J. Chem. Phys.* **32**, 810, 1960

the slopes of the isotherms are proportional to absolute temperature, in agreement with equation (5.96). Finally, as shown in *Figure 68*, the $q-\theta$ relation derived from the isotherms and from desorption data is linear. In contrast to this last result, however, the $q-\theta$ relation on evaporated films is not accurately linear.

Nitrogen and hydrogen chemisorption on iron probably obey the Temkin equation. Isotherms for nitrogen chemisorption on a doubly promoted powder catalyst have been obtained at 396 and 449 °C by EMMETT and BRUNAUER[26]. These are shown in *Figure 69* and have been discussed by BRUNAUER, LOVE and KEENAN[20]. The volumes of nitrogen chemisorbed lie between 2 and 5 cm³, while the volume of nitrogen physically adsorbed into a monolayer at −189 °C was about 18 cm³. Now any promoter atoms in the surface will have been active in physical adsorption but not in chemisorption, and therefore the monolayer value of the iron atoms in physical adsorp-

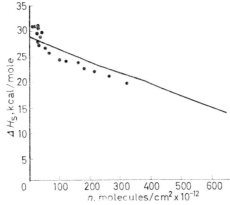

*Figure 68. The heat of adsorption of hydrogen on tungsten: solid line, isosteric heats; points, desorption heats*

By courtesy of Hickmott, T. W. *J. Chem. Phys.* **32**, 810, 1960

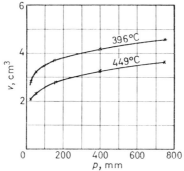

*Figure 69. Isotherms for nitrogen adsorption on iron powders*
By courtesy of Emmett, P. H. and Brunauer, S. *J. Amer. Chem. Soc.* **56**, 35, 1934

tion was rather less than 18 cm³. Assuming close-packing of nitrogen molecules in physical adsorption, and bonding as Fe≡N during chemisorption, we may calculate that the $\theta$ values in chemisorption probably lay between 0·25 and 0·6. These are in the correct range for testing the Temkin equation.

Data for 396 °C are given in Table 25. The figures of the first two columns give reasonable straight lines when plotted either as $\log p$ against $\log v$, as $\sqrt{(p/v)}$ against $\sqrt{p}$, or as $\log p$ against $v$. Thus by plotting it is not possible to decide whether the Freundlich, Langmuir or Temkin equations is obeyed. Furthermore, the data are not sufficiently extensive for distinction to be made on the basis of a $q$–$\theta$ curve.

TABLE 25

Adsorption Isotherm for $N_2$ on Catalyst 931 at 396 °C

| $p$ (mm) | $v_{obs}$(cm³ at S.T.P.) | $v_{calc.}$ (cm³ at S.T.P.) |
|---|---|---|
| 25 | 2·83 | 2·88 |
| 53 | 3·22 | 3·22 |
| 150 | 3·69 | 3·70 |
| 397 | 4·14 | 4·15 |
| 768 | 4·55 | 4·45 |

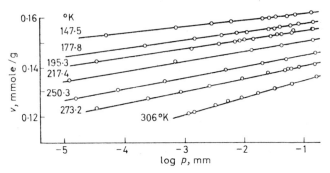

*Figure 70. Isotherms for hydrogen adsorption on iron films*
By courtesy of Porter, A. S. and Tompkins, F. C. *Proc. Roy. Soc.* **A217**, 544, 1953

An alternative method of deciding was used by Brunauer, Love and Keenan, who showed that the constants of the Temkin equation (5.96) may be obtained by measurement of the velocity of chemisorption. Having obtained these, it is then possible to calculate the volumes adsorbed which would be expected at various pressures if the Temkin equation were obeyed. These are shown in column 3 of Table 25. The approach is more sensitive than the method of plotting, and the agreement between calculation and experiment is a strong indication that the Temkin equation is obeyed.

Isotherms, plotted as log $p$ against $v$, for hydrogen chemisorption on evaporated iron films, due to PORTER and TOMPKINS[27], are shown in *Figure 70*. The range of coverages which is involved is uncertain, and may be rather high for testing the Temkin equation. However, *Figure 71* shows that the $q$–$\theta$ relation is exactly linear, and further-

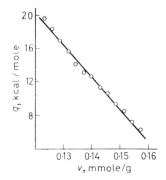

*Figure 71. q–v relation for hydrogen on iron films*
By courtesy of Porter, A. S. and Tompkins, F. C. *Proc. Roy. Soc.* **A217**, 544, 1953

more the slopes of the log $p$–$v$ lines are roughly proportional to the absolute temperature. Both of these conditions are required by the Temkin equation (5.96) and it therefore seems likely that this isotherm applies to the system.

## OTHER ADSORPTION ISOTHERMS

### THE GENERAL CASE

The Langmuir, Freundlich and Temkin isotherms respectively treat the cases where the heat of adsorption is independent of, and falls logarithmically and linearly with coverage. Although many adsorptions will approximate in their behaviour to one of these cases, we may in general write

$$q = q_0 \cdot F(\theta) \qquad (5.98)$$

The isotherms for single site adsorption are then as follows.

### (1) Uniform surface

Inserting equation (5.98) in a Langmuir isotherm (5.87), taking logarithms and transposing, we obtain

$$\ln\frac{p(1-\theta)}{\theta} = -\ln a_0 - \frac{q_0}{RT} \cdot F(\theta) \qquad (5.99)$$

189

## (2) Non-uniform surface

The isotherm is obtained by integration over the surface as

$$\theta = \int_0^1 \frac{a_0 p e^{q_0 F(s)/RT}}{1 + a_0 p e^{q_0 F(s)/RT}} \, ds \qquad (5.100)$$

Neither of these isotherms, however, allow for the possible variation in $a_0$ with $\theta$ due to variation of the partition function of the adsorbed particles.

### CAESIUM ADSORPTION ON TUNGSTEN

A complex isotherm has been observed for the chemisorption of caesium vapour on tungsten[28], and the complexity arises largely because $a_0$ varies markedly with $\theta$. Isosteres are shown in *Figure 72*.

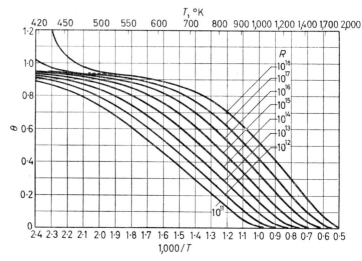

*Figure 72. Isosteres for caesium adsorption on tungsten filaments.*
*R is the rate of collision of Cs atoms with the surface and is*
*proportional to the Cs vapour pressure*
By courtesy of Taylor, J. B. and Langmuir, I. *Phys. Rev.* **44**, 423, 1933

In previous chapters the velocities of adsorption and desorption of caesium on tungsten have been shown to be respectively

$$u = \frac{p}{\sqrt{(2\pi m k T)}} \qquad (5.101)$$

$$\ln u' = \alpha' - E'/RT \qquad (5.102)$$

The values of $a'$ and $E'$ are

$$a' = 61 \cdot 0 + 4 \cdot 8\theta - 2 \cdot 4\theta^2 + \ln\frac{\theta}{1-\theta} + \frac{1}{1-\theta} \quad (5.103)$$

$$E' = \frac{64,000}{1 + 0 \cdot 714\theta} \quad (5.104)$$

The isotherm obtained by equating $\ln u$ and $\ln u'$ and transposing is

$$\ln\frac{p(1-\theta)}{\theta} = \ln\sqrt{(2\pi mkT)} + 61 \cdot 0 + 4 \cdot 8\theta - 2 \cdot 4\theta^2 + \frac{1}{1-\theta}$$
$$- \frac{64,000}{RT(1+0 \cdot 714\theta)} \quad (5.105)$$

This isotherm bears a certain resemblance to the general isotherm (5.99) with

$$q_0 = 64,000 \text{ cal/g atom} \quad (5.106)$$

$$F(\theta) = \frac{1}{1 + 0 \cdot 714\theta} \quad (5.107)$$

and a variation in $a_0$ given by

$$- \ln a_0 = \ln\sqrt{(2\pi mkT)} + 61 \cdot 0 + 4 \cdot 8\theta - 2 \cdot 4\theta^2 + \frac{1}{1-\theta} \quad (5.108)$$

## CASES OF SIMULTANEOUS FORMATION OF TWO DIFFERENT TYPES OF ADSORBED LAYER

Study of chemisorption isotherms is complicated if a second type of adsorption proceeds at the same time as formation of the primary layer. Normally this is not observed because the heat of the initial adsorption is much higher than that for the secondary adsorption. Sometimes, however, the heat of chemisorption for the primary state drops to such low values at high coverage that the different binding states can be populated simultaneously. The secondary state may be either a weak chemisorption or physical adsorption.

Two examples of such behaviour are carbon monoxide and caesium adsorption on tungsten. In the former case the second type of adsorption is thought to be physical in nature whereas in the latter case it is chemical.

Isotherms for carbon monoxide adsorption on evaporated films due to RIDEAL and TRAPNELL[29] are shown in *Figure 73*. Above $-183\,°C$ these give heats too large for physical adsorption, and the coverages are less than 100 per cent, so that chemisorption alone takes place. However, along the isotherms for $-183$ and $-195\,°C$, the heats are low enough for physical adsorption, and also the isotherms show an increase in slope. Both these facts suggest that physical adsorption is commencing. However, part of the adsorption at $-183\,°C$ seems to take place at $\theta < 100$ per cent, and certainly there is no discontinuity between the end of chemisorption

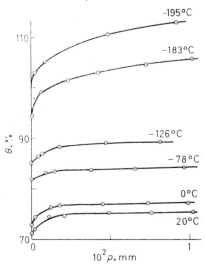

Figure 73. Isotherms for CO adsorption on tungsten films
By courtesy of Rideal, E.K. and Trapnell, B.M.W. Proc. Roy. Soc. A205, 409, 1951

and the commencement of second layer formation. Very probably physical adsorption and chemisorption are taking place simultaneously.

Similarly, the isosteres for caesium adsorption shown in Figure 72, for which $\theta$ exceeds unity at low temperatures, show that the end of first layer formation is continuous with the commencement of second layer formation.

A third possible example of overlap is in hydrogen adsorption on chromia[30].

### REFERENCES

[1] Frankenburg, W. G. J. Amer. Chem. Soc. 66, 1827, 1944
[2] Langmuir, I. J. Amer. Chem. Soc. 40, 1361, 1918
[3] Laidler, K. J. J. Phys. Chem. 53, 712, 1949
[4] Fowler, R. H. Proc. Camb. Phil. Soc. 31, 260, 1935

5 Volmer, M. *Z. physik. Chem.* **115**, 253, 1925
6 Williams, A. M. *Proc. Roy. Soc.* A**96**, 287, 1920
  Henry, D. C. *Phil. Mag.* **44**, 689, 1920
7 Hinshelwood, C. N. *Kinetics of Chemical Change.* London; Oxford University Press, 1940
8 Schwab, G. M. *Catalysis.* London; Macmillan, 1937
9 Hinshelwood, C. N. and Topley, B. *J. Chem. Soc.* **123**, 1014, 1923
10 Hinshelwood, C. N. and Burk, R. E. *J. Chem. Soc.* **127**, 1105, 1925
11 Bodenstein, M. and Ohlmer, F. *Z. physik. Chem.* **53**, 166, 1905
12 Bodenstein, M. and Fink, C. G. *Z. physik. Chem.* **60**, 1, 1907
13 Freundlich, H. *Colloid and Capillary Chemistry.* London; Methuen, 1926
14 Travers, M. W. *Proc. Roy. Soc.* A**78**, 9, 1907
15 Rideal, E. K. *Surface Chemistry.* Cambridge; Cambridge University Press, 1930
16 Zeldowitsch, J. *Acta Physicochim. U.R.S.S.* **1**, 961, 1934
17 Halsey, G. and Taylor, H. S. *J. Chem. Phys.* **15**, 624, 1947
18 Halsey, G. *Adv. in Catalysis* **4**, 259, 1952
19 Frumkin, A. and Slygin, A. *Acta. Physicochim. U.R.S.S.* **3**, 791, 1935
20 Brunauer, S., Love, K. S. and Keenan, R. G. *J. Amer. Chem. Soc.* **64**, 751, 1942
21 Taylor, H. S. and Williamson, A. T. *J. Amer. Chem. Soc.* **53**, 2168, 1931
22 Trapnell, B. M. W. *Proc. Roy. Soc.* A**206**, 39, 1951
23 Ward, A. F. H. *Proc. Roy. Soc.* A**133**, 506, 1931
24 Davis, R. T. *J. Amer. Chem. Soc.* **68**, 1395, 1946
25 Hickmott, T. W. *J. Chem. Phys.* **32**, 810, 1960
26 Emmett, P. H. and Brunauer, S. *J. Amer. Chem. Soc.* **56**, 35, 1934
27 Porter, A. S. and Tompkins, F. C. *Proc. Roy. Soc.* A**217**, 544, 1953
28 Taylor, J. B. and Langmuir, I. *Phys. Rev.* **44**, 423, 1933
29 Rideal, E. K. and Trapnell, B. M. W. *Proc. Roy. Soc.* A**205**, 409, 1951
30 Beebe, R. A. and Dowden, D. A. *J. Amer. Chem. Soc.* **60**, 2912, 1938

# VI

# THE HEAT OF ADSORPTION

## THE REPRODUCIBILITY OF EXPERIMENTAL HEATS

### OF CHEMISORPTION

MEASUREMENTS by different investigators of the heat of physical adsorption of a given gas on a given surface usually agree within the limits of experimental error. However, with chemisorption this is very far from being the case. It is important to discuss the irreproducibility of heats of chemisorption before a satisfactory treatment of them can be made, and the following types of irreproducibility may be discerned.

(1) With the metals the heat often varies from sample to sample. In particular, values obtained using powders tend to vary, and also to be uniformly lower than the values obtained using evaporated films. Films on the other hand tend to give reproducible heats. Thus, for hydrogen chemisorption on nickel, the differential heat on powders at low coverages has varied between 21 kcal/mole[1] and 24 kcal/mole[2], while on evaporated films there is agreement that the value is about 30 kcal/mole[3, 4]. Such effects arise because powders are liable to be contaminated to unknown and variable extents, so that measurements are effectively made on partly covered surfaces.

A similar irreproducibility has arisen in measurements of heats of chemisorption on carbon powders, where values of the initial heat of oxygen chemisorption at room temperatures have varied between 72 and 92 kcal/mole[5, 6].

(2) Recently there have been claims that heats on clean metals may vary from sample to sample. For example, in the case of hydrogen on tungsten, while a number of investigators agree that the calorimetric heat at low coverages on films is 45 kcal/mole[3, 4], HICKMOTT[7] has recently recorded a value of 29 kcal/mole for the initial isosteric heat on a filament. With nitrogen on tungsten, the integral calorimetric heat on films or filaments is 90–95 kcal/mole[8, 9], but on filaments KISLIUK[10] has found a constant isosteric heat amounting to 116 kcal/mole. Possibly heats of chemisorption on metals are structure-sensitive, but at the present juncture it is perhaps best to reserve judgment, and to consider mainly values on films, where there is some reproducibility.

(3) Heats of desorption may differ from heats of adsorption. As indicated in Chapter IV, desorption usually occurs from a mobile layer in which the adsorbed particles have an equilibrium distribution over the various surface sites. On the other hand the layer formed during adsorption may be immobile and far from equilibrium. The average binding energies in the two types of layer can differ, and for this reason the two heats need not be comparable.

(4) Occasionally metal powders seem to be more active than evaporated films. For example, heats of hydrogen adsorption on copper powders have been found to vary between 20 and 9 kcal/mole[11, 12], but on evaporated films, there is general agreement that hydrogen is not chemisorbed at all under identical conditions[3, 13]. Similarly, with carbon monoxide on copper, initial heats as high as 20 kcal/mole have been observed on powders[14], but on evaporated films the initial heat is only 9·3 kcal/mole[15]. These results probably arise because copper powders contain traces of impurity which have a higher adsorptive capacity than the pure copper of evaporated films. Possibly the impurity is nickel. IPATIEFF, CORSON and KURBATOV have found that whereas the purest specimens of copper are inactive in benzene hydrogenation, specimens containing minute traces of nickel show appreciable activity[16].

(5) Quite frequently, the initial heat of chemisorption varies considerably with the temperature at which the measurement is made. For this, there may be two reasons.

(a) Different mechanisms of chemisorption may predominate at different temperatures. With several systems, a weak non-activated chemisorption takes place at low temperatures, while at higher temperatures, the weak adsorption is inappreciable and a stronger activated adsorption is observed, which at the lower temperature could not proceed at a measurable rate. When this effect operates, the heat of chemisorption increases with temperature.

Thus, nitrogen is rapidly chemisorbed on iron films at liquid air temperatures with an initial heat of 10 kcal/mole: at room temperatures, there takes place a slow chemisorption for which the initial heat is 40 kcal/mole[8]. The surface complexes are probably

$$
\begin{array}{ccc}
\text{N}=\text{N} & & \text{N}-\text{N} \\
\diagup \quad \diagdown & \text{or} & \diagup\!\!\diagup \quad \diagdown\!\!\diagdown \\
\text{Fe}\text{------}\text{Fe} & & \text{Fe}\text{------}\text{Fe}
\end{array}
$$

at low temperatures and $FE \equiv N$ at room temperatures.

Hydrogen and oxygen chemisorption on reduced chromia show similar effects. At $-183\,°C$, both gases are very rapidly adsorbed, the initial heats being 5·1 and 25 kcal/mole respectively[17]. At higher temperatures, adsorption tends to be slower, and the initial heats are higher. With oxygen, the values at $0\,°C$[17] and room temperature[18] are 50 and 55 kcal/mole respectively: with hydrogen, the value at room temperature is 36 kcal/mole[18]. With oxygen, it is likely that parts of the surface involving higher activation energies and heats are covered at higher temperatures: with hydrogen, the adsorption at liquid air temperatures is probably on the metal ions, and at room temperatures on the oxygen ions.

(b) The initial heat of a rapid chemisorption may vary with temperature if the layer is immobile at one temperature and mobile at another as indicated in (3).

(6) With the oxides, the crystal structure and stoichiometric formula may both depend on the treatment. For example, GARNER and WARD[19] found that manganese (III) oxide heated in oxygen and then outgassed had a stoichiometric formula $MnO_{1.48}$: heating in CO and then outgassing gave an oxide $MnO_{1.46}$, while heating in hydrogen and then outgassing gave an oxide $MnO_{1.40}$. The changes in stoichiometry were shown, using X-ray analysis, to be associated with changes in the extent to which the lattices of the three oxides, MnO, $Mn_3O_4$ and $Mn_2O_3$ were present. The chemical nature of an oxide adsorbent may therefore vary with its pretreatment, and as a result, heats of chemisorption vary also. Results have been obtained by GARNER and his co-workers on a number of oxides, and are summarized in Table 26[18-20]. In this Table, the oxidized type of surface indicates pretreatment with oxygen, followed by outgassing,

and the reduced surface pretreatment usually in hydrogen, or sometimes in CO, followed by outgassing.

With oxides the great sensitivity of the heat of chemisorption to
the method of pretreatment makes it difficult to assign a single value
to the heat of a particular adsorption.

TABLE 26

Initial Heats of Chemisorption on Oxides at Room Temperatures
(kcal/mole)

| Oxide | $H_2$ | | $O_2$ | | CO | | $CO_2$ | |
|---|---|---|---|---|---|---|---|---|
| | Reduced | Oxidized | Reduced | Oxidized | Reduced | Oxidized | Reduced | Oxidized |
| ZnO | No adsorption | | — | — | 20 | 18 | — | 13 |
| $Cr_2O_3$ | 36 | 72 | 55 | 37 | 28 | 29 | 31 | 18 |
| $Mn_2O_3$ | 30 | 44 | 22 | 24 | 62 | 67 | 17 | 23 |
| ZnO. $Cr_2O_3$ $Mn_2O_3$. | 13 | 48 | 43 | Not adsorbed | 15 | 44 | 18 | 15 |
| $Cr_2O_3$ | No adsorption | | 52 | 22 | 33 | 47 | 14 | 20 |
| $Cu_2O$ | 27 | 42 | 55 | — | 28 | 47 | — | — |

## HEATS OF CHEMISORPTION AND PHYSICAL ADSORPTION

The heat of physical adsorption is always near the heat of liquefaction of the adsorbate. It is therefore decided primarily by the
nature of the adsorbate, with the nature of the adsorbent playing a
secondary role. The range of heats of physical adsorption of a gas
may be predicted from the isotherm of BRUNAUER, EMMETT and
TELLER for multimolecular physical adsorption[21]. This gives the
volume of gas, $v$, adsorbed at pressure $p$, when the saturation vapour
pressure is $p_0$, as

$$\frac{p}{v(p_0-p)} = \frac{1}{v_m c} + \frac{c-1}{v_m c} \cdot \frac{p}{p_0} \tag{6.1}$$

where $v_m$ is the volume adsorbed into a complete monolayer, and $c$
is, to a good first approximation, given by

$$c = e^{(q_1-q_L)/RT} \tag{6.2}$$

where $q_1$ is the heat of adsorption in the first layer and $q_L$ is the latent
heat of liquefaction of the adsorbate. If $p/v(p_0-p)$ is plotted against
$p/p_0$, a straight line should result. The ratio of the slope to the
intercept is $(c-1)$, so that $c$ can readily be evaluated.

o

The isotherm is likely to be only approximate, but it has been applied to many experimental data, and shown to be obeyed. As a result $c$ values for a large number of systems are known. Almost all the values lie between 0·1 and 250, and hence using equation (6.2), the limiting values of $(q_1 - q_L)$ are

$$5 \cdot 5RT \geqslant q_1 - q_L \geqslant -2 \cdot 3RT$$

These limits show the narrow range of heats of physical adsorption and their nearness to the latent heat of liquefaction. Furthermore, using the inequality $q_1 - q_L \leqslant 5 \cdot 5RT$, and inserting for $T$ the highest temperature at which physical adsorption normally occurs, we obtain an upper limit for $q_1$. Values for common gases are given in Table 27. Any heat of adsorption exceeding the prescribed upper limit for the gas in question must indicate chemisorption.

TABLE 27

Maximum Heats of Physical Adsorption

| Gas | $q_L$ (kcal/mole) | $(q_1)_{max}$ (kcal/mole) |
|---|---|---|
| $H_2$ | 0·22 | 2·0 |
| $O_2$ | 1·60 | 5·0 |
| $N_2$ | 1·34 | 5·0 |
| $CO$ | 1·44 | 6·0 |
| $CO_2$ | 6·00 | 9·0 |
| $CH_4$ | 2·18 | 5·0 |
| $C_2H_4$ | 3·50 | 8·0 |
| $C_2H_2$ | 5·74 | 9·0 |
| $NH_3$ | 5·56 | 9·0 |
| $H_2O$ | 10·57 | 14·0 |
| $Cl_2$ | 4·40 | 8·5 |

The range of heats of chemisorption is far wider than that of physical adsorption, largely because chemisorption is a specific interaction between solid and gas, with the heat depending on the nature of both. Thus, the heat of oxygen chemisorption on tungsten is 194 kcal/mole[22], on carbon probably 97 kcal/mole[6], on reduced manganese (III) oxide only 22 kcal/mole[19].

CALORIMETRIC AND ISOSTERIC HEATS OF ADSORPTION

When the Clausius–Clapeyron equation is applied to a set of isotherms at a fixed coverage, *isosteric* heats of adsorption are obtained, which are defined by the equation

$$RT^2 \left( \frac{\partial \ln p}{\partial T} \right)_\theta = q_{\text{isosteric}} \tag{6.3}$$

If heats are measured isothermally at particular $\theta$ values, in such a way that no external work is done during the adsorption, the true differential heat $q_{diff}$ is obtained. It is then possible to show by the use of thermodynamics that

$$q_{diff} = RT^2 \left( \frac{\partial \ln p}{\partial T} \right)_\theta - RT \qquad (6.4)$$

so that

$$q_{isosteric} = q_{diff} + RT \qquad (6.5)$$

The question then arises as to which heat is measured in a calorimeter when small quantities of gas are admitted and adsorbed. In such an experiment, external work is done, but it is not certain how much of this work is transferred to the calorimeter as heat. If none is transferred, $q_{diff}$ is obtained, while if all is transferred, $q_{isosteric}$ is obtained, because equation (6.5) shows that $q_{isosteric}$ exceeds $q_{diff}$ by the amount $RT$, which for an ideal gas is equal to the maximum work done during adsorption. It is very likely that in practice the 'calorimetric differential heat' is intermediate between the true differential heat $q_{diff}$ and the isosteric heat.

Strictly, therefore, when comparing heats of adsorption, isosteric heats should be used, because there is no possible variation of these owing to differences in technique of measurement, as there may be with calorimetric heats. However, with chemisorption, the maximum possible error in comparing isosteric and calorimetric heats, namely $RT$, is less than the normal error of measurement, and for most purposes it is possible to neglect the difference between the two heats.

### THE CALCULATION OF HEATS OF CHEMISORPTION

The calculation of heats of chemisorption has been attempted for carbon and metal adsorbents. With the oxides, the greater complexity of the mechanisms of adsorption has so far proved too great an obstacle to such calculations.

The two most important surface bond types are the ionic and covalent. For purely ionic layers, the ion is assumed to be held to the surface simply by the electrostatic image force. For covalent layers, which are more common, the heat of adsorption is expressed as a difference of bond energies, and these are then elucidated.

Calculated heats should always be compared with differential experimental heats at very low coverages, because no diminution of the latter arises from the operation of repulsive forces between neighbouring adsorbed particles, as may be the case at high coverages.

## HEATS OF CHEMISORPTION ON CARBON

In the chemisorption of simple gases, such as hydrogen, on carbon, covalent surface bonds are formed and the bond energies are assumed to be the same as in simple organic compounds. Then in hydrogen chemisorption according to the equation

$$2C + H_2 \rightarrow 2CH$$

if we assume for the moment that no bonds between carbon atoms are broken in the act of chemisorption, the heat of adsorption at low coverage is

$$q_0 = 2E(C\text{---}H) - E(H\text{---}H) \tag{6.6}$$

where the $E$'s refer to bond energies. Similarly, in oxygen, chlorine and ammonia chemisorption, the last as fragments $NH_2+H$, the heats of adsorption are respectively

$$q_0 = 2E(C = O) - E(O = O) \tag{6.7}$$

$$q_0 = 2E(C\text{---}Cl) - E(Cl\text{---}Cl) \tag{6.8}$$

$$q_0 = E(C\text{---}N) + E(C\text{---}H) - E(N\text{---}H) \tag{6.9}$$

For bond energies values given by COTTRELL[23] are used. Calculated heats are shown in Table 28, and compared with experimental heats on graphite.

### TABLE 28

Calculated and Experimental Heats of Chemisorption on Carbon
(kcal/mole)

| Adsorbate | $q_0$(calc.) | $q_0$(exp.) | Reference |
|-----------|--------------|-------------|-----------|
| $H_2$ | 93 | 50 | Barrer[24] |
| $O_2$ | 239 | 97 | Bull, Hall and Garner[6] |
| $Cl_2$ | 104 | 32 | Keyes and Marshall[5] |
| $NH_3$ | 78 | 17 | Keyes and Marshall[5] |

The calculated heats are uniformly higher than the experimental heats, and for this there may be two reasons. First, the experimental heats may be rather low because the carbon surfaces were not entirely pure—it is doubtful whether a clean carbon surface has yet been prepared. Second, the calculated heats are probably high because energy is taken in the breaking of surface carbon–carbon bonds during adsorption, and this is not allowed for in the calculation.

## HEATS OF CHEMISORPTION ON METALS

### (1) Ionic layers

The nature of a surface bond can be decided from knowledge of its dipole moment at low coverages. High moments suggest ionic bonds and the values for caesium, potassium and sodium layers on tungsten are all exceedingly large, and in close agreement with the values expected for the formation of monovalent positive ions at the surface, as shown in Chapter VII.

For these layers, it is then possible to calculate the heat of adsorption by the following means.

(i) With an adsorbate atom at an infinite distance from the surface, an electron is transferred from it to the tungsten adsorbent. The heat liberated is $\phi - I$, where $\phi$ is the work function of tungsten and $I$ the ionization potential of the adsorbate.

(ii) With the tungsten at zero potential, the adsorbate ion is brought to its equilibrium distance $r_0$ from the surface. $r_0$ is assumed to be the radius of the ion in the adsorbate crystal, namely 1·83 Å for Na, 2·27 Å for K and 2·62 Å for Cs. The tungsten surface is regarded as an infinite plane conducting sheet, so that the force of attraction on the ion at a distance $r$ from the surface, namely the electrostatic image force, is $e^2/4r^2$. The heat liberated in this process is then $e^2/4r_0$.

The heat of adsorption per gram atom is thus

$$q_0 = \phi - I + Ne^2/4r_0 \qquad (6.10)$$

where $N$ is Avogadro's number, and $\phi$ and $I$ are now expressed per gram atom. Values obtained using equation (6.10) are shown in Table 29, and in the case of sodium and caesium layers compared with experimental values[25, 26].

TABLE 29

Calculated and Experimental Initial Heats of Chemisorption
(kcal/g atom)

| System | $\phi$ | $I$ | $Ne^2/4r_0$ | $q_0$(calc.) | $q_0$(exp.) |
|---|---|---|---|---|---|
| Na on W | 104·0 | 118·0 | 44·5 | 30·5 | 32·0 |
| K on W | 104·0 | 99·6 | 35·9 | 40·3 | — |
| Cs on W | 104·0 | 89·4 | 31·1 | 45·7 | 64·0 |

Since $q_0$ depends markedly on $r_0$, and also short range forces of attraction and repulsion, which are not included in equation (6.10), may contribute somewhat to $q_0$, the agreement between calculation and experiment is satisfactory.

*(2) Covalent layers*

Evidence discussed in Chapter VII indicates that the surface bond with gas layers on metals is covalent, and heats of chemisorption have been and are calculated using a method similar to that employed with carbon[27]. Taking hydrogen chemisorption on tungsten as an example, the mechanism of which is given by the equation

$$2W + H_2 \rightarrow 2WH$$

the differential heat at zero coverage is

$$q_0 = 2E(W\text{---}H) - E(H\text{---}H) \tag{6.11}$$

Equation (6.11) assumes that no surface W—W bonds are broken during chemisorption. This is justified by the rapidity of the chemisorption, which suggests that the surface tungsten atoms behave as if they possessed free valencies, and is confirmed by further evidence given in Chapter VII.

The energy $E(W\text{---}H)$ is unknown, but may be evaluated using the Pauling equation for single bond energies[28], namely

$$E(W\text{---}H) = \tfrac{1}{2}\{E(W\text{---}W) + E(H\text{---}H)\} + 23{\cdot}06(X_W - X_H)^2 \tag{6.12}$$

Here $X_W$ and $X_H$ are the respective electronegativities of the two atoms, and the term $23{\cdot}06(X_W - X_H)^2$ allows for the ionic contribution to the bond energy.

Inserting the value for $E(W\text{---}H)$ in equation (6.11), the heat of chemisorption becomes

$$q_0 = E(W\text{---}W) + 46{\cdot}12(X_W - X_H)^2 \tag{6.13}$$

The bond energy $E(W\text{---}W)$ may be obtained from the latent heat of vaporization of the metal, $\lambda$[29]. With face-centred cubic metals, each atom has 12 nearest neighbours, while with body-centred cubic metals, there are 8 nearest and 6 next nearest neighbours. For face-centred cubic metals, remembering that two atoms are involved in each bond, the single bond energy $E(M\text{---}M)$ is then

$$E(M\text{---}M) = \frac{2}{12}\,\lambda \tag{6.14}$$

and to a good first approximation we may assume the same result holds for body-centred cubic metals.

To obtain $(X_W - X_H)$ is more difficult. Two methods, neither ideal, are available. The first, due to ELEY[27], assumes that to a first approximation

$$X_W - X_H = \mu \qquad (6.15)$$

where $\mu$ is the dipole moment of the W—H bond, strictly of course at $\theta \to 0$. Values of $\mu$ can be obtained from surface potentials[30], though in general measurements have only been made at $\theta \to 1$. These values may well be too low, partly because of mutual depolarization, and partly because the later stages of hydrogen chemisorption often produce an electropositive layer, possibly through the operation of a second mechanism, which reduces the calculated dipole for the initial electronegative layer below the true value. Since the term $46·12\mu^2$ could account for about one third of the heat, it is clearly important that the correct value of $\mu$ should be used.

For these reasons a second method of obtaining electronegativity differences has been developed by STEVENSON[31]. It is based on the association of the electronegativity of an atom with the energy of the first ionization potential and the electron affinity. For a metal both of these quantities are equal to the work function, and Stevenson obtains

$$X_M = 0·355\phi \qquad (6.16)$$

where $\phi$ is the work function and $0·355$ is a scaling factor. For the hydrogen atom, Pauling's electronegativity, $2·1$, is used. Thus

$$q_0 = E(W\text{—}W) + 46·12(0·355\phi - 2·1)^2 \qquad (6.17)$$

In Table 30, values obtained by the two methods are compared with experimental values for evaporated films[3, 31, 32].

TABLE 30

Calculated and Experimental Heats of Hydrogen Chemisorption (kcal/mole)

| Metal | $q_0$ (exp.) | $q_0$ (Eley method) | $q_0$ (Stevenson method) |
|:---:|:---:|:---:|:---:|
| Ta | 45 | 33·5 | 50 |
| W | 45 | 36·7 | 46 |
| Mo | 40 | 28·5* | 43 |
| Cr | 45 | 16·2* | 24 |
| Mn | 17 | 13·8* | 38 |
| Ni | 30 | 18·6 | 29 |
| Fe | 32 | 19·0 | 32 |
| Rh | 28 | 24·6* | 32 |
| Pd | 26 | 17·1* | 23 |

* $\mu$ has not been measured and is taken to be the same for related systems

Both methods give results which are of the correct order of magnitude but clearly the Stevenson method is rather better, except in the interesting case of Mn. In the case of Cr, both methods are inaccurate, because the sublimation energy is very low. In the case of Mn, a low sublimation energy allows the Eley method to give an excellent answer, but in the Stevenson method the low value of $\phi$ more than offsets the low sublimation energy and causes a high calculated heat.

The method of calculation may be extended to layers of other gases. Oxygen, nitrogen and carbon monoxide chemisorption may be treated using the equations

$$2M + O_2 \rightarrow 2M = O$$

$$2M + N_2 \rightarrow 2M \equiv N$$

$$2M + CO \rightarrow \begin{matrix} M \\ \\ M \end{matrix}\!\!\!\!\diagdown\!\!\!\diagup C = O$$

If we assume that equations similar to equation (6·12) apply to double and treble bonds between gas and solid, the initial heats of chemisorption are given by the Stevenson method as

$$q_0(O_2) = E(M=M) + 46 \cdot 12(0 \cdot 355\phi - 3 \cdot 5)^2 \qquad (6.18)$$

$$q(N_2) = E(M \equiv M) + 46 \cdot 12(0 \cdot 355\phi - 3 \cdot 0)^2 \qquad (6.19)$$

$$q_0(CO) = E(M-M) + E(C-C) - E(CO) + E(C=O) + \\ 46 \cdot 12(0 \cdot 355\phi - 2 \cdot 5)^2 \qquad (6.20)$$

$E(M=M)$ and $E(M \equiv M)$ may be equated to twice and three times $E(M-M)$ respectively, and heats calculated in this way are compared with experimental values for films in Table 31. In making this comparison it is important to realize that the experimental values[8, 22, 33, 34] are integral heats, not differential heats at low coverages as the latter cannot be measured on films owing to immobility (see Chapter IX). Integral heats are, of course, likely to be lower than differential heats at $\theta \rightarrow 0$. In the case of oxygen chemisorption, care has been taken to use true experimental heats of chemisorption: oxidation quite often takes place even at low temperatures. Agreement between calculation and experiment is clearly less close than with hydrogen. The divergence with oxygen is particularly marked.

Heats of chemisorption for $CO_2$, $C_2H_4$ and $NH_3$ are available on various transition metals[3, 4, 35], and for CO, $C_2H_4$ and $C_2H_2$ on Cu and $Au^{15}$. These are summarized in Tables 32 and 33. No attempt is made to compare these heats with calculated values, as Chapter VII shows that more than one mechanism of chemisorption is operating simultaneously in most of these cases.

TABLE 31

Calculated and Experimental Heats of Chemisorption
(kcal/mole)

| Gas | Metal | q (exp.) | q (calc.) |
|-----|-------|----------|-----------|
| $O_2$ | W | 194 | 239 |
|       | Mo | 172 | 235 |
|       | Rh | 118 | 211 |
|       | Pd | 67 | 184 |
|       | Pt | 70 | 161 |
| $N_2$ | W | 95 | 191 |
|       | Ta | 140 | 194 |
|       | Fe | 70 | 149 |
| CO | Ti | 153 | 73 |
|    | W | 82 | 70 |
|    | Ni | 42 | 53 |
|    | Fe | 46 | 60 |

TABLE 32

Heats of $CO_2$, $C_2H_4$ and $NH_3$ Chemisorption (kcal/mole)

| Gases | Metals | | | | | | | | | | |
|-------|----|----|----|----|----|----|----|----|----|----|----|
|       | Ti | Ta | Nb | W | Cr | Mo | Mn | Fe | Co | Ni | Rh |
| $CO_2$ | 163 | 168 | 132 | 109 | 81 | 89 | 53 | 61 | 35 | 44 | — |
| $C_2H_4$ | — | 138 | — | 102 | 102 | — | — | 68 | — | 58 | 50 |
| $NH_3$ | — | — | — | 72 | — | — | — | 45 | — | 37 | — |

In Table 32, the $CO_2$ heats are integral heats whereas the $C_2H_4$ and $NH_3$ heats are differential heats at $\theta \to 0$. In Table 33, all heats are differential heats at $\theta \to 0$.

The heats of $CO_2$ chemisorption are of interest in that they bear on the question of the mechanism of chemisorption. In particular, if dissociation is taking place, yielding chemisorbed CO and chemisorbed oxygen, the molar heat is given by

$$q_{CO_2} = q_{CO} + \tfrac{1}{2}q_{O_2} - 67.5 \qquad (6.21)$$

where 67·5 kcal/mole is the heat of formation of $CO_2$ from $CO + \tfrac{1}{2}O_2$. Using values of $q_{CO}$ and $q_{O_2}$ from Table 31 we find $q_{CO_2} = 112$ kcal/mole for W, which agrees well with the experimental value, namely, 109 kcal/mole. On W, dissociation may well be occurring, although on a number of other metals further evidence makes this rather doubtful.

TABLE 33

Initial Heats of Chemisorption (kcal/mole)

| Gases | Metals | |
|---|---|---|
| | Cu | Au |
| CO | 9 | 9 |
| $C_2H_2$ | 19 | 21 |
| $C_2H_4$ | 18 | 21 |

THE IONICITY OF BONDS IN GAS CHEMISORPTION ON METALS

According to PAULING[28], the percentage ionic character of a covalent bond is related to the difference in electronegativity of the atoms forming the bond, and for a link between atoms A and B is

$$100[1 - e^{-0.25(X_A - X_B)^2}]$$

This enables an estimate to be made of the percentage ionic character of some of the bonds which we have been considering. That is to say, assuming equation (6.13) is correct for hydrogen adsorption on tungsten

$$(X_W - X_H)^2 = \frac{1}{46.12}[q_0 - E(W\!-\!W)] \qquad (6.22)$$

and $(X_W - X_H)^2$ can be obtained by inserting the experimental value of $q_0$ and the value of $E(W\!-\!W)$ obtained from the sublimation energy. Essentially we are reversing the calculation made in the previous section, in order to obtain $(X_W - X_H)^2$, and hence the ionicity.

Calculations of this kind can be carried out for oxygen, nitrogen and carbon monoxide layers as well as for hydrogen layers, and some results for the four gases are given in Table 34.

206

The ionic character is seen to be larger for oxygen layers than for hydrogen, nitrogen or carbon monoxide layers.

TABLE 34

The Percentage Ionic Character of Surface Bonds

| System | Percentage ionic character |
|--------|----------------------------|
| $H_2$ on W | 6 |
| $H_2$ on Ni | 7 |
| $H_2$ on Rh | 2 |
| $O_2$ on W | 50 |
| $O_2$ on Mo | 48 |
| $O_2$ on Rh | 32 |
| $N_2$ on W | 3 |
| $N_2$ on Ta | 23 |
| $N_2$ on Fe | 11 |
| CO on W | 7 |
| CO on Ni | 3 |
| CO on Fe | 2 |

OTHER METHODS FOR CALCULATING HEATS OF CHEMISORPTION

(1) *Method of Higuchi, Ree and Eyring*[36]

Taking hydrogen on tungsten as an example again, Higuchi, Ree and Eyring consider first a purely covalent bond and a purely ionic bond. For the former the bond energy $E(W—H)_c$ is derived from equation (6.12) by putting $(X_W - X_H)$ equal to zero. This gives

$$E(W—H)_c = \tfrac{1}{2}[E(W—W) + E(H—H)] \qquad (6.23)$$

For a purely ionic bond, $E(W^+H^-)_i$ is obtained as $A_0 - I + (8/9)$ $(e^2/r_{WH})$, where $A_0$ is the electron affinity of hydrogen, $I$ is the ionization potential of a tungsten atom, $e$ is the electronic charge, and $r_{WH}$ is the sum of the radius of the metal atom and the covalent bond radius of the hydrogen atom. The actual bond energy, $E(W—H)$, was then shown by solution of the Schrödinger equation to be given by

$$\frac{E(W—H) - E(W^+H^-)_i}{E(W—H) - E(W—H)_c} = \frac{1}{C} - 1 \qquad (6.24)$$

where $C$ is the fractional ionic character. Thus $E(W-H)$ and hence the heat of chemisorption can be calculated if $C$ is known. This quantity was derived from the surface dipole $\mu$ using the equation

$$C = \mu/er_{WH} \qquad (6.25)$$

The method suffers from the two disadvantages that it depends upon knowledge of $\mu$ and $r_{WH}$, both of which are subject to uncertainty. However, in a case such as hydrogen on tungsten where $C$ is small, this criticism may not be of primary importance. The method in fact gives the same result as the Eley–Stevenson method, namely $q \simeq E(W-W)$. Heats calculated by this method are given in Table 35, together with the experimental heats. The best surface potential measurements available[30] have been used and $E(M-M)$ has been put equal to one-sixth the sublimation energy, $\lambda$, for body-centred cubic metals, not to one-quarter $\lambda$ as in the original calculation of Higuchi, Ree and Eyring.

TABLE 35

Calculated and Experimental Heats of Chemisorption (kcal/mole)

| System | Experimental Heat | Calculated Heat |
|--------|-------------------|-----------------|
| $H_2$ on W | 45 | 37 |
| $H_2$ on Fe | 32 | 20 |
| $H_2$ on Ni | 30 | 18 |
| $O_2$ on W | 194 | 74 |
| $O_2$ on Pt | 70 | 54 |
| $N_2$ on W | 95 | 106 |
| $N_2$ on Ta | 140 | 98 |

(2) *Method of Brodd*[37]

Recently, Brodd has applied Mulliken's theory of charge transfer no-bond links to chemisorption on metals. The ground state for the chemisorbed complex is given by a linear combination of the wave function for a no-bond, and for a dative link. For the latter an electron is transferred, in the case of hydrogen from the metal to the adsorbed atom. The treatment has been rather strongly criticized[38].

HEATS OF CHEMISORPTION AND HEATS OF REACTION

It is interesting to compare heats of chemisorption with heats of similar chemical reactions. For example, one can compare heats of oxygen chemisorption on metals with heats of oxidation, heats of carbon monoxide chemisorption with heats of carbonyl formation, and heats of hydrogen chemisorption with heats of formation of diatomic hydrides. However, it is important to define the conditions under which the heat of chemical reaction is obtained. In particular, if chemisorption involves little or no perturbation of metal–metal bonds, as seems likely, the heat of the corresponding chemical reaction must be obtained in the gas phase. If the heat of a solid-plus-gas reaction is taken, for example the heat of ordinary metal oxidation, a term will be wrongly included for break-up of the metal lattice.

In the case of oxygen, the heat of the reaction[29]

$$W(gas) + 1\tfrac{1}{2}O_2(gas) \to WO_3(gas)$$

is 290 kcal per gram mole of $WO_3$. For one mole of oxygen it is therefore 193 kcal, and this compares with the heat of chemisorption per mole, namely 194 kcal.

In the case of carbon monoxide, the heat of the reaction[39]

$$Ni(gas) + 4CO(gas) \to Ni(CO)_4(gas)$$

is 141 kcal per gram mole of $Ni(CO)_4$. For one gram molecule of CO it is therefore 35 kcal, compared with the heat of chemisorption, 42 kcal/mole.

In the case of hydrogen, the heat of dissociation of the gaseous diatomic molecule NiH has been found from spectroscopic data to be $60\pm7$ kcal per gram atom of hydrogen[23]. This compares with the heat of chemisorption of atomic hydrogen per gram atom, namely 67 kcal.

The agreement is quite striking in all three cases, and suggests that chemisorption on metals is not dissimilar from chemical reactions of metal atoms in the gas phase. This has an interesting implication, namely that in chemisorption metal atoms are acting as isolated units. If this is so, the surface properties of a metal may be determined as much by the properties of the isolated atoms as by the properties of the metal crystal. This possibility receives further consideration in the next section.

## THE VARIATION OF HEATS AMONG DIFFERENT METALS

The heats recorded in Tables 30–33 follow a common pattern, namely that with the seven gases $H_2$, $O_2$, $N_2$, CO, $CO_2$, $C_2H_4$, and $NH_3$ the heats among different metals follows the order

$$Ti, Ta > Nb > W, Cr > Mo > Fe > Mn > Ni, Co > Rh > Pt,$$
$$Pd > Cu, Au$$

The only definite reversal of the order arises from the very weak chemisorption of $H_2$ by Mn.

This result suggests that some single property of the metals decides their relative activity in chemisorption, and a number of attempts have been made to discover the nature of this property. A possible answer can be obtained from the calculated heats of chemisorption. These contain two terms which vary from metal to metal, the heat of sublimation of the metal, and its electronegativity. Since the first term is normally more important than the second, differences in heats of chemisorption of a particular gas on different metals should arise from differences in the heat of sublimation. Hence, the order of heats of chemisorption on different metals should be the order of heats of sublimation. Unfortunately, this order is

$$W > Nb, Ta > Mo > Rh > Pt > Ti > Co, Ni > Fe,$$
$$Pd > Cr > Mn > Au > Cu$$

which differs too greatly from the experimental order of heats to make the explanation feasible.

A rather better answer has been obtained by consideration of the mechanism of chemisorption. In the chemisorption of all gases other than oxygen, transition metals show a far higher activity than non-transition metals. Now isolated transition metal atoms possess incomplete $d$ shells, and transition metal crystals are characterized by a similar property. According to the theory of MOTT and JONES[40], transition metal crystals are said to possess incomplete $d$ bands: according to the theory of PAULING[41] they possess vacant atomic $d$ orbitals. The higher activity of transition metals in chemisorption can then be explained if the surface bond is a covalence with the $d$ band, or with atomic $d$ orbitals. Magnetic evidence shows that $d$-orbitals are in fact used in chemisorption[42, 43].

Now according to both theories of metals, the metal–metal bond which gives rise to cohesion may differ from the surface bond formed during chemisorption. The older theory suggests that cohesion is due to interaction of the outermost $s$ electrons of the metal atoms: the newer theory that it is due to formation of hybrid ($dsp$) orbitals similar to those found in certain complex ions. But the calculation of heats of chemisorption, and in particular the use of equations such as (6.12), assumes that the surface bond is similar to the metal–metal bond. It may be because of this that an incorrect answer as to the cause of the variation of heats of chemisorption among metals is obtained by considering calculated heats.

Now if chemisorption is a covalence with atomic $d$ orbitals (or a $d$ band), it is reasonable to suppose that the heat of chemisorption will increase as the number of available orbitals increases. The question is then whether there is any quantity which is a measure of this availability. The Pauling percentage $d$ character[41] could be such a quantity. It is obtained from certain known constants of the metal crystal, and high $d$ character indicates a high participation of $d$ electrons in cohesion, and therefore a low availability for formation

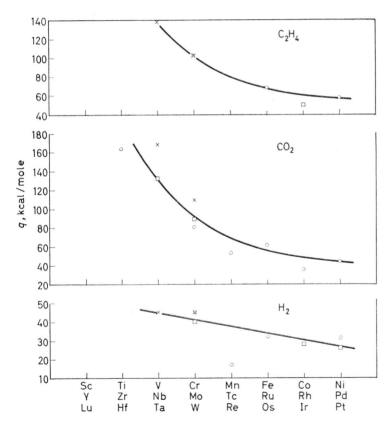

*Figure 74. Heats of chemisorption for the transition metals, plotted according to Periodic Classification.*

o, □ *and* x *denote 1st, 2nd and 3rd transition periods, respectively*

of covalent bonds at the surface. The order of heats of chemi-sorption should therefore be the inverse order of $d$ characters, and this is

Ti>Ta, Cr, Nb>Co>Fe>Ni,
Mn>Mo>W>Pt>Pd>Rh>Cu, Au

Once again, however, the order differs considerably from the true order.

Examination of the actual order shows that the heats tend to fall in passing across the Periodic Table from left to right. This is shown in *Figure 74*, where the heats for hydrogen, ethylene and carbon dioxide are plotted against the Group of the Periodic Table in which the metal is situated. Once again only the low heat for $H_2$ on Mn is an exception. Similar curves may be obtained for nitrogen and ammonia, but it is only fair to say that with carbon monoxide and oxygen the plot is less satisfactory. With oxygen, however, the mechanism of chemisorption is probably different, so that no such correlation need be expected.

A correlation between heat and position in the Periodic Table, while implying that the availability of $d$-orbitals controls the heat, may imply as well that surface atoms are like isolated atoms. Position in the Periodic Table is after all an indication of the configuration of free atoms rather than of atoms in the crystal.

### VARIATION OF THE HEAT OF ADSORPTION WITH THE VOLUME OF GAS ADSORBED

Differential heats of chemisorption usually fall with increasing volume adsorbed: many cases of apparent constancy are due to an artefact whereby integral and not differential heats are measured (see Chapter IX).

The only sound evidence for a constant heat of chemisorption is in the case of nitrogen adsorbed on tungsten filaments and ribbons. Here, independent measurements have been made of the calori-metric heat of adsorption[9], the activation energy of desorption (i.e. the heat of desorption)[44] and the isosteric heat of adsorption[10]. All three are independent of coverage, and the values of the first two, namely 95 and 81 kcal/mole are in reasonable agreement. However, the isosteric heat of adsorption, 116 kcal/mole, is noticeably larger.

Some observers have reported maxima in the $q$–$\theta$ curve at low $\theta$ values, but these are now known to be due to faulty technique of calorimetric measurement.

The way in which the heat of chemisorption falls with increasing coverage varies both with the adsorbate and with the adsorbent.

For nitrogen chemisorption on tantalum[45] the $q$–$\theta$ curve, shown in *Figure 75*, is concave to the origin, but for ethylene on tantalum[3] it is indistinguishable from a straight line: for hydrogen on an outgassed tungsten powder[46] it is logarithmic, but for ethylene on tungsten[3] it is sigmoid (*Figure 75*), and for caesium on tungsten[26] it is convex (*Figure 76*). The curve for oxygen on charcaol[6] (*Figure 76*) shows no simple form. $q$–$\theta$ curves for the same gas on different surfaces[3] are likewise different, as shown in *Figure 77*.

To account for heat falls, three main explanations have been advanced. The earliest explanation, due initially to CONSTABLE[47]

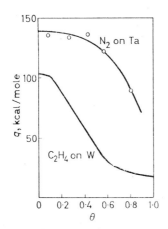

*Figure 75. q–θ curves*

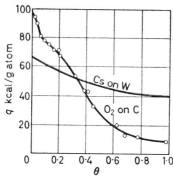

*Figure 76. q–θ curves*

213

P

and to TAYLOR[48], is that the fall is due to surface heterogeneity. On a heterogeneous surface, there will be a tendency for the most active sites to be covered first, both because adsorption is likely to proceed more rapidly on them, and also because in a mobile layer, even if there has been random coverage initially, there will subsequently take place a spreading to the most active points. Thus, as the coverage increases, sites of lessening activity will be covered so that the heat of adsorption continuously decreases.

The second explanation, due to ROBERTS[49], is that falling heats are due to forces of repulsion between molecules in the adsorbed layer.

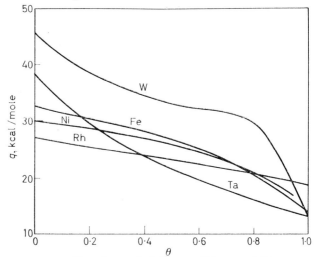

*Figure 77. q–θ curves for hydrogen on different metal films*
By courtesy of Beeck, O. *Disc. Faraday Soc.* **8**, 118, 1950

That is to say the heat of adsorption per molecule, $q$, at a coverage $\theta$ is the decrease in energy of the system when one molecule is adsorbed and is given by

$$q = u - \frac{\partial U}{\partial (n_s \theta)} \qquad (6.26)$$

where $u$ is the energy of a molecule in the gas phase, $n_s$ the total number of sites, and $U$ the total energy of all molecules in the adsorbed layer. $U$ is given by

$$U = U_0 + \bar{U} \qquad (6.27)$$

where $U_0$ is the energy of the adsorbed layer, when there are no interactions and $\bar{U}$ is the interaction energy. $\bar{U}$ thus affects $q$, and increasing surface repulsions cause a progressive fall in $q$.

214

The third explanation, due to ELEY[50] and to SCHWAB[51], considers the electron transfers which constitute formation of the surface bond. If either an electron is donated by the gas or a covalency is formed, electrons from the gas enter the solid. Since in crystals there are bands of permitted electron energies, the first electron will enter the lowest unoccupied level of the band system and then higher and higher levels will be used as adsorption proceeds. Thus the heat will fall. If on the other hand electrons are donated by the solid to the gas, the first electron will come from the highest occupied state, and then deeper and deeper levels will be used. Again, the heat will fall.

We now consider the three explanations in more detail.

HETEROGENEITY

A certain physical basis for heterogeneity was provided by TAYLOR[48], namely that edges, corners and boundaries of crystals, lattice defects and pores might show greater adsorptive capacity than the free surface. More recently, emphasis has been placed on the fact that a number of properties of a crystal surface, notably the work function[52], have different values on different crystal faces. The calculation of heats of adsorption suggested that this quantity may affect heats of chemisorption, and so heats may differ on different faces. This amounts to surface heterogeneity, and BEECK and his co-workers[53, 54] have observed such heterogeneity in catalysis. In a number of reactions, oriented metal films show a different catalytic activity per unit area from non-oriented films. In ethylene hydrogenation, for example, oriented nickel films, which preferentially expose (110) planes, are five times as active at $0\,^{\circ}C$ as randomly oriented films.

In addition it is sometimes possible effectively to inhibit a catalytic reaction by the addition of poison in quantities far less than are required to cover the whole surface. This suggests that catalytic activity on these surfaces is largely confined to a few surface atoms. Thus, PEASE and STEWART[55] found that 1 per cent coverage of a copper powder catalyst by carbon monoxide reduced the activity in ethylene hydrogenation at $0\,^{\circ}C$ by a factor of 9.

Recently, interesting data have been obtained by EHRLICH[56] and by REDHEAD[57] in an investigation of the desorption of CO from tungsten filaments. Curves due to Redhead, shown in *Figure 78*, represent the pressure rise due to desorption as the temperature of the filament is raised. The numbers against the curves are the times of adsorption in minutes and are an indication of the amount on the surface before desorption is commenced. From these curves, Redhead concludes not only that there are two main phases, $\alpha$ and $\beta$, which are known from infra-red work to be single site adsorption as

$M-C\equiv O$ and two site adsorption as $\dfrac{M}{M}\!\!\diagdown\!\!C{=}O$, but also that the $\beta$

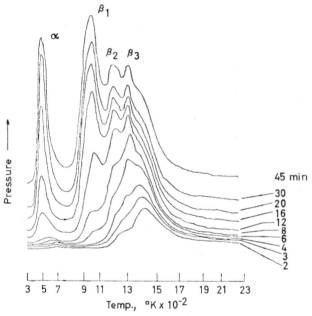

Figure 78. Desorption spectra for various adsorption times at a temperature of 300°K. The zero levels of the curves have been shifted to prevent overlap

By courtesy of Redhead, P. A. Trans. Faraday Soc. **57**, 641, 1961

mechanism subdivides into binding states $\beta_1$, $\beta_2$, and $\beta_3$, possibly owing to adsorption on different spacings or planes. At any rate, from the curves it is possible to calculate heats of desorption for the four states, and mean values for two tungsten samples due to Redhead, together with similar, but less complete data due to EHRLICH[56] are given in Table 36. For each individual state[57] the heat is constant and independent of coverage.

These heats vary by some 50 kcal/mole among the different phases, part arising from different binding states within the $\beta$ mechanism, and part from the difference in heat between the two

216

different mechanisms. While heats of desorption may differ from heats of adsorption, it is worth noting that the variation in the former is of the same magnitude as the fall in the heat of adsorption. However, it is doubtful whether the heat falls in other chemisorptions, such as that of hydrogen on tungsten, can be accounted for in the same way.

TABLE 36

Heats of Desorption of CO from Tungsten
(kcal/mole)

| Phase | Heat of desorption[57] | Heat of desorption[56] |
|---|---|---|
| $\alpha$ | 29 | 20 |
| $\beta_1$ | 59 | — |
| $\beta_2$ | 69·5 | 75 |
| $\beta_3$ | 75·5 | 100 |

A change in mechanism of chemisorption may account for the result of TAYLOR and his co-workers[58], namely that with a number of systems a rise in temperature while adsorption is proceeding causes a fairly rapid desorption followed by slow readsorption. Typical results are shown in *Figure 79*. Certainly they show that

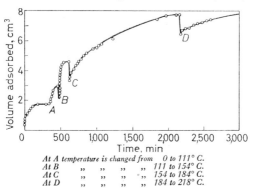

At A temperature is changed from 0 to 111° C.
At B    ,,    ,,    ,,    ,,   111 to 154° C.
At C    ,,    ,,    ,,    ,,   154 to 184° C.
At D    ,,    ,,    ,,    ,,   184 to 218° C.

*Figure 79. Effect of temperature on adsorption velocity of hydrogen on
ZnO at 1 atmosphere pressure*

By courtesy of Taylor, Sir Hugh and Liang, S. C. *J. Amer. Chem. Soc.* **69**, 1306, 1947

two types of adsorption are taking place, so that when the temperature is raised, gas is desorbed from places where the activation energy and heat of adsorption are relatively low, and readsorbed on areas where they are high. Occurrence of different mechanisms, a rather particular type of heterogeneity, may best explain the phenomenon. It has also been observed for a number of adsorptions on oxide and metal powders, as well as in hydrogen chemisorption on tungsten films[59].

Lastly, it is worth recalling that if an adsorption obeys the Freundlich isotherm, the differential heat falls logarithmically with increasing coverage. HALSEY and TAYLOR[60] have shown this to be explicable only in terms of an exponential distribution of energy among sites on a heterogeneous surface. Rapid heat falls at low $\theta$ values should in general be regarded as indicative of heterogeneity, as interactions are not large under these conditions.

SURFACE INTERACTIONS

As with heterogeneity, the problem in dealing with surface interactions is the lack of quantitative data. It is very difficult to calculate the forces acting between adsorbed particles, and only in this way can it be decided whether heat falls are due to surface interactions. Nevertheless, study of interactions has produced two interesting results.

(a) Almost all experimental $q$–$\theta$ curves belong to one of four types. They are either linear, sigmoid, concave or convex; and curves of all these forms can be derived from interaction theory.

(b) In one or two cases calculation of the magnitude of surface interactions has been made, and the resulting heat fall compared with the experimental value.

The simpler theory of surface interactions[61] makes two assumptions. The first is that the interaction energy between two adsorbed particles at a given distance apart is independent of the state of occupation of nearby sites. The second is that the force of repulsion decreases sufficiently quickly with distance for the interaction energy to be significant only between particles on nearest neighbour sites. These assumptions mean that we may assign to each nearest neighbour interaction a magnitude $V$, which is independent of $\theta$, and to all other interactions a value zero.

The interaction energy $\bar{U}$ is given by

$$\bar{U} = \bar{X}V \tag{6.28}$$

where $\bar{X}$ is the average number of interacting pairs at the particular value of $\theta$. To obtain the form of the $q$–$\theta$ curve we derive $\bar{X}$ statistically as a function of $\theta$, which gives $\bar{U}$ as a function of $\theta$, and insert the value of $\bar{U}$ in equations (6.27) and (6.26). This will now be done for the various types of layer treated in Chapters III and IV.

*Adsorbed molecule occupying one site—immobile layer*

If we consider a particular occupied site with $z$ nearest neighbours, the average number of particles adsorbed on these neighbouring sites at coverage $\theta$ will be $z\theta$. The interaction energy is therefore $z\theta V$, so that

$$q = q_0 - z\theta V \qquad (6.29)$$

where $q_0$ is the heat of adsorption at $\theta=0$. Since $z$ is normally equal to 4, the heat will fall linearly from $q_0$ to $q_0-4V$ as $\theta$ increases from 0 to 1.

*Adsorbed molecule occupying one site—mobile layer[62]*

Here the chance that a site next to an occupied site is itself occupied is less than $\theta$, and is $(\eta\epsilon/1+\eta\epsilon)$ where

$$\frac{\theta}{1-\theta} = \frac{\epsilon(1+\eta\epsilon)}{1+\epsilon} \quad \text{and} \quad \eta=e^{-V/RT} \qquad (6.30)$$

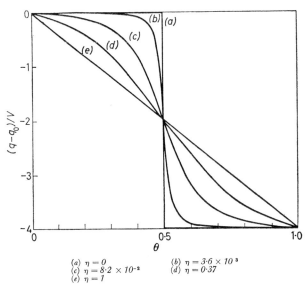

(a) $\eta = 0$      (b) $\eta = 3\cdot6 \times 10^3$
(c) $\eta = 8\cdot2 \times 10^{-2}$    (d) $\eta = 0\cdot37$
(e) $\eta = 1$

*Figure 80. q–θ curves for mobile layers*
By courtesy of Wang, J. S. *Proc. Roy. Soc.* **A161**, 127, 1937

The number of pairs of occupied sites is therefore given by

$$\bar{X} = \tfrac{1}{2}zn_s \frac{\theta\eta\,\epsilon}{1+\eta\,\epsilon} \qquad (6.31)$$

$n_s$ being the total number of surface sites. From this the heat curve may be calculated. However its form depends on $\eta$ (that is, on $V$) and therefore it is necessary to plot curves for various values of $\eta$. This is done in *Figure 80*, $(q-q_0)V$ being plotted against $\theta$.

The curves are characterized by a sigmoid form, which is different from the linear fall obtained with immobile layers. An important feature is the relatively slow heat fall at low $\theta$ values, when spreading can take place efficiently and minimize interactions.

*Adsorption with dissociation to two particles each occupying one site—immobile layer*[63]

The chance that two adjacent sites are both occupied has been shown in Chapter IV to be

$$\frac{(z-1)^2}{z(z-\theta)} \cdot \theta^2$$

Since each site is surrounded by $z$ nearest neighbours, the total number of occupied adjacent site pairs per unit area is $\tfrac{1}{2}n_s z$ times this expression.

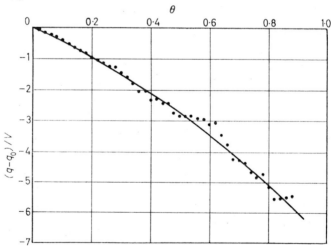

*Figure 81. q–θ curve for immobile layer formed by dissociation of diatomic molecules to atoms*

By courtesy of Miller, A. R. *Proc. Camb. Phil. Soc.* **37**, 82, 194

That is

$$\bar{X} = \tfrac{1}{2}n_s \frac{(z-1)^2}{z-\theta} \cdot \theta^2 \tag{6.32}$$

where the factor $\tfrac{1}{2}$ arises so that an interaction between two particles is not counted twice.

The interaction energy $\bar{U}$ is then

$$\bar{U} = \tfrac{1}{2}n_s V \frac{(z-1)^2}{z-\theta} \cdot \theta^2 \tag{6.33}$$

and from this the $q$–$\theta$ curve may be calculated. As shown in *Figure 81* for the case where $z=4$, it is somewhat concave with respect to the origin.

*Adsorption with dissociation to two particles each occupying one site—mobile layer*

Here precisely similar considerations apply as to the case o mobile layers adsorbed without dissociation. That is to say there is spreading owing to repulsions, and the same mathematical approach is used. The results are identical with those shown in *Figure 80*.

*Variation of V with θ*

So far it has been assumed that $V$ is independent of $\theta$. Since repulsion forces depend on the distance between the particles concerned, this implies that the distance between neighbouring particles is fixed. In practice, this is unlikely to be the case. At high $\theta$ values, a particle will tend to be symmetrically surrounded by other particles, and as a result it will remain at the lowest point of the potential well in which it is situated. At low $\theta$ values, however, it will tend to be unsymmetrically surrounded, and hence tend to climb out of the well in order to increase its distance from the repelling particles. Thus, the distance separating two neighbouring particles will be lower at higher $\theta$ values, and $V$ will increase with $\theta$. An approximate method for dealing with the effect has been developed by MILLER and ROBERTS[64]. Their results differ only in detail from those given above.

*The magnitude of surface repulsions*

If only nearest neighbour interactions are important, short range forces must be operating. These arise from the overlapping of electron clouds, and the energy to which they give rise is exponentially dependent on distance:

$$V = be^{-r/\rho} \tag{6.34}$$

where $b$ and $\rho$ are constants and $r$ is the internuclear distance. These forces would however be too small to cause an appreciable heat fall in most cases, because the chemisorbed particles are not sufficiently near for electron clouds to overlap. This is the case for the adsorption of hydrogen and nitrogen on metals, and for many chemisorptions on oxides where there is only limited coverage of the surface. However, GRIMLEY[65] has suggested that surface orbitals may extend over several atomic diameters, while TOMPKINS[66] has suggested that there may be a local pile-up of electron density. In either of these cases short range forces would become appreciable. Both these effects, and indeed normal short range forces, are difficult to calculate quantitatively.

In addition to short range forces, longer range forces must operate, due to dipole–dipole interaction. For two dipoles of moment $\mu$ at a distance $r$ apart

$$V = \mu^2/2r^3 \qquad (6.35)$$

With these forces it is necessary to sum all repulsions between particles up to 100 Å apart. The results are similar to those obtained for short range forces, provided $\mu$ is constant. However, the fall in $\mu$ with increasing $\theta$, arising from mutual depolarization, should be allowed for, and when this is done curves for immobile layers tend to be convex to the origin, while for mobile layers the sigmoid character is less apparent.

Quantitative calculation can be made for dipole–dipole forces, provided $\mu$ is known. For gas layers on metals they indicate that only a small fraction of the total fall can be ascribed to these forces. Thus for hydrogen on tungsten, assuming $\mu=0\cdot3$D, dipole forces cause a heat fall of 0·6 kcal/mole, compared with an observed fall amounting to over 40 kcal/mole[67]. For hydrogen on nickel, assuming $\mu=0\cdot2$D, the dipole forces give a heat fall of 1 kcal/mole, which is only about 5 per cent of the actual fall[3].

However, for layers where the dipole moments are very high, appreciable heat falls can arise from dipole–dipole repulsion. For caesium layers on tungsten $\mu=1\cdot8$D at $\theta=1$ (see Table 1), from which a heat fall amounting to 3 kcal/g atom is obtained, some 12 per cent of the total[26]. For sodium on tungsten $\mu=2\cdot7$D at $\theta=0\cdot75$[68], and electrostatic forces account for a heat fall amounting to 2·5 kcal/g atom compared with the experimental value, 15 kcal/g atom[25].

USE OF DIFFERENT ELECTRON LEVELS IN THE SOLID

At first sight it is attractive to ascribe heat falls to the filling of different electron energy levels in the solid. However, in the case of the metals, the number of electron levels in the crystal is very much greater than the number engaged in forming a chemisorbed monolayer. As a result, chemisorption will not involve an appreciable change in the energy of the occupied levels in the metal. This type of explanation can in fact only apply if a separate band is formed by the surface atoms of the metal. In this case, the total number of levels would be comparable with the number of chemisorbed atoms or molecules. Since band widths are normally at least 100 kcal, appreciable heat falls could then result. This idea has in fact been developed by TEMKIN[69]. However, it has been criticized by GUNDRY and TOMPKINS[38] on the ground that a surface electron band would be in equilibrium with the band system of the crystal, which during chemisorption would act as an almost infinite reservoir for replenishment or depletion of the surface band. Again, if an effect of this kind was operating, the solution of hydrogen as protons in metals should take place with a continuously decreasing heat, while in fact the heat is normally constant.

There is, however, one case where heat falls may arise from use of different electron levels, and this is in certain chemisorptions on oxides. Here chemisorption may involve a limited number of orbitals arising from the small number of defects or impurities associated with non-stoichoimetry. When depletion of the states takes place in chemisorption, whether by abstraction of a limited number of electrons, or by filling of a limited number of vacancies, the necessary replenishment from the bulk can be very difficult. That is, we are dealing effectively with an isolated surface band. The case has been discussed by STONE[70], who shows that a large parabolic heat fall may result.

## REFERENCES

[1] Eucken, A. $Z$. Elektrochem. **53**, 285, 1949
[2] Shield, L. S. and Russell, W. W. $J$. Phys. Chem. **64**, 1592, 1960
[3] Beeck, O. Disc. Faraday Soc. **8**, 118, 1950
[4] Wahba, M. and Kemball, C. Trans. Faraday Soc. **49**, 1351, 1953
[5] Keyes, F. G. and Marshall, M. J. $J$. Amer. Chem. Soc. **49**, 156, 1927
[6] Bull, H. I., Hall, M. H. and Garner, W. E. $J$. Chem. Soc. 837, 1931
[7] Hickmott, T. W. $J$. Chem. Phys. **32**, 810, 1960
[8] Beeck, O. Adv. in Catalysis **2**, 151, 1950
[9] Kisliuk, P. $J$. Chem. Phys. **31**, 1605, 1959
[10] Kisliuk, P. $J$. Chem. Phys. **30**, 174, 1959
[11] Taylor, H. S. and Kistiakowsky, G. B. $Z$. physik. Chem. **125**, 341, 1927
[12] Beebe, R. A. and Taylor, H. S. $J$. Amer. Chem. Soc. **46**, 43, 1924
[13] Kington, G. L. and Holmes, J. M. Trans. Faraday Soc. **49**, 417, 1953
[14] Beebe, R. A. and Wildner, E. L. $J$. Amer. Chem. Soc. **56**, 642, 1934

[15] Trapnell, B. M. W. *Proc. Roy. Soc.* A**218**, 566, 1953

[16] Ipatieff, V. N., Corson, B. B. and Kurbatov, I. D. *J. Phys. Chem.* **43**, 589, 1939

[17] Beebe, R. A. and Dowden, D. A. *J. Amer. Chem. Soc.* **60**, 2912, 1938

[18] Dowden, D. A. and Garner, W. E. *J. Chem. Soc.* 893, 1939

[19] Garner, W. E. and Ward, T. *J. Chem. Soc.* 857, 1939

[20] Garner, W. E. and Veal, F. J. *J. Chem. Soc.* 1487, 1935
Ward, T. *J. Chem. Soc.* 1244, 1947
Garner, W. E., Gray, T. J. and Stone, F. S. *Proc. Roy. Soc.* A**197**, 294, 1949
Garner, W. E., Stone, F. S. and Tiley, P. F. *Proc. Roy. Soc.* A**211**, 472, 1952

[21] Brunauer, S., Emmett, P. H. and Teller, E. *J. Amer. Chem. Soc.* **60**, 309, 1938

[22] Brennan, D., Hayward, D. O. and Trapnell, B. M. W. *Proc. Roy. Soc.* A**256**, 81, 1960

[23] Cottrell, T. L. *The Strengths of Chemical Bonds.* London; Butterworths, 1958

[24] Barrer, R. M. *Proc. Roy. Soc.* A**149**, 253, 1935

[25] Bosworth, R. C. L. *Proc. Roy. Soc.* A**162**, 32, 1937

[26] Taylor, J. B. and Langmuir, I. *Phys. Rev.* **44**, 423, 1933

[27] Eley, D. D. *Disc. Faraday Soc.* **8**, 34, 1950

[28] Pauling, L. *The Nature of the Chemical Bond.* London; Oxford University Press, 1960

[29] *U.S. Nat. Bur. Stand. Circ.* No. 500: Washington, 1952

[30] Culver, R. V. and Tompkins, F. C. *Adv. in Catalysis* **11**, 67, 1959

[31] Stevenson, D. P. *J. Chem. Phys.* **23**, 203, 1955

[32] Greenhalgh, E., Hayward, D. O. and Trapnell, B. M. W. *J. Phys. Chem.* **61**, 1254, 1957

[33] Bagg, J. and Tompkins, F. C. *Trans. Faraday Soc.* **51**, 1071, 1955

[34] Hayes, F. *Ph.D. Thesis.* Liverpool University, 1962

[35] Hayward, D. O. *Ph.D. Thesis.* Liverpool University, 1958

[36] Higuchi, I., Ree, T. and Eyring, H. *J. Amer. Chem. Soc.* **79**, 1330, 1957

[37] Brodd, R. J. *J. Phys. Chem.* **62**, 54, 1958

[38] Gundry, P. M. and Tompkins, F. C. *Quart. Rev.* **14**, 257, 1960

[39] Fischer, A. K., Cotton, F. A. and Wilkinson, G. *J. Amer Chem. Soc.* **79**, 2044, 1957

[40] Mott, N. F. and Jones, H. *The Theory of the Properties of Metals and Alloys.* London; Oxford University Press, 1936

[41] Pauling, L. *Proc. Roy. Soc.* A**196**, 343, 1949

[42] Dilke, M. H., Maxted, E. B. and Eley, D. D. *Nature, Lond.* **161**, 804, 1948

[43] Moore, L. E. and Selwood, P. W. *J. Amer. Chem. Soc.* **78**, 697, 1956

[44] Hickmott, T. W. and Ehrlich, G. *J. Phys. Chem. Solids* **5**, 47, 1958

[45] Beeck, O., Cole, W. A. and Wheeler, A. *Disc. Faraday Soc.* **8**, 314, 1950

[46] Frankenburg, W. G. *J. Amer. Chem. Soc.* **66**, 1827, 1944

[47] Constable, F. H. *Proc. Roy. Soc.* A**108**, 355, 1925

[48] Taylor, H. S. *Proc. Roy. Soc.* A**108**, 105, 1925

[49] Roberts, J. K. *Proc. Roy. Soc.* A**152**, 445, 1935

[50] Eley, D. D. *J. Phys. Chem.* **55**, 1017, 1951

[51] Schwab, G. M. *Trans. Faraday Soc.* **42**, 689, 1946
[52] Nichols, M. H. *Phys. Rev.* **57**, 297, 1940
[53] Beeck, O., Smith, A. E. and Wheeler, A. *Proc. Roy. Soc.* A**177**, 62, 1940
[54] Beeck, O. and Ritchie, A. W. *Disc. Faraday Soc.* **8**, 159, 1950
[55] Pease, R. N. and Stewart, L. *J. Amer. Chem. Soc.* **47**, 1235, 1925
[56] Ehrlich, G. *J. Chem. Phys.* **34**, 39, 1961
[57] Redhead, P. A. *Trans. Faraday Soc.* **57**, 641, 1961
[58] Taylor, H. S. and Liang, S. C. *J. Amer. Chem. Soc.* **69**, 1306, 2989, 1947
Sadek, H. and Taylor, H. S. *J. Amer. Chem. Soc.* **72**, 1168, 1950
[59] Rideal, E. K. and Trapnell, B. M. W. *J. chim. Phys.* **47**, 126, 1950
[60] Halsey, G. D. and Taylor, H. S. *J. Chem. Phys.* **15**, 624, 1947
[61] Miller, A. R. *The Adsorption of Gases on Solids.* London; Cambridge University Press, 1949
[62] Wang, J. S. *Proc. Roy. Soc.* A**161**, 127, 1937
[63] Miller, A. R. *Proc. Camb. Phil. Soc.* **43**, 232, 1947
[64] Miller, A. R. and Roberts, J. K. *Proc. Camb. Phil. Soc.* **37**, 82, 1941
[65] Grimley, T. B. in *Chemisorption* (ed. W. E. Garner). London; Butterworths, 1957
[66] Culver, R. V., Pritchard, J. and Tompkins, F. C. *Z. Elektrochem* **63**, 741, 1959
[67] Trapnell, B. M. W. *Proc. Roy. Soc.* A**206**, 39, 1951
[68] Bosworth, R. C. L. and Rideal, E. K. *Proc. Roy. Soc.* A**162**, 1, 1937
[69] Temkin, M. *Problems of Chemical Kinetics, Catalysis and Reactivity, Akad. Nauk. U.S.S.R.* 1955
[70] Stone, F. S. in *Chemistry of the Solid State* (ed. W. E. Garner). London: Butterworths, 1955

# VII

# MECHANISMS OF CHEMISORPTION ON METALS

## THE SURFACE BOND

### THE THEORY OF METALS

THE early theory, due to MOTT and JONES[1], makes two assumptions. The first is that the cohesive forces in a metal crystal are due to interaction of the outermost $s$ electrons alone. The second is that the electrons are considered as a whole, without reference to individual atoms. That is, the theory is a collective electron theory, with the electron wave function confined simply to the metal crystal, not to the neighbourhood of individual atoms.

The theory indicates that the electrons in metals retain much of the character which they possess in the isolated atom—it is still possible, for example, to talk of $s$, $p$ and $d$ electrons in the crystal, as in the isolated atom. A difference, however, is that in the isolated atom the energy of each spectroscopic state is discrete and single-valued, but the energy of each state in the crystal has a band of permitted values, the breadth of which is larger for the outermost electrons.

The number of electrons per atom in the shells of isolated atoms may differ from the number in the bands of the crystals. With iron and nickel, for example, the configurations of the outer electrons of the atoms are respectively $3d^6 \, 4s^2$ and $3d^8 \, 4s^2$, but in the crystal the band structures are on the average $3d^{7\cdot8} \, 4s^{0\cdot2}$ and $3d^{9\cdot4} \, 4s^{0\cdot6}$. Nevertheless, it is the important distinguishing feature of the transition metals that their crystals possess incomplete $d$ bands, in the same way that the isolated atoms possess incomplete $d$ shells.

In a more recent approach, due to PAULING[2, 3], the electron wave function is localized round a particular atom or pair of atoms. Also, cohesion is ascribed to resonance between all possible structures in which the electrons form definite one or two electron bonds between atoms in the crystal. In the transition metals, the bonding orbitals are hybrid orbitals of $d$, $s$, and $p$ states similar to those found in complex ions.

If, in passing along a transition period, the increase in the number of $d$ electrons merely resulted in an increase in the number of bonding orbitals, the cohesion would continuously increase. This, however, is not the case, for taking the melting point as a convenient index of bond strength, the maximum value always occurs before the end of a transition period. This and other evidence led Pauling to conclude that there are three types of $d$ orbital, namely

($a$) bonding $d$ orbitals, which form ($dsp$) hybrid bonds.

($b$) atomic $d$ orbitals, associated with individual atoms, but not used in bonding.

($c$) metallic $d$ orbitals, participating in electric conduction.

In passing along a transition period, the electrons at first primarily enter bonding $d$ orbitals, but after about Group VII, these are full, and the electrons then primarily enter atomic $d$ orbitals. At the end of the period these also are full. The characteristic of the transition metals according to this theory is that they possess vacant atomic $d$ orbitals, and to some extent these correspond to the incomplete $d$ band of the older theory.

UNSATURATION AT METAL SURFACES

Two general types of unsaturation may be distinguished at a metal surface.

($a$) Unsaturation arising because the surface atoms do not possess their full complement of nearest neighbours. This should be common to all metal surfaces. On the basis of the band theory, it has been suggested[4] that the asymmetric environment of the surface atoms leads to the formation of special electron energy levels at the surface, and unsaturation arises from partial occupation of these. In the Pauling theory, 'dangling' metal–metal hybrid bonds will be present at the surface, and although the surface bonds may well rehybridize in order to lower the energy, a considerable degree of unsaturation should persist.

(*b*) Both bulk and surface atoms of a transition metal crystal show a further type of unsaturation. On the collective electron theory this arises because the *d*-band is only partially occupied, and in the Pauling theory because all atoms have vacant atomic *d*-orbitals. This type of unsaturation operates in the formation of interstitial hydrides. Generally, however, it can only be used by the surface atoms, because the atoms in the bulk are inaccessible to reactants.

Table 37 summarizes the results of this section.

TABLE 37

Surface Unsaturation of Metals

| Type of unsaturation | Collective electron theory | Pauling theory |
|---|---|---|
| (*a*) surface only (all metals) | unfilled surface states | vacant (*dsp*) or (*sp*) hybrid orbitals |
| (*b*) bulk and surface (transition metals only) | unfilled *d*-band | vacant atomic *d*-orbitals |

### THE SURFACE BOND FORMED IN CHEMISORPTION OF GASES

*Surface Potential Data*

In the chemisorption of gases on metals the surface dipole, measured at $\theta \rightarrow 1$, is always small[5, 6] and, except in the case of oxygen, less than about 0·5D. This suggests covalence, although as the moments are measured at full coverage, where depolarization effects are pronounced, it is not proof of covalence. However, since the surface potential change is nearly always negative for strong chemisorption, the alternative to covalence is negative ion formation, and it can readily be shown that for most gases this is highly endothermic and therefore impossible[7].

*Magnetic Data*

The magnetic susceptibility of a strongly paramagnetic or ferromagnetic metal is largely determined by the number of unpaired *d*-electrons associated with its ion cores. If chemisorption involves pairing of an electron from the adsorbate with one of these unpaired electrons in the metal, the susceptibility of the surface atoms will be reduced. If, on the other hand, surface bonding takes place in some other way, e.g. through the breaking of $(dsp)$ electron pair bonds employed in cohesion, followed by covalence with these electrons, there will be almost no change in susceptibility because the electrons before and after will be paired.

On this basis, measurements of the change in the magnetic susceptibility of palladium on adsorption of dimethyl sulphide have suggested that metal–metal bonds are not broken[8]. The susceptibility changes which were observed are shown in Table 38.

TABLE 38

Susceptibility of Palladium Powders

| Moles $(CH_3)_2S$ per grm atom Pd | $100\left(\dfrac{\Delta x}{x}\right)$ | $100\left(\dfrac{\Delta x}{x}\right)_{Pd}$ | $100\left(\dfrac{\Delta x}{x}\right)_{calc.}$ |
|---|---|---|---|
| 0·27 | 10·1 | 8·0 | 13·5 |
| 0·23 | 7·9 | 6·0 | 11·5 |

The second column shows the percentage change in the susceptibility, $x$, of the solid on chemisorption, and the third column the change in the susceptibility of the palladium alone, after subtracting from the total change the diamagnetic susceptibility of the adsorbed dimethyl sulphide. The last column gives the decrease in susceptibility of the palladium calculated on the assumption that the susceptibility of the surface atoms is reduced to zero.

The calculated decrease is larger than the observed decrease, probably because the powder was incompletely freed of initial contamination, so that not all the surface atoms were able to enter into chemisorption. However, the experimental change is of the same order of magnitude as would be expected for bonding with unpaired $d$-electrons in the metal.

Further evidence has been provided by SELWOOD and his co-workers[9, 10, 11], from studies of the change in magnetization of nickel powders on chemisorption of various gases. In the case of hydrogen the saturation magnetization decreases linearly with chemisorbed amount, and from the slope of the line DIETZ and SELWOOD[10] calculate that 0·7 unpaired $d$-electrons are used per hydrogen atom adsorbed.

In the case of oxygen[9] the saturation magnetization increases, which might be expected if electrons are leaving the metal to form partially negative oxygen ions. It should be noted, however, that

BROEDER et al.[12] found that, as with hydrogen, there is a decrease in magnetization on adsorption of oxygen.

Ethylene and ethane also decrease the magnetization[11], and the slope of the graph relating magnetization and volume adsorbed can give interesting information. Thus, if in the case of hydrogen, the slope is associated with the formation of one bond per hydrogen atom, and if the bond types with ethylene and ethane are the same as with hydrogen, the slopes for the latter gases can, by simple proportionality, be converted to the number of bonds formed per molecule adsorbed. The assumptions are probably justified, and at room temperatures the method indicates the formation of two bonds per molecule with ethylene and between four and six with ethane. That is, chemisorption involves some breakdown of the ethane molecule, but two point attachment of ethylene, probably through opening of the double bond. At higher temperatures, though, breakdown also occurs with ethylene.

One further point should be noted. According to the Pauling theory of metals, it is the unpaired atomic $d$-electrons that give rise to strong paramagnetism and to ferromagnetism, and hence, a fall in the magnetic property would appear to suggest covalent bond formation with sharing of an electron from the adsorbate with an electron from the atomic $d$-orbitals of the metal. However, cancellation of the spins of unpaired electrons in $(dsp)$ hybrid orbitals in the surface would also account for the decrease in magnetization on adsorption.

Thus, while $d$-electrons are undoubtedly used in chemisorption, it is difficult to decide unequivocally whether, in terms of the Pauling theory, these are in atomic $d$-orbitals or $(dsp)$ hybrid orbitals.

### Conductivity data

The conductivity of a metal is determined by the number of electrons engaged in conduction, and by their mean free path.

Increases in resistance have been obtained for oxygen[13] and hydrogen[14] adsorbed on nickel and for carbon monoxide adsorbed on nickel, iron and titanium[15]. This could be due to removal of electrons from the conduction band in order to form covalent bonds. Equally, however, the presence of chemisorbed atoms, by altering the periodicity of the potential at the surface, could decrease the mean free path of the electrons and hence increase the resistance.

### The Pattern of Activity in Chemisorption

In Table 39 is shown data due to TRAPNELL[16] on the activities of some 20 metals between $0\,°C$ and $-183\,°C$ towards the gases nitrogen, hydrogen, carbon monoxide, ethylene, acetylene and oxygen. These are expressed as 'gas chemisorbed' or 'gas not chemisorbed'. The latter means that no adsorption was observed between $0\,°C$ and the temperatures at which physical adsorption begins: the former usually means that chemisorption takes place over a large part of the surface with great rapidity.

TABLE 39

The Activities of Metal Films in Chemisorption

+ *gas chemisorbed.* — *gas not chemisorbed.*

| Group | Metals | Gases | | | | | |
|-------|--------|-------|-------|-------|-------|-------|-------|
| | | $N_2$ | $H_2$ | CO | $C_2H_4$ | $C_2H_2$ | $O_2$ |
| A | W, Ta, Mo, Ti, Zr, Fe, Ca, Ba | + | + | + | + | + | + |
| B | Ni, Pt, Rh, Pd | — | + | + | + | + | + |
| C | Cu, Al | — | — | + | + | + | + |
| D | K | — | — | — | — | + | + |
| E | Zn, Cd, In, Sn, Pb, Ag* | — | — | — | — | — | + |
| F | Au | — | — | + | + | + | — |

* CO is known to adsorb on silver[17].

The metals divide into six groups, designated in order of decreasing activity, *A* to *F*, and with few exceptions, high activity is associated with transition metals. The activity rises with increasing atomic number as a transition period is approached and entered, and dies away as the period ends. This rhythm is shown most clearly by the sequence K (atomic number 19), Ca(20), Ti(22), Fe(26), Ni(28), Cu(29) and Zn(30). Falling activity is shown by the sequence Mo(42), Rh(45), Pd(46), Ag(47), Cd(48), In(49) and by W(74), Pt(78), Au(79), Pb(82).

No transition metal is in the less active groups *C–F*, while the most active Groups *A* and *B*, with the exception of Ca and Ba, contain only transition metals. Also, while Ca and Ba are not usually classed as transition metals because their isolated atoms contain no outer electrons in $3d$ and $5d$ states respectively, there is good evidence[18] that in the metal crystals, some electrons are in $3d$ and $5d$ bands. In this case Ca and Ba share with the transition metals the property of a partly filled $d$ band. K, which precedes Ca in the Periodic Table, does not show this effect, and its lower activity is of interest on this account.

Evidence presented so far suggests that activity in chemisorption is in general confined to the transition metals, and that chemisorption involves covalent bonding with the partly filled $d$-band or with unpaired electrons in atomic $d$-orbitals. Non-transition metals are then inactive because their $d$-bands or atomic $d$-orbitals are completely filled.

There are, however, some exceptions to this rule. Thus, oxygen appears to be adsorbed by all metals except gold. Here, there is good evidence that oxygen uptakes on many metals are due to oxidation rather than to true chemisorption[19], resulting in the breaking of metal–metal bonds. In this case it is the properties of the individual metal ions that are important, not the unsaturation of the metal surface, the reaction being the start of a bulk chemical reaction.

The heats of adsorption of CO on Cu and Au[16] are in the border region between those expected for physical and chemical adsorption. In addition these adsorptions give positive surface potentials, whereas on the transition metals CO gives negative values[6, 17]. Thus, adsorption may be largely physical and this is confirmed in the case of copper by infrared data[20].

Strong physical adsorption may also explain why $C_2H_4$ and $C_2H_2$ are adsorbed by Cu, Au and Al, while in the case of $C_2H_2$ on K, compound formation is probably taking place. The interaction proceeds with liberation of hydrogen and is probably similar to the formation of acetylides, which are ionic salts.

An alternative explanation with Cu and Au is that they immediately succeed transition periods, and although they possess complete $d$ bands, the energies required for $d$–$s$ promotion are uniquely small. For Au, the energy is $3.25\text{eV}$[21], for Cu about $3.0\text{eV}$[22], and it is possible that such promotions might accompany chemisorption to create $d$ band vacancies and hence allow covalence with the $d$ band. In this case the reason why Ag does not chemisorb $C_2H_4$, and $C_2H_2$ could be that the $d$–$s$ promotion energy for Ag is higher, being about $4.0\text{eV}$[23].

Chemisorption of $N_2$ as atoms does not proceed on all transition metals, for the Group B metals do not dissociate nitrogen. These metals contain either 1 or 2 vacancies in the $d$ shell of the isolated atom, whereas the Group A metals have 3 or more vacancies. The requirement of 3 vacancies may be due either to the high valency of the nitrogen atom or to the high dissociation energy of the nitrogen molecule.

Later TRAPNELL[24] and also COLLINS and TRAPNELL[25] investigated the chemisorption of $CH_4$, $C_2H_6$ and $CO_2$. Results are shown in Table 40.

With $CH_4$ and $C_2H_6$ most of the transition metals are sufficiently active for appreciable coverages to be obtained at room temperatures. However, the ferromagnetic metals Fe, Co and Ni are inactive. This is surprising, as Rh and Pd are active, and these metals are usually weaker chemisorbing agents than Fe, Co and Ni.

TABLE 40

Chemisorption of $CH_4$, $C_2H_6$ and $CO_2$

| Gas | Active metals | Inactive metals |
|---|---|---|
| $CH_4$ and $C_2H_6$ | Ti, W, Mo, Ta, Cr, Rh, Pd | Fe, Co, Ni |
| $CO_2$ | W, Mo, Fe, Ni, Al | Rh, Pt, Pd, Cu, Zn, Cd |

With these two gases an activation energy is required for chemisorption on all active metals and on Fe, Co and Ni the stable alignment of $d$-electrons associated with ferromagnetism may raise the activation energy and preclude low temperature chemisorption. Films of these metals are active at higher temperatures[26], and an increase of a few kilocalories was shown to be sufficient to explain the results. Such an increase could well be attributed to ferromagnetism.

With $CO_2$, the non-transition metals other than Al are inactive, while with Al dissociation of $CO_2$ occurs, oxygen atoms being adsorbed and CO liberated in the gas phase. The high affinity of Al for oxygen may be responsible for this. Rh, Pt and Pd are also inactive, and among the transition metals these are normally the least active chemisorbing agents.

An interesting observation is that hydrogen *atoms* are adsorbed on the metals Cu, Ag, Au[17] and on Pb, Cd, Zn, Al[27]. However, desorption as hydrogen molecules commences at temperatures above about $-78\,°C$ so that the heat of adsorption of hydrogen molecules is low, probably because it involves an endothermic term for the dissociation of the molecule. Nevertheless, HICKMOTT and EHRLICH[28] suggest that the electronic requirements for bond formation are better revealed by chemisorbing a beam of atoms than by chemisorbing undissociated molecules. Certainly M–H bond energies can be appreciable on non-transition metals. In Table 41 the bond energies and surface potentials[6] of hydrogen layers on a series of metals are given. The bonding of a hydrogen atom on Cu is only slightly weaker than on a neighbouring transition metal such as Ni, though sufficiently so to make the heat of adsorption of hydrogen molecules very low. Heats of chemisorption of molecules on Ni[29] and Cu[30] are 30 and about 8 kcal/mole respectively.

TABLE 41

Bond Energies and Surface Potentials for Hydrogen Adsorption

| Metal | W | Ni | Cu | Ag | Au |
|---|---|---|---|---|---|
| $E$ (M–H) (kcal/mole) | 75 | 67 | 56 | $<52$ | $<52$ |
| Surface potential (volts) | −0·48 | −0·35 | −0·36 | −0·36 | −0·17 |

PRITCHARD and TOMPKINS[30] have concluded from this type of data that the '$d$-character' contributes only about 15 per cent of the total bond energy. However, with CO there seems to be a definite change in the nature of the surface bond in going from Ni to Cu. The surface potential[6] and infra-red[20] data indicate chemisorption with Ni, but only strong physical adsorption with Cu. The respective heats of adsorption are 42 kcal/mole[31] and 9 kcal/mole[16], but with Ni the carbon–oxygen bond of the CO is considerably weakened on adsorption, and when allowance is made for this the energy of the metal–carbon bond works out to be about 119 kcal/mole. Thus, in this case, the bond energy falls markedly once the $d$-band is full.

In conclusion, it would appear that both of the types of surface unsaturation discussed earlier are involved in chemisorption and that the degree of participation of the two types may depend on the nature of the adsorbate. In the case of hydrogen the role of the $d$-band may be less important than with CO.

## CO-ORDINATE LINKS

Evidence for the existence of co-ordinate links in chemisorption has been provided by MAXTED and his co-workers[32], who have studied the poisoning of transition metal catalysts. Poisoning activity by non-metals towards a variety of catalytic reactions in solution was found to be largely confined to such compounds of elements of Groups V and VI of the Periodic Table as possess lone electron pairs. Some results are shown in Table 42.

Since catalyst poisons normally act through being very strongly adsorbed, and poisoning activity is limited to compounds capable of co-ordination, it seems likely that the poisons are adsorbed in this way, possibly with donation to a metal $d$ band.

The adsorptions of $NH_3$, $PH_3$ and $AsH_3$ may however be exceptions to the rule. With ammonia, evidence will be given later that chemisorption involves dissociation of hydrogen, and formation of covalent surface bonds, and the same may also apply to $PH_3$ and $AsH_3$.

TABLE 42

Influence of Electronic Configuration on Toxicity

| Element | Toxic compounds | Non-toxic compounds |
|---------|-----------------|---------------------|
| N | $NH_3$ | $NH_4^+$ |
| P | | |
| As | | |
| S | | |

IONIC BONDS

In a few cases, the surface dipole produced on adsorption is in agreement with the value expected for an ionic bond, and larger than could be ascribed to a covalent or co-ionic bond.

When deciding bond types from dipole moment data, it is important to use moments measured at $\theta \rightarrow 0$, since mutual depolarization can occur at high coverages, and reduce the moment appreciably, as shown in Table 1. True moments may be calculated from surface potential data using the formula

$$\mu = \Delta\phi/4\pi n_s\theta \qquad (7.1)$$

where $\Delta\phi$ is the change in work function and $n_s\theta$ is the number of ions adsorbed per cm² of surface. Moments calculated in this way from experimental data for the chemisorption of Na[33], K[34], Cs[35] and Th[36] on tungsten are given in Table 43 together with those calculated on the assumption that monovalent positive ions, Na⁺ etc., are formed in adsorption. These moments are the product of the electronic charge and the distance, $d$, between the positive charge and the conducting surface. $d$ is the radius of the positive ion and may be equated to the normal ionic radius in the crystal of the element in question.

TABLE 43

| System | $\mu$ (exp.) | $d$ $(\text{Å})$ | $\mu$ (calc.) |
|--------|--------------|------------------|---------------|
| Na on W | 11·3 | 1·83 | 8·75 |
| K on W | 11·5 | 2·27 | 10·85 |
| Cs on W | 8·1 | 2·62 | 12·5 |
| Th on W | 2·0 | 1·78 | 8·65 |

With Na, K and Cs layers the agreement between calculation and experiment is sufficiently good to conclude that almost purely ionic bonds are formed. With Th layers, however, the experimental moment is so far below the calculated moment that the surface bond must be largely covalent.

### THE SURFACE RADICALS

HYDROGEN LAYERS

Only metals which chemisorb hydrogen catalyse the exchange between hydrogen and deuterium.

$$H_2 + D_2 \rightarrow 2HD$$

Since the reaction is a breaking and remaking of H—H and D—D bonds, hydrogen atoms are presumably formed on the surface in chemisorption.

The diameter of the hydrogen atom is less than the distances between adjacent atoms in metal surfaces, and in saturated hydrogen layers there should therefore be one hydrogen atom per surface metal atom. The equation for chemisorption then becomes

$$2M + H_2 \rightarrow 2MH$$

Volumetric work indicates that this is the case. Thus ROBERTS[37] showed that the volume of hydrogen chemisorbed at room temperatures by a flashed tungsten filament corresponded to within 15 or 20 per cent to one atom per surface atom, if the roughness factor of the filament was taken to be 1·4, the value determined by TAYLOR and LANGMUIR[35].

BEECK and RITCHIE[38] have compared the volume of hydrogen chemisorbed by an evaporated nickel film with the volumes, $v_m$, of various gases physically adsorbed into a monolayer. These volumes were obtained from adsorption isotherms by application of the Brunauer–Emmett–Teller equation for multilayer adsorption[39]. From this the volume of gas, $v_m$, physically adsorbed into a monolayer can be obtained.

Then if each physically adsorbed molecule occupies an area $a_1$ Å² on the surface, and $v_2$ cm³ of hydrogen are chemisorbed, the area $a_2$ Å² occupied by each chemisorbed molecule is

$$a_2 = \frac{a_1 v_m}{v_2} \tag{7.2}$$

Hence $a_2$ may be obtained provided $a_1$ is known. For simple molecules such as krypton, methane and nitrogen, it may be assumed that there is close packing in physically adsorbed monolayers, with $a_1$ equal to the cross-sectional area in the liquid phase. For more complex molecules it is necessary to assume some definite configuration on the surface. With $n$-butane, it has proved valid to assume that the molecule lies flat, in the form of a cylinder of diameter 4·75 Å and length 5·16 Å.

Values of $a_2$ obtained by Beeck and Ritchie are shown in Table 44 and are seen to be independent of the gas used in physical adsorption. $v_2$ was measured as the volume chemisorbed at $-196\,^{\circ}\text{C}$ and 0·1 mm pressure.

The nickel films were randomly oriented, and are likely to have exposed in their surfaces the low index planes (100), (110) and (111) to roughly equal extents. The areas per site in these three planes are respectively 6·15, 8·70 and 5·32 Å$^2$, the mean being 6·72 Å$^2$. If in the saturated layer one hydrogen atom is present per nickel atom, the area covered by each hydrogen molecule would be $2 \times 6·72 = 13·44$ Å$^2$. This is in good agreement with the experimental value, and suggests 1:1 bonding.

TABLE 44

Hydrogen Chemisorption on Nickel Films

| Gas physically adsorbed | $v_m$ (mols/ 100 mg Ni $\times 10^{-18}$) | $a_1$ ($\mathring{A}^2$) | $v_2$ (mols/ 100 mg Ni $\times 10^{-18}$) | $a_2$ ($\mathring{A}^2$) |
|---|---|---|---|---|
| Kr | 6·15 | 14·6 | 7·28 | 12·33 |
| Kr | 5·85 | 14·6 | 6·9 | 12·38 |
| CH$_4$ | 5·40 | 15·68 | 6·9 | 12·27 |
| $n$-C$_4$H$_{10}$ | 3·48 | 24·5 | 6·9 | 12·36 |

More recent work has been concerned to discover whether more than one mechanism of chemisorption may be operating within the monolayer. This was first suggested by MIGNOLET[40, 41], as a result of studies of the change in work function on adsorption. Often $\mu$–$\theta$

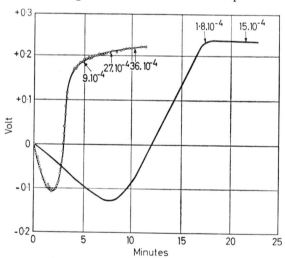

Figure 82. Change in surface potential of a Pt film with time on continuous addition of hydrogen at −190°C; numbers represent the equilibrium hydrogen pressure above the film

By courtesy of Mignolet, J. C. P. J. chim. phys. **54**, 19, 1957

curves are non-linear, showing an apparent decrease in the surface dipole as adsorption proceeds. Hitherto this had been ascribed to mutual depolarization, but the case of platinum is more extreme[42]. As shown in *Figure 82*, the work function initially increases on adsorption, but then decreases, eventually giving an electropositive layer. Clearly, mutual depolarization cannot explain the result, and Mignolet suggested that in the later stages a weak molecular chemisorption is taking place through a Mulliken charge transfer bond. However, infra-red work by PLISKIN and EISCHENS[43] shows that this cannot be the case. These workers found bands at 4·86 and 4·76 microns respectively for the strong and weak chemisorptions of hydrogen, and at 6·8 and 6·7 microns in the case of deuterium. The results confirm that there are two mechanisms of chemisorption, but if the weak adsorption is molecular, a band should appear at about 5·4 microns when HD is adsorbed. However, when an equilibrated $H_2/D_2$ mixture was contacted with the platinum sample, no absorption occurred at this wavelength. Both strong and weak adsorptions must therefore be atomic, and representing the species as $H_s$ and $H_w$, Pliskin and Eischens suggest two possible structures, namely

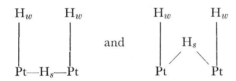

That is, the two chemisorptions are associated with different topographical positions on the surface, the strong adsorption being part way towards solution in the metal.

In the case of tungsten, there is no reversal of the dipole as adsorption proceeds[41], but simply a decrease. However, if a filament is covered with gas at liquid air temperatures and then flashed, the curve relating the rise in pressure due to desorption with rise in temperature shows two peaks[44]. Other peaks have at various times been claimed[45], suggesting the presence of further binding states, but later work showed that these arise from impurity in the system[28]. The weak chemisorption of hydrogen on tungsten is small in extent and pressure dependent, and is confined to temperatures below 200 °K. It may well be molecular, and take place in gaps in the strongly adsorbed layer, though as yet this must be regarded as unproved.

Certainly the balance of evidence supports the existence of two mechanisms, and this is confirmed by the effect hydrogen chemisorption has on the conductivity of metal films[15]. In the case of iron films, the resistance first increases on admission of hydrogen, but then decreases, eventually reaching almost the initial value for the clean surface. Those who have used the resistance method tend to agree with those who have used infra-red spectra, not only that two mechanisms exist, but also that these are due to adsorption at different lattice points[7]. The alternative possibility, namely that the second weak adsorption takes place in the gaps in an immobile atomic layer, does not at present find favour.

OXYGEN LAYERS

The study of oxygen chemisorption on metals is complicated by the occurrence of oxidation, even at low temperatures. Thus, BRENNAN, HAYWARD and TRAPNELL[19] have compared the volume of krypton physically adsorbed on evaporated films with the extent of oxygen chemisorption at room temperatures on the same film. Using the BET technique it is then possible to obtain the ratio, $\theta$, of the number of oxygen to surface metal atoms. These ratios varied according as the BET area was obtained before or after oxygen chemisorption, probably because the sudden liberation of the heat of chemisorption caused the film to sinter. However, with most metals (Ti, Cr, Mn, Ta, Fe, Co, Ni, Nb, Al) the results gave values of $\theta$ in excess of 2 and in some cases as high as 8, indicating that oxidation was taking place. Only with Mo, W, Rh, Pt and Pd, did $\theta$ approach unity, as shown in Table 45.

TABLE 45

Oxygen Coverages at Room Temperature

| Metal | Mo | W | Rh | Pd | Pt |
|---|---|---|---|---|---|
| $\theta$ (from initial area) | 1·27 | 1·15 | 0·84 | 0·65 | 0·62 |
| $\theta$ (from mean area) | 1·41 | 1·33 | 0·97 | 0·74 | 0·63 |

In the cases of Mo, W and Rh, Table 45 gives the mechanism of chemisorption as

$$2M + O_2 \rightarrow 2MO$$

with the beginnings of oxidation commencing on Mo and W. This mechanism would be expected since the oxygen atom is rather smaller than the metal atoms concerned, permitting 1:1 bonding, yet not so small that further adsorption may take place. With Pt and Pd incomplete monolayers, PtO and PdO seem to be formed. In the case of Pt some evidence was obtained that this is due to a low heat of chemisorption in dense layers.

As with hydrogen, there have been suggestions that more than one mechanism of chemisorption may operate within oxygen mono-layers. MORRISON and ROBERTS[46], using the accommodation coefficient technique, found oxygen layers on a tungsten filament to evaporate in two different temperature ranges. The less stable portion, evaporating at 800 °C, was believed to be a molecular film, and the more stable portion, evaporating at 1,400 °C, an atomic film. Some 8 per cent of single sites are in fact left over when an immobile layer is formed by dissociation of diatomic molecules to atoms, and it was suggested that on these a strong molecular chemi-sorption might take place. Evaporation data are however even more difficult to interpret with oxygen than with hydrogen, owing to the possibility of desorption as oxide.

CARBON MONOXIDE LAYERS

A good deal of volumetric work has been carried out on carbon monoxide layers with the aim of obtaining the ratio of adsorbed molecules to surface metal atoms. BRUNAUER and EMMETT[47], for example, compared the low temperature adsorption of nitrogen on iron powders with the extent of CO chemisorption. Unfortunately their work is difficult to interpret as some low temperature nitrogen chemisorption was almost certainly taking place in addition to physical adsorption. However, similar work by BEECK et al.[48] on evaporated nickel films suggested that a single site chemisorption of CO was taking place, indicating a surface complex NiCO, analagous to nickel carbonyl.

On molybdenum and rhodium films on the other hand LANYON and TRAPNELL[49] found the CO and $H_2$ chemisorptions to be almost equal in extent, suggesting a two-site mechanism, while on iron and tungsten films the CO chemisorption was respectively 1·23 and 1·40 times the hydrogen chemisorption, suggesting mixed one and two sites mechanisms. Only on platinum and palladium films did the CO chemisorption correspond to a single site mechanism.

The CO molecule can cover two sites in one of three ways, namely,

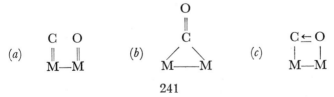

and no final decision between these is possible on volumetric grounds. This question and others have, however, been resolved by EISCHENS and his co-workers[50, 51], who have obtained infra-red spectra of CO adsorbed on a number of metals, normally supported on silica or alumina. Their most important results are the following:

($i$) both one and two site adsorption occur,

($ii$) one site adsorption involves a single bond between metal and carbon atoms, and should therefore be represented as M—C≡O,

($iii$) two site adsorption takes place via mechanism ($b$) above,

($iv$) the relative amounts of one and two site chemisorption vary

    ($a$) with the metal

    ($b$) with the nature of the support

    ($c$) with the surface coverage.

Thus *Figure 83* shows spectra for CO on supported palladium at room temperatures, curves A to E corresponding to 20 per cent,

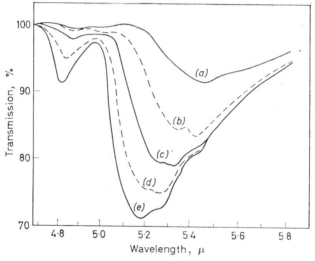

*Figure 83. Effect of increasing surface coverage of the spectrum of* CO *chemisorbed on* Pd

By courtesy of Eischens, R. P., Francis, S. A. and Pliskin, W. A. *J. Phys. Chem.* **60**, 194, 1956

45 per cent, 65 per cent, 85 per cent and 100 per cent coverage respectively. The band in the region $5\cdot2$–$5\cdot5\mu$ is due to two site adsorption and the band at $4\cdot85\mu$ to single site adsorption. While the initial adsorption takes place primarily by a two site mechanism, single site adsorption clearly becomes important as the surface

coverage increases. Probably the effect is due to surface hetero-geneity rather than to adjacent pairs of sites being filled and leaving only single sites. On nickel, mixed one and two site adsorption was also observed, but both on supported platinum and on evaporated films single site adsorption predominated[51]. However, the relative proportions of the two types of adsorption varies with the nature of the support. As shown in *Figure 84*, two site chemisorption is rather

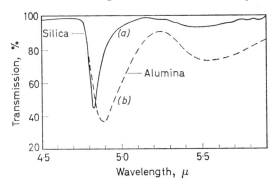

*Figure 84. Spectrum of* CO *chemisorbed on* (a) *silica-supported* Pt, *and* (b) *alumina-supported* Pt

By courtesy of Eischens, R. P. and Pliskin, W. A. *Adv. in Catalysis* **10**, 1, 1958

more extensive on alumina supported than on silica supported platinum. This result may show that the nature of the support influences the electronic structure of the metal, since a relatively greater donation of electrons by the metal is required for two site than one site adsorption.

YANG and GARLAND[52] find one and two site adsorption on rhodium, together with a third mechanism in which one rhodium atom adsorbs two molecules of CO.

The relative proportions of the various types of adsorption again depend on the coverage and on the concentration of rhodium on the support. In recent work with evaporated metal films[53], both single site and two site adsorption has been found with the metals W, Mo, Fe, Co, Ni, Pt and Pd.

Desorption studies on tungsten filaments by EHRLICH[54] and by REDHEAD[55] confirm the existence of two mechanisms. Redhead finds that two-site chemisorption takes place both first and to a greater extent, and concludes that the small amount of single-site chemisorption (some 10 per cent of the total) is a gap-filling process. Both Ehrlich and Redhead agree that there are three sub-phases within the two-site mechanism, as shown in *Figure 78*. These have different heats of chemisorption, and may arise from adsorption on different lattice spacings.

An unexpected result which relates to CO chemisorption is that isotopic exchange between CO molecules takes place on iron powders at temperatures as low as $-35\,^{\circ}C$[56].

$$^{13}CO + C^{18}O \rightleftharpoons \, ^{13}C^{18}O + CO$$

At face value the result is difficult to explain. However, iron powders are undoubtedly contaminated, presumably with oxygen, and exchange might take place through association of the chemisorbed CO with this oxygen. On several oxides isotopic exchange of CO with surface oxide ions has been observed at low temperatures, and if a similar process occurs on contaminated iron powders, exchange between CO molecules would result.

CARBON DIOXIDE LAYERS

A dissociative chemisorption of $CO_2$ might be expected according to an equation such as

$$2M + CO_2 \rightarrow MCO + MO$$

On several metals there is evidence for such chemisorption at about $100\,^{\circ}C$. For example, BRENNAN, GREENHALGH and TRAPNELL[57] have found that with Ta, Ti and Nb appreciable CO is liberated in the gas phase on contacting evaporated films with $CO_2$ at $100\,^{\circ}C$. Again, on W and Mo films isotopic exchange takes place between CO and $CO_2$ at $100\,^{\circ}C$,

$$CO + \, ^{14}CO_2 \rightleftharpoons \, ^{14}CO + CO_2$$

probably via dissociative $CO_2$ chemisorption. However on the more weakly adsorbing metals Fe, Co and Ni, no CO was liberated during $CO_2$ chemisorption, nor did isotopic exchange take place between CO and $CO_2$.

The conclusion drawn from this work, namely that $CO_2$ tends to dissociate at $100°C$ on metals at the beginning of transition periods but not on metals such as Fe, Co and Ni, is supported by three further results.

(*1*) Brennan, Hayes and Hayward[58] have measured heats of chemisorption of $CO_2$ and CO on a number of metal films. Their values suggest dissociative chemisorption with Ti, W, Ta, Nb, Mo and Mn, but not with Fe, Co and Ni (see Chapter VI).

(*2*) Hayward and Gomer[59] have studied the chemisorption of $CO_2$ on tungsten in the field emission microscope and observed surface diffusions at temperatures between 400°K and 750°K which correspond closely with those found for $O_2$ and CO layers. They conclude from their results that $CO_2$ is completely dissociated on tungsten at 400 °K and possibly at lower temperatures.

(*3*) Eischens and Pliskin[60] find that on nickel powders the infrared spectrum of $CO_2$ layers only shows the presence of chemisorbed CO above 100 °C. At lower temperatures the spectrum is that of a carboxylate ion, suggesting a surface complex

A surprising feature of $CO_2$ chemisorption is its limited extent. Collins and Trapnell[25] agree with Brennan, Hayes and Hayward[58] that on tungsten and molybdenum films between 4 and 5 sites are covered by each molecule, while the latter workers claim a 10 site chemisorption on Fe, Co and Ni, about a 3 site chemisorption on Ta, and between a 2 and 3 site chemisorption on Ti. These values are high to be interpreted in steric terms and, furthermore, there is no correlation of saturation coverage with lattice spacing. The best correlation is with heat of chemisorption, the coverage increasing with increasing heat. However, chemisorption does not cease because the heat has fallen to a low value—in all cases high heats were recorded at saturation. Probably an activation energy is required above a certain coverage, and this coverage is higher for the stronger adsorbing metals.

NITROGEN LAYERS

Nitrogen chemisorption by metals may take place by one of two mechanisms, the characteristics of which may be seen by reference to iron[61].

At low temperatures, iron films chemisorb nitrogen instantaneously over the whole surface. The differential heat of adsorption is initially 10 kcal/mole, and falls to 5 kcal/mole as $\theta \rightarrow 1$. The

R

volume of nitrogen chemisorbed at saturation is equal to the hydrogen chemisorption, so that the nitrogen molecule occupies two sites.

At room temperatures and above this adsorption is too weak to proceed to an appreciable extent. Instead there is found to take place a slow, activated adsorption, and at room temperatures the volume adsorbed at saturation corresponds to about 1 nitrogen atom per 5 surface atoms. The heat of adsorption is initially high—values between 70 and 40 kcal/mole have been recorded[61] and falls to 16 kcal/mole with increasing coverage.

The two adsorptions clearly proceed by different mechanisms. The high temperature adsorption almost certainly takes place as atoms, because it is known to be active in the catalytic synthesis of ammonia. The mechanism of the low temperature chemisorption is uncertain. It presumably takes place without complete dissociation of the nitrogen molecule, giving one of the complexes

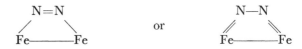

Other metals behave differently in nitrogen chemisorption. The Group B metals of Table 39 show only the weak chemisorption[16], while the Group A metals other than iron show both the strong and the weak chemisorption, but the former is fast and takes place first. The weakly chemisorbed gas then goes onto the residual surface.

In the weak chemisorption, each molecule probably always covers two sites, but the properties of the atomic chemisorption vary from metal to metal. At room temperatures on Mo and Cr the ratio of adsorbed nitrogen atoms to surface metal atoms is 0·42, on W it is 0·36, while on Ta, the figure given by GREENHALGH, SLACK and TRAPNELL[62], corrected for a fallacious surface area measurement, is about 0·5.

Greenhalgh et al. suggest that chemisorption ceases when there are no further groups of metal atoms possessing the necessary 6 unpaired electrons for forming covalences with two nitrogen atoms. Since nitrogen layers are immobile at these temperatures, groups of uncovered metal atoms possessing 2, 3, 4 or 5 unpaired electrons will be left over. These should be able to chemisorb hydrogen, and were in fact found to do so. The differences between Group A and Group B metals may be that the latter possess too few available

246

orbitals to enter into atomic nitrogen chemisorption, all being in Group VIII of the Periodic Table.

It should be noted that as a result of desorption studies, EHRLICH[63] claims that the weak chemisorption of nitrogen on tungsten filaments contains two types of adsorbed gas, one adsorbed with a heat of 9 kcal/mole, the other with a heat of 20 kcal/mole, as mentioned in Chapter IV.

AMMONIA LAYERS

With ammonia, adsorption involves dissociation of hydrogen, the extent of which increases with rising temperature. At very high temperatures, many metals decompose ammonia to nitrogen and hydrogen, and this suggests that the ammonia molecule is completely dissociated in chemisorption. Confirmatory evidence that nitrogen atoms are present on the surface is that on tungsten[64], ammonia decomposition and the nitrogen exchange reaction

$$^{14}N_2 + {}^{15}N_2 \rightarrow 2\,{}^{14}N^{15}N$$

both commence at similar temperatures.

At room temperatures, WAHBA and KEMBALL[65] have studied ammonia chemisorption on tungsten, iron and nickel films. The following two results are important.

(a) With nickel and iron, the ammonia chemisorption at room temperatures and low pressures on a given film area is roughly equal to the hydrogen chemisorption. Under these conditions the surfaces will not have been completely covered, but the $\theta$ values for both gases will have been high, and not greatly different from one another: since the hydrogen molecule covers two sites in chemisorption, the ammonia molecule must cover roughly two sites also.

(b) With tungsten and iron, when more than a certain quantity of ammonia has been admitted, hydrogen appears in the gas phase. Some hydrogen is liberated in the absence of excess ammonia in the gas phase, but the extent and velocity of hydrogen evolution is increased if ammonia is present. The volume of hydrogen liberated after exposure to 0·1 mm pressure of ammonia for 24 hours is about 1·5 times the initial ammonia chemisorption. With nickel there is almost no liberation of hydrogen.

The most reasonable explanation of these results is that with these metals there is an initial two site chemisorption, according to the equation

$$2M + NH_3 \rightarrow MNH_2 + MH$$

247

When this layer is exposed to excess ammonia, there will be a tendency for the chemisorbed hydrogen to be displaced by amine radicals, provided the heat of ammonia chemisorption somewhat exceeds the heat of hydrogen chemisorption. With tungsten and iron this state of affairs holds, but with nickel it does not, and so very little hydrogen is liberated. The mechanism of displacement is probably through desorption of hydrogen

$$2MH \rightarrow 2M + H_2$$

followed by ammonia chemisorption on the resulting vacant sites. The overall equation for displacement is then

$$MH + NH_3 \rightarrow MNH_2 + H_2$$

If chemisorption as amine and displacement of hydrogen were the only processes, the volume of hydrogen liberated would be equal to the initial ammonia chemisorption. However, with both iron and tungsten the volume approaches $1 \cdot 5$ times the ammonia chemisorption, and the most likely reason for this is a further slow breakdown of amine radicals to imine radicals, or possibly to nitrogen. The fact that some hydrogen is slowly liberated in the absence of gaseous ammonia offers some support for this idea.

PARAFFIN LAYERS

(1) Methane

Methane is chemisorbed to some extent by most transition metals at room temperature[24], and by Fe, Co and Ni at temperatures of $100\,°C$ and above[26]. In each case there is a progressive dissociation of hydrogen, which increases both with time and with rising temperature.

Thus, WRIGHT, ASHMORE and KEMBALL[26] have analysed the amounts of hydrogen and methane above evaporated films of W, Fe and Ni to which methane has been admitted. From their results they calculate the amount of methane adsorbed, and then the overall composition of the adsorbed layer. That is, representing adsorption as

$$CH_{4(gas)} \rightarrow (CH_n)_{(ads)} + \tfrac{1}{2}(4 - n)H_{2(gas)}$$

the experiments enable the quantity $n$ to be determined. It is, however, important to realise that as some chemisorbed hydrogen may be present on the surface as such, the method only gives an upper limit for the number of hydrogen atoms attached to each hydrocarbon radical. In order to obtain the actual composition of the radicals it would be necessary to obtain the extent of chemisorbed hydrogen, and while this could in theory be done by exchange with a large excess of deuterium at low temperatures and measurement of the liberated HD, the quantities involved with films are too small for this to be possible. Nevertheless, overall compositions are of interest and *Figure 85* shows the result of a typical run on Ni films at 156 °C. The value of $n$ is seen to fall from an initial value of 4 to about 2·3 after 3 hours. In another run at 200 °C, $n$ fell to 1·0 after 3 hours. Similarly on W after 3 hours, $n$ fell to 3·15 at 76 °C and to 2·2 at 98 °C. On Fe at 211 °C, $n$ fell to about 2 after 3 hours.

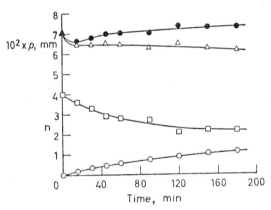

*Figure 85. Decomposition of $CH_4$ on 20·8 mg nickel at 156° C; total pressure* ●
$p_{CH_4}$ △, $p_{H_2}$ ○, n□
By courtesy of Wright, P. G., Ashmore, P. G. and Kemball, C. *Trans. Faraday Soc.* **54**, 1692, 1958

## (2) Ethane

With all hydrocarbons other than methane the most important question to be decided is whether in chemisorption C—C bonds or C—H bonds break. With ethane and propane there is good evidence that the primary process is breakage of C—H bonds. Thus early work by MORIKAWA et al.[66, 67] compared the rate of deuterium exchange with the rate of cracking by hydrogen. With ethane the equations are

$$C_2H_6 + D_2 \rightarrow C_2H_5D + HD$$

$$C_2H_6 + H_2 \rightarrow 2CH_4.$$

In the former, chemisorption with breaking of a C—H bond necessary: in the latter C—C bonds must eventually be broken. On nickel, exchange proceeded at far lower temperatures than cracking, and with a lower activation energy. Furthermore later work on the kinetics of cracking, by KEMBALL and TAYLOR[68], showed that even in this reaction the first step is dissociation of hydrogen from the ethane molecule. Again, magnetic evidence due to SELWOOD[11], which suggests that between 4 and 6 bonds are formed on chemisorption of an ethane molecule on nickel, can only be explained in terms of dissociation.

TRAPNELL[24] showed that dissociation of ethane occurred on Rh and W films because of the presence of hydrogen in the gas phase. Representing the overall composition of the surface layer as $C_2H_n$ he obtained values for $n$ after 30 minutes at 70°C of 4·8 on W and 3·9 on Rh. More detailed work on W, Fe and Ni by WRIGHT, ASHMORE and KEMBALL[26] using the same technique gave results such as those shown in *Figure 86*, indicating that, as with methane, there is increasing dissociation of hydrogen with increasing time. After 3 hours at 90°C, ethane layers on W films show considerable dissociation of hydrogen, with overall compositions in the neighbourhood of $C_2H_2$.

In the case of nickel, infrared spectra[51] confirm these conclusions.

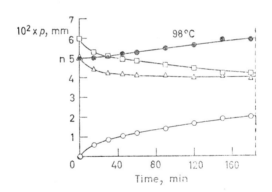

*Figure 86. Decomposition of $C_2H_6$ on 31·3 mg nickel at 98° C; total pressure ●, $p_{C_2H_6}$ △, $p_{H_2}$ ○, n □*

By courtesy of Wright, P. G., Ashmore, P. G. and Kemball, C. *Trans. Faraday Soc.* **54**, 1692, 1958

### (3) Other paraffins

In the case of some higher paraffins, namely *n*-pentane, isopentane, cyclohexane, and 2:3-dimethylbutane, GALWEY and KEMBALL[69] have obtained the actual number of hydrogen atoms dissociated during chemisorption on supported nickel by admitting sufficiently small quantities of adsorbate for them to be quantitatively adsorbed, and then obtaining the extent of chemisorbed hydrogen by low temperature exchange with excess deuterium. Once again, as the temperature was raised hydrogen dissociated increasingly, but a ceiling was in each case reached in the sense that further raising of the temperature did not cause increased dissociation. Results for cyclohexane are shown in *Figure 87*, indicating a maximum dissociation of 4 hydrogen atoms. Magnetic studies[70] again confirm this result. The most reasonable model for these adsorbed species is the boat form of the molecule in which the four valencies directed below the plane of the ring are bonded to the surface.

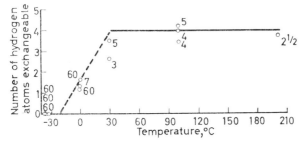

*Figure 87. Number of hydrogen atoms initially exchangeable with deuterium from cyclohexane adsorbed at 0° C on nickel and held at various temperatures. Numbers on the graph refer to the time in minutes for which the sample was held at the temperature concerned*

By courtesy of Galwey, A. K. and Kemball, C. *Trans. Faraday Soc.* **55,** 1959, 1959

Similarly, with *n*-pentane up to 5 hydrogen atoms could be dissociated, probably one hydrogen atom from each carbon atom, while with isopentane and 2:3-dimethylbutane the maximum numbers were respectively 5 and 4 hydrogen atoms.

ETHYLENE LAYERS

The first work to bear on the question of ethylene chemisorption is that of TWIGG and RIDEAL[71] who claimed that their results on ethylene hydrogenation at nickel surfaces could best be explained if a C—C bond broke in chemisorption, giving a complex bound by two point attachment.

$$CH_2=CH_2 \qquad\qquad CH_2—CH_2$$
$$\rightarrow$$
$$Ni————Ni \qquad\qquad Ni————Ni$$

Subsequent work by CONN and TWIGG[72] seemed to confirm the result.

The plausibility of such a mechanism depends on the distance between the two metal atoms being suitable. TWIGG and RIDEAL[73] were able to show that favourable spacings were available both on nickel, and on all other metals active in catalysing ethylene hydrogenation.

Magnetic work by SELWOOD[11] on nickel powders confirms that a two-bond chemisorption is taking place at room temperatures. While this mechanism may apply on powders, work by BEECK and his collaborators[74] using nickel films suggests that over the main surface chemisorption of ethylene involves breakage of C—H rather than C—C bonds. The result which leads to this conclusion is that when excess ethylene is admitted to a nickel film at room temperatures ethane appears in the gas phase. This can be explained if ethylene dissociates hydrogen, which is chemisorbed and reacts with further ethylene to produce ethane.

$$2NiH + C_2H_4 \rightarrow 2Ni + C_2H_6$$

According to this equation, vacant sites are produced in self-hydrogenation, on which further adsorption should be possible. This in fact occurs on both nickel[29] and tungsten[75]. Beeck found that, with nickel, $7.5 \times 10^{18}$ molecules of ethylene were adsorbed during self-hydrogenation on a 100 mg film, compared with $5.0 \times 10^{18}$ molecules taken up in the initial chemisorption. The latter figure, being about one half the hydrogen chemisorption on a clean film, suggests that the initial chemisorption takes place by a four site mechanism. Again, ethylene was shown to be capable of reacting with a chemisorbed layer of hydrogen with great speed to produce ethane, as the mechanism requires.

As a result of these observations Beeck[74] suggested that the initial chemisorption is a dissociation to an acetylenic complex covering two sites, and two hydrogen atoms.

$$4Ni + C_2H_4 \rightarrow 2NiH + Ni_2C_2H_2$$

The overall process of chemisorption and self-hydrogenation combined, is then represented by the equation

$$2Ni + 2C_2H_4 \rightarrow Ni_2C_2H_2 + C_2H_6.$$

These equations indicate an initial four site chemisorption, and a final two site chemisorption, and are in fair agreement with the experimental results.

Ethylene chemisorption on tungsten films has been studied by TRAPNELL[75]. The initial chemisorption is again a four site process, and the final adsorption after self-hydrogenation a two site process. Also, the equation for self-hydrogenation, obtained by combining the previous equations, is

$$2WH + 3C_2H_4 \rightarrow W_2C_2H_2 + 2C_2H_6$$

This indicates that during self-hydrogenation, one-third of the admitted molecules should be adsorbed, and was found to be closely obeyed.

The course of self-hydrogenation on nickel was later followed by JENKINS and RIDEAL[76] who found that 40 per cent rather than one-third of the admitted molecules were adsorbed. The result fits a rather more complex equation[51] in which some ethylene is adsorbed as such, and some as acetylenic complexes.

$$10NiH + 10C_2H_4 \rightarrow 3Ni_2C_2H_4 + Ni_4C_2H_2 + 6C_2H_6$$

This equation may well represent the reaction on nickel more closely than the previous equation, for when ethylene is allowed to interact with hydrogen layers on nickel the infrared spectrum[51, 77] indicates the presence of ethylene adsorbed as such, as well as some which is dissociatively adsorbed.

Infrared spectra give certain other interesting results. Thus, the intensity of C—H bands on admitting ethylene to a bare nickel surface is rather less than when it is admitted to a hydrogen-covered surface. Furthermore, when hydrogen is admitted to an ethylene layer on clean nickel the intensity of the C—H bands increases. These results were believed to confirm that ethylene chemisorption on the bare surfaces is mainly dissociative, with a low ratio of hydrogen to carbon atoms in the hydrocarbon radicals, but that this ratio increases on admitting hydrogen. The spectra in fact suggest that the ratio is rather variable, and depends on temperature and catalyst activity as well as on hydrogen pressure. Thus, to speak simply of acetylenic complexes may be too simple. Also, even when the surface layer consists mainly of radicals with low hydrogen-to-carbon ratio, the position of the C—H bands is such that the radicals must be mainly paraffinic rather than olefinic. That is, the structure of a $C_2H_2$ complex should probably be represented as

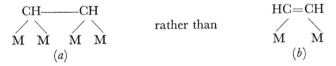

(a)   rather than   (b)

253

although a second possibility is that complexes of type $(b)$ are initially formed, but tend to polymerize, thereby reducing the number of olefinic groups.

The idea that the nature of the radicals formed during ethylene chemisorption varies with the activity of the metal sample may well explain why Selwood's nickel powder gave a non-dissociative, two bond adsorption at room temperatures, whereas on films there is a dissociative chemisorption under the same conditions.

### ACETYLENE LAYERS

The interaction of acetylene with nickel supported on kieselguhr has been studied by DOUGLAS and RABINOVITCH[78], who observed self-hydrogenation to ethylene. By analogy with the case of ethylene chemisorption, this suggests that acetylene also dissociates hydrogen. However, some hydrogen was initially present on the catalyst surface, having remained after a reduction treatment, and the ethylene might have been formed by interaction of gaseous acetylene with this hydrogen.

Attempts to overcome the difficulty were made by interacting $C_2D_2$ with the catalyst. This gave a mixture of $C_2H_2$, $C_2HD$, $C_2D_4$, $C_2HD_3$ and $C_2H_2D_2$. The main ethylene constituent was $C_2D_4$, and this was cited as proof of true self-hydrogenation.

Infrared spectra of acetylene layers have been obtained by EISCHENS and PLISKIN[51], who confirm these conclusions. Thus ethyl radicals may be observed either after adsorption of acetylene on bare nickel, or after interaction of acetylene with chemisorbed hydrogen. This again suggests an initial dissociative chemisorption followed by self-hydrogenation. However, the extent of the latter seems rather larger in the experiments of Eischens and Pliskin than in those of Douglas and Rabinovitch.

## REFERENCES

[1] Mott, N. F. and Jones, H. *The Theory of the Properties of Metals and Alloys.* London; Oxford University Press, 1936
[2] Pauling, L. *J. Amer. Chem. Soc.* **69**, 542, 1947
[3] Pauling, L. *Proc. Roy. Soc.* A**196**, 343, 1949
[4] Tamm, I. *Z. Phys. (U.S.R.R.)* **1**, 733, 1932
[5] Eberhagen, A. *Fortschr. Phys.* **8**, 245, 1960
[6] Culver, R. V. and Tompkins, F. C. *Adv. in Catalysis* **11**, 67, 1959
[7] Gundry, P. M. and Tompkins, F. C. *Quart. Rev.* **14**, 257, 1960
[8] Dilke, M. H., Maxted, E. D. and Eley, D. D. *Nature, Lond.* **161**, 804, 1948
[9] Moore, L. E. and Selwood, P. W. *J. Amer. Chem. Soc.* **78**, 697, 1956
[10] Dietz, R. E. and Selwood, P. W. *J. Chem. Phys.* **35**, 270, 1961

[11] Selwood, P. W. *J. Amer. Chem. Soc.* **79**, 3346, 1957

[12] Broeder, J. J., van Reijen, L. L., Sachtler, W. M. H. and Schmit, G. C. A. *Z. Elektrochem.* **60**, 838, 1956

[13] Suhrmann, R. and Schulz, K. *Z. phys. Chem. (Frankfurt)* **1**, 69, 1954

[14] Sachtler, W. M. H. *J. Chem. Phys.* **25**, 751, 1956

[15] Zwietering, P., Koks, H. L. T. and van Heerden, C. *J. Phys. Chem. Solids* **11**, 18, 1959

[16] Trapnell, B. M. W. *Proc. Roy. Soc.* A**218**, 566, 1953

[17] Culver, R. V., Pritchard, J. and Tompkins, F. C. *Proc. 2nd Int. Congr. Surface Activity* (ed. J. H. Schulman). London; Butterworths, vol. 2, p. 243, 1957

[18] Manning, M. F. and Krutter, H. M. *Phys. Rev.* **51**, 761, 1937

[19] Brennan, D., Hayward, D. O. and Trapnell, B. M. W. *Proc. Roy. Soc.* A**256**, 81, 1960

[20] Eischens, R. P., Pliskin, W. A. and Francis, S. A. *J. Chem. Phys.* **22**, 1786, 1954

[21] Goos, F. *Z. Phys.* **100**, 95, 1936

[22] Krutter, H. M. *Phys. Rev.* **48**, 664, 1935

[23] Meier, W. *Ann. Phys. Lpz.* **31**, 1017, 1910

[24] Trapnell, B. M. W. *Trans. Faraday Soc.* **52**, 1618, 1956

[25] Collins, A. C. and Trapnell, B. M. W. *Trans. Faraday Soc.* **53**, 1476, 1957

[26] Wright, P. G., Ashmore, P. G. and Kemball, C. *Trans. Faraday Soc.* **54**, 1692, 1958

[27] Herley, P. and Tompkins, F. C.—Private communication

[28] Hickmott, T. W. and Ehrlich, G. *J. Phys. Chem. Solids* **5**, 47, 1958

[29] Beeck, O. *Disc. Faraday Soc.* **8**, 118, 1950

[30] Pritchard, J. and Tompkins, F. C. *Trans. Faraday Soc.* **56**, 540, 1960

[31] Hayes, F. *Ph.D. Thesis.* Liverpool University, 1962

[32] Maxted, E. B. *Adv. in Catalysis* **3**, 129, 1951

[33] Bosworth, R. C. L. and Rideal, E. K. *Proc. Roy. Soc.* A**162**, 1, 1937

[34] Bosworth, R. C. L. *Proc. Roy. Soc.* A**154**, 112, 1936

[35] Taylor, J. B. and Langmuir, I. *Phys. Rev.* **44**, 423, 1933

[36] Langmuir, I. *J. Chem. Soc.* 511, 1940

[37] Roberts, J. K. *Proc. Roy. Soc.* A**152**, 445, 1935

[38] Beeck, O. and Ritchie, A. W. *Disc. Faraday Soc.* **8**, 159, 1950

[39] Brunauer, S., Emmett, P. H. and Teller, E. *J. Amer. Chem. Soc.* **60**, 309, 1938

[40] Mignolet, J. C. P. *Disc. Faraday Soc.* **8**, 105, 1950

[41] Mignolet, J. C. P. *J. Chem. Phys.* **20**, 341, 1952

[42] Mignolet, J. C. P. *J. chim. phys.* **54**, 19, 1957

[43] Pliskin, W. A. and Eischens, R. P. *Z. phys. Chem. (Frankfurt)* **24**, 11, 1960

[44] Hickmott, T. W. *J. Chem. Phys.* **32**, 810, 1960

[45] Hickmott, T. W. and Ehrlich, G. *J. Chem. Phys.* **24**, 1263, 1956

[46] Morrison, J. L. and Roberts, J. K. *Proc. Roy. Soc.* A**173**, 1, 1939

[47] Brunauer, S. and Emmett, P. H. *J. Amer. Chem. Soc.* **62**, 1732, 1940

[48] Beeck, O., Smith, A. E. and Wheeler, A. *Proc. Roy. Soc.* A**177**, 62, 1940

[49] Lanyon, M. A. H. and Trapnell, B. M. W. *Proc. Roy. Soc.* A**227**, 387, 1955
[50] Eischens, R. P., Francis, S. A. and Pliskin, W. A. *J. Phys. Chem.* **60**, 194, 1956
[51] Eischens, R. P. and Pliskin, W. A. *Adv. in Catalysis* **10**, 1, 1958
[52] Yang, A. C. and Garland, C. W. *J. Phys. Chem.* **61**, 1504, 1957
[53] Hayward, D. O.—Unpublished results
[54] Ehrlich, G. *J. Chem. Phys.* **34**, 39, 1961
[55] Redhead, P. A. *Trans. Faraday Soc.* **57**, 641, 1961
[56] Webb, A. N. and Eischens, R. P. *J. Amer. Chem. Soc.* **77**, 4710, 1955
[57] Brennan, D., Greenhalgh, E. and Trapnell, B. M. W.—Unpublished experiments
[58] Brennan, D., Hayes, F. and Hayward, D. O.—Unpublished experiments
[59] Hayward, D. O. and Gomer, R. *J. Chem. Phys.* **30**, 1617, 1959
[60] Eischens, R. P. and Pliskin, W. A. *Adv. in Catalysis* **9**, 662, 1957
[61] Beeck, O. *Adv. in Catalysis* **2**, 151, 1950; Bagg, J. and Tompkins, F. C. *Trans. Faraday Soc.* **51**, 1071, 1955
[62] Greenhalgh, E., Slack, N. and Trapnell, B. M. W. *Trans. Faraday Soc.* **52**, 865, 1956
[63] Ehrlich, G. *J. Chem. Phys.* **34**, 29, 1961
[64] Joris, G. G. and Taylor, H. S. *J. Chem. Phys.* **7**, 893, 1939
[65] Wahba, M. and Kemball, C. *Trans. Faraday Soc.* **49**, 1351, 1953
[66] Morikawa, K., Benedict, W. S. and Taylor, H. S. *J. Amer. Chem. Soc.* **58**, 1795, 1936
[67] Morikawa, K., Trenner, N. R. and Taylor, H. S. *J. Amer. Chem. Soc.* **59**, 1103, 1937
[68] Kemball, C. and Taylor, H. S. *J. Amer. Chem. Soc.* **70**, 345, 1948
[69] Galwey, A. K. and Kemball, C. *Trans. Faraday Soc.* **55**, 1959, 1959
[70] Selwood, P. W. *J. Amer. Chem. Soc.* **79**, 4637, 1957
[71] Twigg, G. H. and Rideal, E. K. *Proc. Roy. Soc.* A**171**, 55, 1939
[72] Conn, G. K. T. and Twigg, G. H. *Proc. Roy. Soc.* A**171**, 70, 1939
[73] Twigg, G. H. and Rideal, E. K. *Trans. Faraday Soc.* **36**, 533, 1940
[74] Beeck, O. *Rev. Mod. Phys.* **17**, 61, 1945
[75] Trapnell, B. M. W. *Trans. Faraday Soc.* **48**, 160, 1952
[76] Jenkins, G. I. and Rideal, E. K. *J. Chem. Soc.* 2490, 2496, 1955
[77] Pliskin, W. A. and Eischens, R. P. *J. Chem. Phys.* **24**, 482, 1956
[78] Douglas, J. E. and Rabinovitch, B. S. *J. Amer. Chem. Soc.* **74**, 2486, 1952

# VIII

# MECHANISMS OF CHEMISORPTION ON SEMICONDUCTORS

## THE SURFACE BOND

In dealing with oxides, two types of adsorption centre are immediately apparent, namely the metal and oxygen ions, and it is tempting to suggest that each may be active in chemisorption. To some extent this proves to be the case.

Oxygen ions can, for example, combine with certain gases to form new ions, the simplest example being the chemisorption of carbon dioxide as carbonate[1].

$$CO_2 + O^{2-} \rightarrow CO_3^{2-} \qquad (8.1)$$

Similarly water is probably chemisorbed as hydroxide, while $SO_2$ could be chemisorbed as sulphite. Again CO can, under certain circumstances, undergo isotopic oxygen exchange with oxide surfaces[2], suggesting a combination with oxygen ions.

Since metals usually enter into chemisorption by using their $d$-electrons, one might expect the metal ions of an oxide to be similarly active. There is very little direct evidence for such chemisorption, although it is worth noting that the activity of transition metal oxides of the first transition period in $H_2/D_2$ exchange appears to be determined by the metal ion configuration[3]. This suggests a metal ion to hydrogen bond involving $d$-electrons.

Such a picture accounts for one very important feature of chemisorption on oxides, namely that a gas is often adsorbed by more than one mechanism. Frequently, a rapid, relatively weak chemisorption occurs at low temperatures, and a slow strong chemisorption at high temperatures. Similar behaviour is occasionally found with the metals. Examples in the case of the oxides are the adsorption of $O_2$ and $H_2$ on $ZnO$[4, 5] and $Cr_2O_3$[6, 7], and of CO on $Cu_2O$[8]. The two types of adsorption have been distinguished by calorimetric determinations of heats, by measurements of the velocities of adsorption and desorption, and by derivation of adsorption isobars.

However this picture of chemisorption on oxides proves far too simple. For one thing it neglects the electronic structure of the oxides, consideration of which shows that other mechanisms of adsorption are possible using different electrons from those so far considered. Again, our picture is incapable of explaining many basic facts of oxide chemisorption and catalysis. Why is it, for example, that nickel oxide will adsorb appreciable quantities of oxygen but very little hydrogen, whereas with zinc oxide the reverse is true[9], or that in the decomposition of $N_2O$ cuprous oxide is extremely active, alumina moderately active, and ferric oxide almost inactive[10]? In order to answer these and other questions we must consider how electrons in oxides are arranged.

## THE ELECTRONIC STRUCTURE OF OXIDES

### (1) Lattice defects in oxides

Very few oxides are stoichiometric. A stoichiometric oxide should normally be an insulator, as no electrons are available to carry current, but in fact most oxides are at least semi-conducting and a few, such as zinc oxide, can show conductivity approaching that of the metals.

Zinc oxide, in fact, contains an excess of zinc metal. In cases where the excess is fairly considerable a film of metallic zinc is formed on the walls of the containing vessel when the oxide is heated in vacuo. Such a metal-excess semiconductor is called n-type.

On the other hand, nickel oxide, when prepared at temperatures below 500 °C, is black, and contains a slight excess of oxygen. This type of oxide is called a p-type oxide.

Deviations from stoichiometry are accommodated in an oxide lattice by various types of defect. In the case of an oxygen-rich oxide, such as nickel oxide, one simple possibility is that some nickel-ion sites are unoccupied. While this is in fact the case, it would in itself leave the specimen negatively charged. This is only prevented by two nearby cations existing in the tervalent state as $Ni^{3+}$, for every $Ni^{2+}$ which is missing. These units are called positive holes, and conduction occurs by transfer of electrons between $Ni^{2+}$ and $Ni^{3+}$ ions: when an electron moves from the former to the latter in order to carry current the two entities are interchanged.

A second possibility whereby excess oxygen can be accommodated is by some oxygen ions being present interstitially in the lattice, though once again this must be associated with an appropriate number of cations in a higher valence state. While being rarer than the first type of defect, interstitial oxygen ions are present in a few oxides, notably $UO_2$.

With a metal-excess semiconductor such as ZnO, one possibility is that certain of the oxygen ion sites are unoccupied. To preserve neutrality two electrons would have to be present in the lattice for every oxygen vacancy, and these would permit a measure of conductivity. This type of defect does not in fact occur in ZnO but may be present in $CeO_2$ and $ThO_2$. In ZnO the excess zinc is present as interstitial metal atoms. In the oxide medium these atoms can ionize very readily—the ionization energy for removal of the first electron is only $0.04eV$ and as a result the equilibrium

$$Zn_{(i)} \leftrightharpoons Zn_{(i)}^{+} + e \qquad (8.2)$$

where the subscript $i$ represents an atom or ion held interstitially, permits appreciable liberation of electrons, and hence appreciable conductivity.

### (2) The band structure of oxides

When atoms come together to form a crystal, a broadening of energy levels into bands tends to occur. For the crystal to conduct there must in general be at least one partly filled band, so that electronic transfers between filled and empty states is a possibility. The only other mechanism, which is rare, is for the top of a completely filled band to be so near the bottom of an empty band that thermal promotion can take place.

In the oxides, the metal ions form the deeper energy states, and the wavefunctions of neighbouring metal ions do not overlap. As a result banding of metal ion states proves to be inappreciable, and we only have to concern ourselves with the oxygen anion bands. With an isolated $O^{2-}$ ion, the $2s$ and $2p$ states are filled, and consequently in an oxide crystal the $sp$ band should be filled, and separated by some distance from the empty $sp$ band formed from the $3s$ and $3p$ states. In the stoichiometric oxides this is the case, and virtually no conduction is observed. However, in non-stoichiometric oxides this is not so. Thus, in the case of zinc oxide, while the electrons liberated from the interstitial zinc atoms cannot enter the full $sp$ band of the oxygen ions they can enter the empty band, partly filling it and creating the conditions for conductivity. That is to say, conductivity arises from the donor zinc atoms transferring electrons from their donor levels to the so-called conduction band. This is shown in *Figure 88*. Precisely similar conditions apply when the metal excess arises from anion vacancies with electrons present in the lattice—a donor condition yielding electrons is essentially present.

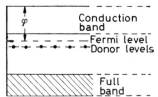

*Figure 88. Arrangement of electrons in a metal-excess (n-type) semi-conductor*

When oxygen is in excess the reverse applies, in that acceptor states are present. In the case of nickel oxide the rather unstable $Ni^{3+}$ ions act as acceptors according to the equation

$$Ni^{3+} + e \rightarrow Ni^{2+} \tag{8.3}$$

That is, electrons are abstracted from the full band, partly emptying it and therefore giving the conditions for conductivity. The state of affairs is shown in *Figure 89*. Precisely similar effects apply when there are interstitial anions.

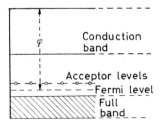

*Figure 89. Arrangement of electrons in an oxygen-excess (p-type) semi-conductor*

In the case of $n$-type oxides the conductivity is decided by the number of electrons in the conduction band: in the case of $p$-type oxides by the number of holes in the full band.

## THE BOUNDARY-LAYER THEORY—QUALITATIVE TREATMENT

Of all the electrons in an oxide crystal, those in the bands which we have been considering happen to have the highest energy. They are therefore likely to be used in chemisorption. Some important qualitative results immediately arise from this principle. Now, oxygen tends to be adsorbed as negative ions, either $O^-$ or $O^{2-}$. As an example we may consider adsorption as $O^{2-}$.

$$\tfrac{1}{2}O_2 + 2e \rightarrow O^{2-} \tag{8.4}$$

With zinc oxide the electrons for negative ion formation must come from the partly full conduction band. However, few electrons are present in this band, and if appreciable adsorption is to take place, levels deep in the crystal will have to be employed. Such a process of abstraction in depth will set up a potential barrier as it proceeds, and quite soon we should expect adsorption to cease. That is, only a small fraction of a monolayer should be formed. Also, the reduction in the number of conduction electrons due to adsorption should reduce the conductivity of the sample. Both of these results are found in practice[9]. This kind of chemisorption, causing a reduction in the number of charge carriers, is referred to as depletive chemisorption.

On the other hand in oxygen adsorption on nickel oxide or cuprous oxide, both of which are $p$-type, there is no such limitation. There are sufficient electrons available in the almost full band for a monolayer to be formed by using electrons from levels very near the surface. Again, chemisorption provides extra holes, and the conductivity should increase as adsorption proceeds. Both of these results occur in practice[8, 11, 12]. Such chemisorption, causing an increase in the charge carrier, is referred to as cumulative chemisorption.

As an example of a chemisorption which, in contrast to oxygen chemisorption, causes electrons to be liberated, we may consider hydrogen adsorption as hydroxide

$$\tfrac{1}{2}H_2 + O^{2-} \rightarrow OH^- + e \tag{8.5}$$

On $n$-type oxides such as ZnO the electrons will enter the almost empty conduction band. There is no barrier to this so that a monolayer should be formed, while the increase in the number of charge carriers will cause the conductivity to increase. Both these results are found[13]. On $p$-type oxides, however, the electrons have to enter an almost full band: there are few vacancies, and for appreciable adsorption the electrons will have to enter levels deeper and deeper

261

S

in the crystal. The process again sets up a potential barrier which soon stops further adsorption, while the reduction in the number of charge-carrying holes causes the conductivity to fall. Once more depletive chemisorption is limited in extent, and only cumulative chemisorption can proceed to a monolayer.

### THE BOUNDARY-LAYER THEORY—QUANTITATIVE TREATMENT

Depletive chemisorption may be treated quantitatively[9, 14, 15, 16], using an approach almost identical with that used in considering the rectifying contact between a metal and a semiconductor. In both cases a charge transfer is taking place across an interface until the potential energy of the electrons in the semiconductor is equal to the potential energy on the other side of the interface.

We use oxygen chemisorption on zinc oxide as an example. Considering adsorption as $O^-$, the energy of chemisorption for the first atom adsorbed will be

$$(a - \phi)e + K$$

where $a$ is the electron affinity of the atom, $\phi$ is the work function of the oxide (i.e. the distance of the Fermi level below the zero of energy) and $K$ is the interaction energy of the ion $O^-$ with the surface. As adsorption proceeds a potential barrier $V$ builds up. The Fermi level falls by this amount, the work function increasing to $\phi + V$. Eventually when $V$ as a value $V_f$ a state is reached such that the energy of chemisorption $(a - \phi - V_f)e + K$ is zero, and further chemisorption is precluded. In the adsorption of hydrogen on nickel oxide according to equation (8.5) electrons are entering the oxide causing the work function to fall. Here the initial heat of chemisorption is $(\phi - I)e + K$, where $I$ is the ionization potential, and chemisorption proceeds until $(\phi - I - V_f) + K$ is zero.

At this stage let the number of adsorbed ions be $N_f$, and the thickness of the boundary layer from which electrons have been abstracted (ZnO case) or into which they have been inserted (NiO case) be $l$. We assume that the charge density in the boundary layer, $\rho$, is constant, because every defect has yielded its electron (ZnO) or been filled (NiO). Thus, if $n_0$ is the concentration of defects

$$\rho = e n_0 \qquad (8.6)$$

Applying Poisson's equation

$$\frac{d^2V}{dx^2} = \frac{4\pi\rho}{\kappa} \qquad (8.7)$$

262

where $x$ is the distance into the boundary layer and $\kappa$ is the dielectric constant, and integrating between $x=0$ and $x=l$, we obtain

$$V_f = \frac{2\pi\rho}{\kappa} \cdot l^2 \tag{8.8}$$

Substituting for $\rho$ we find

$$V_f = \frac{2\pi e n_0 l^2}{\kappa} \tag{8.9}$$

Since the total charge in the boundary layer is equal to that in the chemisorbed layer

$$N_f = n_0 l \tag{8.10}$$

and substituting for $l$ in (8.9) we obtain

$$V_f = \frac{2\pi e N_f^2}{n_0 \kappa} \tag{8.11}$$

or

$$N_f = \sqrt{\left(\frac{n_0 \kappa V_f}{2\pi e}\right)} \tag{8.12}$$

Assuming $V_f$ is about 1 volt, $\kappa \sim 10$ and $n_0 \sim 10^{18}$ per cc,

$$N_f \sim 2 \cdot 5 \times 10^{12} \text{ per sq. cm.}$$

The number of surface sites on an oxide is of the order of $10^{15}$ per sq. cm, and therefore coverages between 1 per cent and 0·1 per cent only are predicted. If the surface has a high roughness factor, the values might be further reduced by a factor of 10 or more. These results are in accordance with experiment. For example, in the chemisorption of $H_2$ on $Cu_2O$, or of $CO$ on $NiO$, while there are detectable reductions in conductivity, such small amounts are adsorbed that the coverage cannot be determined[9]. Similar effects usually apply in the chemisorption of $O_2$ on $ZnO$, although in one case where the concentration of interstitial zinc was unusually high, coverages up to 16 per cent were observed[4].

The theory has also been extended to the variation of heat of chemisorption with coverage in cases of depletive chemisorption. The relation is of the form

$$q = a - b\theta^2 \tag{8.13}$$

where $a$ and $b$ are constants. Owing to the difficulty of determining $\theta$ the relationship has not so far been confirmed.

The theory has achieved the following successes.

(*1*) It has suggested that chemisorption will, in many cases, involve the defects of the oxide, so that changes of semi-conductivity in a predictable direction will accompany adsorption. This often proves to be so.

(*2*) The theory shows that depletive chemisorption will be limited in extent, whereas cumulative chemisorption can proceed virtually to a monolayer. This is generally the case.

(*3*) As an extension of the last point one would expect marked differences between $p$-type and $n$-type oxides towards a particular catalytic reaction, with insulators occupying an intermediate position. For example, in the decomposition of $N_2O$, where adsorbed oxygen ions are formed on the surface, $n$-type oxides would be expected to show relatively little activity because they can only adsorb oxygen to a limited extent, whereas $p$-type oxides should be very active. This proves to be so, and it is possible[10] to arrange the oxides according to their activity in this reaction in the order

$$p\text{-type oxides}>\text{insulators}>n\text{-type oxides}.$$

In the case of CO oxidation[9], $p$-type oxides are again most active, though $n$-type oxides appear to be more active than insulators.

(*4*) In the case of $H_2/D_2$ exchange on ZnO, the conductivity of the oxide may be systematically altered by incorporation of foreign ions in the lattice. If the conduction electrons are involved in chemisorption, changes in conductivity should cause changes in activity.

Thus if a cation of valency greater than 2, such as $Ga^{3+}$, is dissolved in ZnO and takes the place of a $Zn^{2+}$ ion, electrical neutrality must be maintained by an increased concentration of free electrons in the lattice, some $Zn_i^+$ ions disappearing at the same time. The conductivity should increase, which proves to be the case, and possibly the catalytic activity also, though why is not perhaps altogether clear. On the other hand incorporation of a monovalent ion such as $Li^+$ should have reverse effects. For $H_2/D_2$ exchange at 25°C and above MOLINARI and PARRAVANO[17] in fact obtained an activity order

$$ZnO + 1\% \ Li_2O < ZnO < ZnO + 1\% \ Ga_2O_3$$

Similar effects are observed in the case of the activity of doped nickel oxides towards CO oxidation[18], where the adsorption of oxygen as negative ions is important. When $Li^+$ ions are incorporated in the lattice, extra $Ni^{2+}$ ions must be oxidized to the $Ni^{3+}$ state to maintain neutrality. However, these acceptors are, as it were, competing with the adsorbed oxygen for electrons, and the extra $Ni^{3+}$ ions produced by doping should therefore tend to decrease the activity. On the other hand a trivalent ion such as $Cr_2O_3$ should increase the activity. These ideas were confirmed experimentally, an order being obtained

$$NiO + 0.01\% \, Li_2O < NiO < NiO + 0.01\% \, Cr_2O_3$$

(5) A further consequence of the boundary-layer theory is that photoeffects might be expected in chemisorption. Photodesorption is not of great significance because the light may merely be activating the surface bond, but photoadsorption can be of interest. This has recently been observed by BARRY and STONE[4] in the adsorption of oxygen on a sample of ZnO with high interstitial zinc content. For such a sample, irradiation might be expected to produce an appreciable number of extra electrons from interstitial zinc atoms within the boundary layer, thereby assisting adsorption. In several cases irradiation increased the velocity of adsorption, while on one occasion irradiation at a temperature sufficiently high for desorption to be taking place caused this to cease and adsorption to commence instead.

In spite of the many successes of the boundary-layer theory there are a number of cases where it appears inapplicable. For example, it has already been mentioned that more than one mechanism of chemisorption can occur with a particular gas on a particular oxide. Sometimes different types of binding can be envisaged each of which may obey the boundary-layer theory, but not all examples of dual mechanism can be so explained. With the two mechanisms of oxygen chemisorption on ZnO the surface species being formed are probably $O^-$ and $O^{2-}$

$$\tfrac{1}{2}O_2 + e \rightarrow O^- \qquad\qquad (8.14)$$

$$\tfrac{1}{2}O_2 + 2e \rightarrow O^{2-} \qquad\qquad (8.15)$$

and in both cases conduction band electrons will be employed. However, the reactive chemisorption of $H_2$ on ZnO which is responsible for $H_2/D_2$ exchange at low temperatures does not change the semi-conductivity of the sample[13]. This immediately places the adsorption outside the confines of the theory. Only in the high temperature chemisorption at $100\,^\circ C$ or above does the expected increase in conductivity occur, due to surface hydroxide formation according to equation (8.5).

WOLKENSTEIN[19, 20] has suggested that in weak, low temperature chemisorption the defects in the oxide do not contribute to the surface bond and the adsorbed radical plus its adsorption centre remains electrically neutral. For the chemisorption of a particle C on the surface of an oxide, MO, he distinguishes the six types of

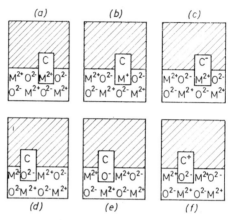

*Figure 90. Modes of chemisorption on an oxide*
By courtesy of Wolkenstein, Th. *Adv. in Catalysis* **12**, 189, 1960

chemisorption shown in *Figure 90*. Of these (*a*) and (*d*) represent weak adsorption on the $M^{2+}$ or $O^{2-}$ ions and do not involve defects. (*b*), (*c*), (*e*) and (*f*) Wolkenstein regards as strong chemisorptions—all involve interaction with defects and can therefore be treated using boundary-layer theory. Of these four types, (*b*) and (*c*) involve transfer of electrons to the surface layer, (*e*) and (*f*) transfer to the bulk of the oxide.

The idea that the reactive low temperature hydrogen chemisorption falls outside the boundary-layer theory receives further support from the work of DOWDEN, MACKENZIE and TRAPNELL[3], who found no correlation between the semi-conductivity of an oxide and its activity in $H_2/D_2$ exchange. Results for the oxides of the first transition series are shown in *Figure 91*, values of the rate constant, $k$, per unit surface area being plotted across the period. For a hydrogen-type reaction, the theory suggests that $n$-type oxides should be most active, and $p$-type oxides least active. In fact, among the three most active oxides, NiO and $Co_3O_4$ are $p$-type, while $Cr_2O_3$ is neither strongly $n$- or $p$-type. In the group of moderate activity the $k$ values for $Cu_2O$ ($p$-type) and ZnO ($n$-type) are indistinguishable. MnO and $Co_3O_4$ are both $p$-type but differ greatly in activity. The best correlation appears to be with position in the Periodic Table, the condition for high activity being the presence of a fair but not extensive number of unpaired $d$-electrons. High activity is associated with the structures $3d^3(Cr_2O_3)$, $3d^6$ or

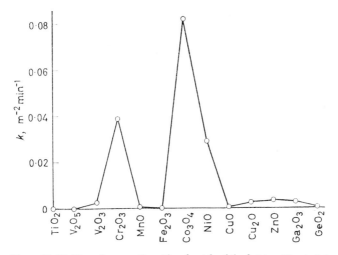

*Figure 91.* $H_2/D_2$ *exchange on the oxides of metals of the first transition period*
By courtesy of Dowden, D. A., Mackenzie, N. and Trapnell, B. M. W. *Proc. Roy. Soc.* **A237**, 245, 1956

$3d^7(Co_3O_4)$ and $3d^8(NiO)$. This, of course, implies a bonding to metal ions not dissimilar to hydrogen chemisorption on the metals. It was suggested that if there are very few unpaired $d$-electrons or none at all, ($TiO_2$, $V_2O_5$, $V_2O_3$, $CuO$) chemisorption is slow and catalysis poor on this account: if the $d$-shell is full ($Cu_2O$, $ZnO$, $Ga_2O_3$, $GeO_2$) chemisorption may likewise be inhibited: 5 unpaired $d$-electrons ($MnO$, $Fe_2O_3$) are known to form a stable arrangement, and slow chemisorption would result. Nevertheless the nature of the low temperature chemisorption of $H_2$ on ZnO remains a mystery, since the $d$-shell is full. If some $O^-$ ions are present in the surface, chemisorption as hydroxide is possible without a change in semi-conductivity

$$O^- + \tfrac{1}{2}H_2 \rightarrow OH^- \qquad (8.16)$$

but it is doubtful whether after baking ZnO in vacuo any $O^-$ ions remain on the surface—all oxygen should have been incorporated in the lattice.

Dowden *et al.* suggested that some of the defects in ZnO surfaces are anion, with electrons present to maintain neutrality, and that the reactive hydrogen chemisorption takes place on zinc ions near these.

$$
\begin{array}{ccc}
\overset{\displaystyle H}{\underset{\displaystyle Zn^{2+}}{|}} & \qquad & \overset{\displaystyle H}{\underset{\displaystyle Zn^{2+}}{|}} \\[2em]
& 2e & \\[1em]
\overset{\displaystyle H}{\underset{\displaystyle Zn^{2+}}{|}} & \qquad & \overset{\displaystyle H}{\underset{\displaystyle Zn^{2+}}{|}}
\end{array}
$$

Then if increase of conductivity by doping is partly due to an increase in anion vacancies, an increase in catalytic activity should result, in accordance with experiment.

Reactive hydrogen chemisorption has also been observed on $\gamma$-alumina[21], which has a very high activity in $H_2/D_2$ exchange, even at $-100\,°C$. This result is inexplicable in terms of simple boundary-layer theory, since the oxide is normally regarded as an insulator, and should therefore have only moderate activity in the reaction. Possibly the very attenuated lattice of $\gamma$-alumina means that many defects are available for low temperature chemisorption, but equally adsorption may be taking place on metal ions by a weak covalence—aluminium metal shows unexpectedly high surface activity for an $sp$ metal[22], possibly because the high density of occupied and unoccupied states is similar to that found in the active $d$ band of transition metals.

Some of the results obtained with elemental semiconductors, notably Ge and Si, are likewise not explicable in terms of boundary layer theory. BRENNAN, HAYWARD and TRAPNELL[23] have studied the properties of films of these elements, evaporated from $n$-type samples. In each case oxygen chemisorption caused a fall in conductivity, as expected, but with both elements virtually a monolayer was readily formed at room temperatures. Even at $-195\,°C$ half a monolayer was instantly adsorbed. Both these coverages are far higher than would be expected, and furthermore, in comparing their results on Si with those of EISINGER and LAW[24], who used $p$-type samples, Brennan *et al.* came to the conclusion that the characteristics of oxygen chemisorption on Si did not seem to depend on the semiconductor type. Again, hydrogen, which should be chemisorbed more easily than oxygen on $n$-type semiconductors is not chemisorbed at room temperatures with any ease on either $Ge^{25}$ or $Si.^{26}$

Finally the question of the mobility of defects requires brief discussion. As an example we may consider the adsorption of oxygen as negative ions on the surface of cuprous oxide. Chemically we may represent this adsorption by the equation

$$2Cu^+ + \tfrac{1}{2}O_2 \rightarrow 2Cu^{2+} + O^{2-} \qquad (8.17)$$

That is to say, positive holes are produced, and the conductivity of the $p$-type cuprous oxide should be enhanced. However, there will be a very strong coulombic attraction between the cupric ions and the adsorbed oxygen ions. Clearly the migration of holes into the lattice will take place with difficulty, and the change in conductivity due to adsorption may be reduced. At room temperatures this is in fact the case, and only after adsorption at $200\,°C$ are large changes observed[8].

## THE SURFACE RADICALS

### CARBON MONOXIDE LAYERS

Chemisorbed carbon monoxide is sometimes desorbed as such, but often it can only be desorbed as $CO_2$: the first type of chemisorption is termed reversible, and the second type irreversible.

On some oxides, only one type of adsorption has been observed, on others both. At room temperatures CO chemisorption is wholly reversible on $ZnO^{27}$; on $Cu_2O^8$, and on the mixed oxide $ZnO \cdot Cr_2O_3^{27}$, it is partly reversible and partly irreversible; on $Mn_2O_3 \cdot Cr_2O_3^{28}$, wholly irreversible.

In cases where both mechanisms can operate simultaneously, the proportion of reversible adsorption seems to be higher the lower the temperature. On $Cr_2O_3$, adsorption at room temperatures is largely irreversible[7], but at liquid air temperatures[6] it is probably mainly reversible. When $Cu_2O$ is covered with CO, Table 46 shows that an increasing fraction of gas is desorbed as $CO_2$ as the temperature is raised[29].

When two different types of chemisorption predominate in different temperature ranges, the low temperature adsorption is weak but rapid, and the high temperature adsorption strong but slow.

$CO_2$ can most reasonably be desorbed by decomposition of surface carbonate

$$CO_3^{2-} \rightarrow CO_2 + O^{2-} \qquad (8.18)$$

TABLE 46

Desorption of CO from $Cu_2O$

| Temp (°C) | % of total adsorbed gas desorbed as CO | % of total adsorbed gas desorbed as $CO_2$ |
|---|---|---|
| 20 | 30 | 0 |
| 20–100 | 20 | 25 |
| >100 | 0 | 25 |

Formation of such carbonate in irreversible CO chemisorption involves the formation of an anion vacancy containing two electrons according to the equation

$$CO + 2O^{2-} \rightarrow CO_3^{2-} + 2e \qquad (8.19)$$

If this is the true mechanism of irreversible CO chemisorption, we should expect it to produce an enhancement of the oxygen chemisorption to the extent of one half the CO chemisorption, in order to fill the anion vacancies. For a divalent metal oxide the production and satisfaction of this unsaturation towards oxygen may be represented diagrammatically as follows:

With a $p$-type oxide the electrons liberated by the CO adsorption will neutralize positive holes, whereas with an $n$-type oxide they will enter the conduction band.

In practice, surface unsaturation towards oxygen is always produced by irreversible CO chemisorption, and this is strong confirmatory evidence for the postulated mechanism. With some oxides, such as CuO[12] and ZnO . $Cr_2O_3$[27], the ratio of the extra $O_2$ chemisorption to the irreversible CO chemisorption is almost exactly one half, as expected. With $Cr_2O_3$[7] and $Mn_2O_3$[30] it is not as high as one half. Data are given in Table 47. However, as shown in the next section, the $CO_3^{2-}$ structure is unlikely to be that of a normal carbonate ion.

Reversible CO adsorption, on the other hand, does not produce unsaturation towards oxygen. On zinc oxide at room temperature CO chemisorption is entirely reversible, and GARNER and VEAL[27] report that when a mixture of $0.224$ cm³ of CO and $0.112$ cm³ of $O_2$ was admitted to the oxide all the CO, but only $0.006$ cm³ of the $O_2$, was adsorbed. This shows that carbonate is not formed in reversible CO chemisorption.

TABLE 47

$O_2$ and CO Chemsiorption on Oxides

| Oxide | $O_2$ chemi-sorption before CO chemi-sorption (cm³) | Irreversible CO chemi-sorption (cm³) | $O_2$ chemi-sorption after CO chemi-sorption (cm³) | $\dfrac{Extra\ O_2}{CO}$(%) |
|---|---|---|---|---|
| ZnO . $Cr_2O_3$ | Nil | 0·132 | 0·064 | 48·5 |
| $Mn_2O_3$ . $Cr_2O_3$ | Nil | 0·602 | 0·132 | 21·9 |
| $Cr_2O_3$ | 0·05 | >0·4 | — | <50 |
| $Mn_2O_3$ | Nil | 1·44 | 0·5 | 34·7 |
| CuO | 0·05 | 4·08 | 2·15 | 51·4 |

The nature of the reversible chemisorption remains, however, something of a mystery. It is tempting to suggest that it takes place on metal ions and is similar in nature to CO chemisorption on metals. However, the following three results make such a mechanism unlikely in certain cases.

(a) The reversible chemisorption of CO on ZnO would not be easy to explain in such terms, the configuration of the $Zn^{2+}$ ion hardly being favourable.

(b) The extent of reversible CO chemisorption appears to be determined by the semi-conducting property rather than by the configuration of the metal ion, $n$-type oxides being most active. This suggests that reversible CO chemisorption involves donation of electrons to the oxide band system.

(c) On $Cu_2O$[8] reversible CO chemisorption decreases the conductivity, again indicating electron donation to the oxide.

(d) WINTER[2] has found that reversibly adsorbed CO can undergo isotopic oxygen exchange with $Cu_2O$ at low temperatures, exchange taking place over a large part of the surface even at 78°C. This result confirms that surface bonding involves oxygen ions in this case.

It seems most likely that some process such as

$$O^{2-} + CO \rightarrow (CO_2)^- + e \qquad (8.20)$$

is involved, but the nature of the complex remains uncertain. In particular it is unlikely that a carboxylate ion is being formed. Reversible chemisorption requires that the surface complex should readily decompose to give CO, but carboxylate ions do not do so.

### CARBON DIOXIDE LAYERS

Chemisorbed $CO_2$ may always be desorbed as such. Furthermore, $CO_2$ layers are indistinguishable from layers formed when CO is first adsorbed irreversibly and then a quantity of oxygen is added equal to half the volume of CO adsorbed. The net result of this process is, of course, the formation of a $CO_3^{2-}$ complex according to the equation

$$CO + \tfrac{1}{2}O_2 + O^{2-} \rightarrow CO_3^{2-} \qquad (8.21)$$

which suggests that $CO_2$ is adsorbed by the very similar mechanism

$$CO_2 + O^{2-} \rightarrow CO_3^{2-} \qquad (8.22)$$

Thus on manganese oxide[30] the calorimetric heat of $CO_2$ adsorption was 23 kcal/mole. When CO was adsorbed irreversibly and the stoichiometric quantity of oxygen added, $CO_2$ was readily desorbed on pumping, and the calorimetric heat of desorption was 22 kcal/mole. Within the limits of experimental error the two surface layers were identical.

With other oxides[1] the molar heat liberated on adsorbing CO irreversibly and then $O_2$ in the volume ratio 2:1 is equal to the heat of adsorption of $CO_2$ plus the heat of formation of $CO_2$ from $CO + \tfrac{1}{2}O_2$. This again shows that $CO_2$ layers are identical with those formed by adsorbing $(CO + \tfrac{1}{2}O_2)$.

The $CO_3$ complex which is formed in $CO_2$ chemisorption on NiO has been studied by EISCHENS and PLISKIN[31] using infrared spectra.

They claim that in the complex the oxygen atoms are not all equivalent, as is the case in a normal carbonate ion. Instead the complex appears to be of the form shown, with surface bonding through one of the oxygen atoms.

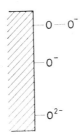

This structure is surprising, being more like a bicarbonate than a carbonate ion. Furthermore, WINTER[2] has found that exchange of oxygen between $CO_2$ and oxide surfaces takes place readily, implying a more mobile complex than that shown.

$CO_2$ adsorption as carbonate or bicarbonate, unlike the similar chemisorption of CO, clearly produces no anion vacancies. Therefore no unsaturation of the surface towards oxygen would be expected, nor is any ever found.

OXYGEN LAYERS

Oxygen chemisorption decreases the conductivity of $n$-type oxides and increases the conductivity of $p$-type oxides. For example, GARNER and his co-workers[8] observed a decrease in the resistance of a thin cuprous oxide film from 2·68 to 1·8 M$\Omega$ on contacting with oxygen at 20 °C, and from 650 to 70 $K\Omega$ on contacting at 200 °C. These results are only explicable if oxygen chemisorption is taking place as negative ions. The possible ions are $O_2^-$, $O^-$ and $O^{2-}$, which may be represented on the surface as shown.

So far there is evidence for the occurrence of $O^-$ and $O^{2-}$ ions, but not for $O_2^-$ ions. Thus at zinc oxide surfaces BARRY and

STONE[4] have shown that oxygen desorption, as given by the accumulation of gas in an initial vacuum, takes place rapidly at room temperatures, slowly at 200 °C, and rapidly again at 400 °C. Their results are shown in *Figure 92*, and are indicative of at least two mechanisms of chemisorption. Further experiments then

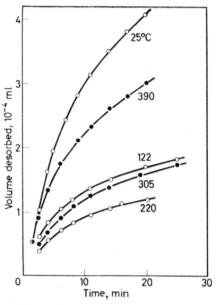

*Figure 92. Oxygen desorption from* ZnO *as a function of time at various temperatures*
By courtesy of Barry, T. I. and Stone, F. S. *Proc. Roy. Soc.* **A255**, 124, 1960

showed that the low temperature chemisorption could catalyse the oxygen exchange reaction

$$^{18}O_2 + {^{16}O_2} \rightleftharpoons 2{^{16}O^{18}O} \qquad (8.23)$$

It is doubtful whether a molecular chemisorption such as $O_2^-$ could participate in exchange, and the most likely interpretation of the results is that the low temperature adsorption is taking place as $O^-$ and the high temperature adsorption as $O^{2-}$.

However, further experimental results in the case of cuprous oxide[12] show that, in addition to chemisorption, penetration of the lattice may occur.

(*a*) The surface area of the adsorbent may be measured by physical adsorption of krypton at low temperatures, and the approximate number of cuprous ions in the surface calculated from it. Using this number, the expected oxygen chemisorption can be obtained. On a particular specimen this was 2·9 cm.³ The experimental chemisorption at room temperature was, however, some 5·4 cm³. Thus a second process occurs, which at room temperature accounts for almost half the oxygen uptake.

(b) Not all the oxygen which is taken up by cuprous oxide is in a catalytically reactive state: if CO is admitted to an oxygenated surface, some $CO_2$ is liberated, but the volume is less than corresponds to the volume of oxygen adsorbed.

(c) The fraction of the oxygen which will react with $CO_2$ decreases with time.

These results can be explained if, in addition to forming a reactive adsorbed layer, oxygen can be slowly built into the crystal, probably by a diffusion of metal ions to the surface, as in the oxidation of metals. This causes positive holes ($\square^+$) to form in the interior of the crystal. The process may be represented schematically as follows

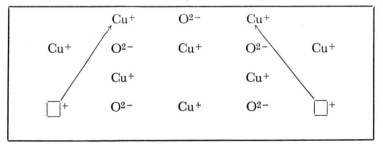

If this mechanism is correct, some $Cu^+$ ions are exposed to the gas phase at the end of penetration, and should be able to adsorb CO reversibly. This was found to occur.

### HYDROGEN LAYERS

Hydrogen and carbon monoxide chemisorption are similar in that, as mentioned previously, there are two possible modes of chemisorption—one rapid, weak and tending to predominate at low temperatures, the other slower, stronger and predominating at high temperatures. Furthermore, while the former is reversible, the latter is irreversible, desorption in the case of hydrogen only taking place as water.

On $Cr_2O_3$[6, 7] and $ZnO \cdot Cr_2O_3$[27], both mechanisms have been observed. On $Cr_2O_3$ at liquid air temperatures[6], hydrogen is reversibly chemisorbed with an initial heat of 5 kcal/mole, and the adsorption is active in the exchange between hydrogen and deuterium[3], while at room temperatures[7] hydrogen adsorption is irreversible, and the initial heat of adsorption is 72 kcal/mole. On $ZnO \cdot Cr_2O_3$ at room temperatures[27], part of the adsorption is reversible, part irreversible. The irreversible adsorption is again stronger, the initial heats probably being 13 and 48 kcal/mole respectively.

Desorption as water suggests the presence of surface hydroxide,

$$2OH^- \rightarrow O^{2-} + H_2O \qquad (8.24)$$

The mechanism of irreversible hydrogen adsorption is then represented by the equation

$$\tfrac{1}{2}H_2 + O^{2-} \rightarrow OH^- + e \qquad (8.25)$$

In the case of $p$-type oxides the liberated electrons will remove positive holes: with $n$-type oxides they will enter the conduction band. In either case they might well be available for subsequent oxygen chemisorption:

$$\tfrac{1}{2}O_2 + 2e \rightarrow O^{2-} \qquad (8.26)$$

Although the available data on hydrogen chemisorption are rather few, there are indications that unsaturation towards oxygen is produced by irreversible hydrogen chemisorption. With $ZnO \cdot Cr_2O_3$[27] there is an enhancement of the oxygen chemisorption by some 15 per cent of the hydrogen chemisorption: with $Cr_2O_3$[7] there is again enhancement, but this seems to vanish rapidly, and its extent is consequently difficult to measure: with $Mn_2O_3$[30] the same probably applies.

The mechanism of reversible hydrogen chemisorption has been mentioned earlier, the important facts being as follows.

(a) The adsorption is active in $H_2/D_2$ exchange and is therefore presumably atomic, while the activity of an oxide in exchange appears to be related to its metal ion configuration[3].

(b) With zinc oxide at least, there is no change in semi-conductivity on adsorption, so that the conduction band is not involved.

Possibly chemisorption is proceeding on metal ions and is similar to hydrogen chemisorption on metals.

SULPHUR DIOXIDE LAYERS

Sulphur dioxide chemisorption has been observed at room temperatures on cuprous oxide[12]. There was an initial heat liberation amounting to 26 kcal/mole but the total heat liberated increased slowly with time, and after 12 minutes had reached 37 kcal/mole. This suggests that two mechanisms may operate, the secondary heat evolution arising from a slow change from one type of layer to a second.

Of the two mechanisms, one is irreversible, desorption taking place only as $SO_3$: very little is known of the other mechanism. Irreversible adsorption probably forms surface sulphate:

$$SO_2 + 2O^{2-} \rightarrow SO_4^{2-} + 2e \qquad (8.27)$$

The second mechanism may be similar to that of $CO_2$ chemisorption, and form surface sulphite.

$$SO_2 + O^{2-} \rightarrow SO_3^{2-} \qquad (8.28)$$

NITROGEN LAYERS

Nitrogen chemisorption has been observed on chromia at liquid air temperatures[6]. It is rapid, and desorption seems to take place as nitrogen.

The adsorption is unlikely to proceed through combination with oxygen ions and formation of surface nitrite or nitrate. Adsorption on the metal ions is more probable, either as atoms, or with formation of the molecular complex formed in the adsorption of nitrogen on iron and the Group B metals of Table 39, namely

$$\begin{array}{ccc} N{=}N & & N{-}N \\ \diagup \quad \diagdown & \text{or} & \diagup\!\!\diagup \quad \diagdown\!\!\diagdown \\ Cr^{3+} \quad Cr^{3+} & & Cr^{3+} \quad Cr^{3+} \end{array}$$

277

T

HYDROCARBON LAYERS

Oxides are active in the chemisorption and catalytic reactions of a number of hydrocarbons. Ethylene, for example, is chemisorbed at room temperature by $ZnO$[27], $ZnO.Cr_2O_3$[27], $Cu_2O$[12] and $CoO$[32] while ethane chemisorption takes place on $NiO$[33] at $-25°C$, and on $Fe_2O_3$[33] at $200°C$. Again, $MoO_3$, $ZnO.Cr_2O_3$ and other oxides catalyse the hydrogenation of ethylene, while $Cr_2O_3$ catalyses its polymerization. Several transition metal oxides are active in aromatization of long chain aliphatics.

Unfortunately there are few data which give information as to the mechanisms of chemisorption. In particular, conductivity data appear to be non-existent, so that it is uncertain whether changes in the defect structure accompany chemisorption. Since such adsorption tends to arise from bonding to oxygen ions (cf. CO and $H_2$) and this is difficult to envisage chemically in the case of hydrocarbons, bonding to metal ions might seem more feasible. The adsorption would in this case be similar to that on a metal. However, two points should be noted.

(a) THOMAS[33] has observed that in the chemisorption of ethane on stoichoimetric nickel oxide, the colour of the latter changes from green to grey. As a colour change is usually associated with an increase in the number of defects (stoichiometric NiO is green, but $p$-type NiO is black) chemisorption may be altering the defect structure.

(b) WOLKENSTEIN[19] has implied that a defect, such as a free electron, represents a potential unit for surface bonding, and that it is possible to designate surface bonds by indicating the defects involved, but without specifying participation of the surface metal or oxygen ions. In the chemisorption of ethane on stoichiometric nickel oxide as an ethyl radical and a hydrogen atom, it is just conceivable that electrons for covalent surface bonding are drawn to the surface from the full band. This would produce the $p$-type character in the oxide, in agreement with experiment. In Wolkenstein's representation chemisorption might be represented as follows

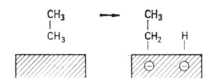

Nevertheless, Herington and Rideal, noting similarities in the behaviour of hydrocarbons at metal and oxide surfaces, have suggested bonding to metal ions. Thus, in dehydrogenation of cyclic paraffins[34] and in aromatization[35], according to the equations

$$CH_2\text{---}CH_2$$

$$CH_2 \qquad CH_2 \quad \rightarrow \quad \bigcirc \qquad +3H_2$$

$$CH_2\text{---}CH_2$$

$$CH_3 . CH_2 . CH_2 . CH_2 . CH_2 . CH_2 . CH_3 \rightarrow \bigcirc CH_3 + 3H_2$$

only C—H bonds break, and it was suggested that this process commences in two-point chemisorption on metal ions, such adsorption being geometrically possible in all the cases studied.

$$CH_2\text{---}CH_2 \qquad\qquad CH_2\text{---}CH_2$$

$$CH_2 \qquad CH_2 \quad \rightarrow \quad CH_2 \qquad CH_2 + 2H$$

$$CH_2\text{---}CH_2 \qquad\qquad CH\text{---}CH$$

$$M^{2+} \qquad M^{2+} \qquad M^{2+} \qquad M^{2+}$$

$$CH_2\text{---}CH_2 \qquad\qquad CH_2\text{---}CH_2$$

$$CH_3\text{--}CH_2 \qquad CH_2 \rightarrow CH_3\text{--}CH_2 \qquad CH_2 + 2H$$

$$CH_3\text{---}CH_2 \qquad\qquad CH_2\text{---}CH$$

$$M^{2+} \qquad M^{2+} \qquad M^{2+} \qquad M^{2+}$$

A certain additional support for the mechanism in the case of cyclohexane is that small quantities of cyclohexene are found in the products of dehydrogenation.

## REFERENCES

[1] Garner, W. E. *J. Chem. Soc.* 1239, 1947
[2] Winter, E. R. S. *Adv. in Catalysis* **10**, 196, 1958

[3] Dowden, D. A., Mackenzie, N. and Trapnell, B. M. W. *Proc. Roy. Soc.* A**237**, 245, 1956

[4] Barry, T. I. and Stone, F. S. *Proc. Roy. Soc.* A**255**, 124, 1960

[5] Taylor, H. S. and Strother, C. O. *J. Amer. Chem. Soc.* **56**, 586, 1934
Smith, E. A. and Taylor, H. S. *J. Amer. Chem. Soc.* **60**, 362, 1938

[6] Beebe, R. A. and Dowden, D. A. *J. Amer. Chem. Soc.* **60**, 2912, 1938

[7] Dowden, D. A. and Garner, W. E. *J. Chem. Soc.* 893, 1939

[8] Garner, W. E., Gray, T. J. and Stone, F. S. *Proc. Roy. Soc.* A**197**, 294, 1949

[9] Stone, F. S. in *Chemistry of the Solid State* (ed. W. E. Garner). London;
Butterworths, p. 367, 1955

[10] Dell, R. M., Stone, F. S. and Tiley, P. F. *Trans. Faraday Soc.* **49**, 201, 1953

[11] Dell, R. M. and Stone, F. S. *Trans. Faraday Soc.* **50**, 501, 1954

[12] Garner, W. E., Stone, F. S. and Tiley, P. F. *Proc. Roy. Soc.* A**211**, 472, 1952

[13] Kubokawa, Y. and Toyama, O. *J. Phys. Chem.* **60**, 833, 1956

[14] Aigrain, P. and Dugas, C. *Z. Elektrochem.* **56**, 363, 1952

[15] Hauffe, K. and Engel, H. J. *Z. Elektrochem* **56**, 366, 1952

[16] Weisz, P. B. *J. Chem. Phys.* **20**, 1483, 1952; **21**, 1531, 1953

[17] Molinari, E. and Parravano, G. *J. Amer. Chem. Soc.* **75**, 5233, 1953

[18] Parravano, G. *J. Amer. Chem. Soc.* **75**, 1452, 1953

[19] Wolkenstein, T. *Adv. in Catalysis* **12**, 189, 1960

[20] Wolkenstein, T. and Roginsky, S. Z. *J. Phys. Chem.* (*U.S.S.R.*) **29**, 485,
1955

[21] Hindin, S. G. and Weller, S. W. *Adv. in Catalysis* **9**, 70, 1957

[22] Trapnell, B. M. W. *Proc. Roy. Soc.* A**218**, 566, 1953

[23] Brennan, D. Hayward, D.O. and Trapnell, B. M. W. *J. Phys. Chem.
Solids* **14**, 117, 1960

[24] Eisinger, J. and Law, J. T. *J. Chem. Phys.* **30**, 410, 1959

[25] Bennett, M. J. and Tompkins, F. C. *Trans. Faraday Soc.* **58**, 816, 1962

[26] Law, J. T. *J. Chem. Phys.* **30**, 1568, 1959

[27] Garner, W. E. and Veal, F. J. *J. Chem. Soc.* 1487, 1935

[28] Ward, T. *J. Chem. Soc.* 1244, 1947

[29] Garner, W. E., Gray, T. J. and Stone, F. S. *Disc. Faraday Soc.* **8**, 246, 1950

[30] Garner, W. E. and Ward, T. *J. Chem. Soc.* 857, 1939

[31] Eischens, R. P. and Pliskin, W. A. *Adv. in Catalysis* **9**, 662, 1957

[32] Stone, F. S., Rudham, R. and Gale, R. L. *Z. Elektrochem.* **63**, 129, 1959

[33] Thomas, W. J. *Trans. Faraday Soc.* **53**, 1124, 1957

[34] Herington, E. F. G. and Rideal, E. K. *Proc. Roy. Soc.* A**190**, 289, 309, 1947

[35] Herington, E. F. G. and Rideal, E. K. *Proc. Roy. Soc.* A**184**, 434, 447, 1945

# IX

# THE MOBILITY OF ADSORBED LAYERS

IT IS probable that chemisorption is invariably localized. Consequently the movement of adsorbed particles from site to site is activated. Chemisorbed layers therefore tend to be freely mobile only above certain minimum temperatures.

With localized layers, the activation energy of migration is normally less than the activation energy of desorption. The surface bond breaks in desorption, but is only weakened during migration, and consequently the energy level from which migration can occur lies below that from which desorption is possible. Mobility may therefore be expected at temperatures well below those at which desorption commences. For this reason, reversibly adsorbed layers tend to be mobile. There are, however, certain exceptions to this rule.

(1) If adsorption involves dissociation, so that desorption involves association, the rule may not apply. For example, the activation energy of migration of a chemisorbed hydrogen atom is no doubt less than that of desorption of an *atom*, but it may well be greater than the activation energy for desorption of two atoms as a *molecule*, and this is, of course, the normal mechanism of desorption. Hydrogen layers may therefore be immobile even when reversibly adsorbed.

(2) Some reversibly adsorbed layers are immobile, although they are formed without dissociation. So far this behaviour is mainly limited to layers which are physically adsorbed either very strongly or at very low temperatures[1], but there are also a few examples among chemisorbed layers.

Two factors would appear to decide whether or not a layer is mobile under defined conditions. The first is the magnitude of the activation energy of migration. The more strongly adsorbed layers have a greater tendency to immobility, so that there must be a general increase of activation energy of migration with heat of adsorption. Since differential heats of adsorption decrease with increasing surface coverage, mobility will also proceed more easily at high coverages than at low coverages. The second factor deciding mobility is temperature.

Mobility may either be studied directly or indirectly. In direct investigations, the change in the density of adsorbed material is observed as spreading proceeds.

Two indirect methods of investigating mobility are available. Potentially the more important method is the calculation of the entropy of adsorption. From this quantity it is in theory possible to decide how many degrees of freedom have been lost on adsorption. The second indirect method is to observe the form of the curve relating the experimental heat of adsorption and the amount of gas adsorbed. There is evidence that this may vary according as the layer is mobile or immobile, provided the adsorbent is porous and possesses a considerable internal surface. Similar information can be obtained from plots of surface potential against coverage.

### DIRECT INVESTIGATIONS OF MOBILITY

#### THE FIELD EMISSION MICROSCOPE

The field emission microscope[2] has been described in Chapter II. It consists of a small metal tip (or point) placed behind a conducting fluorescent screen. On applying a high accelerating potential

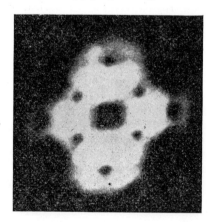

*Figure 93 (a) Field emission pattern of a clean tungsten tip*
By courtesy of Lodge, G. W. and Jacobs, P. W. M.

between the two, electrons are emitted from the tip and travel radially outwards to the screen where they produce a highly magnified picture of the emission from corresponding parts of the tip surface. Regions of high and low work function appear respectively dark and bright.

*Figure 93 (a)* shows the emission pattern of a clean tungsten tip. It is not uniform because various crystal faces are exposed in the surface and the work functions of these are different. The faces can be identified from the crystallographic projection shown in *Figure 93 (b)*.

In this apparatus it is possible to coat one side of the tip with adsorbate and to follow migration over the surface in terms of changes in the field emission pattern.

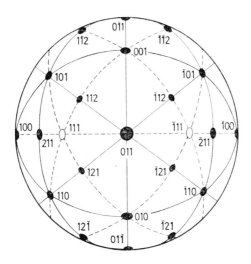

*Figure 93 (b) Crystallographic projection diagram of a tungsten single crystal hemisphere*

*The migration of metals over tungsten*

Some typical results[3] are illustrated in *Figure 94* which shows the patterns observed at room temperature with thorium layers on a single crystal tungsten tip.

The emission from the clean tip, obtained with 7,300 volts applied between screen and tip is shown in (*a*).

In (*b*) is shown the pattern obtained with 5,000 V applied after thorium had been deposited at room temperature over the left hand

(a)

(b)

(c)

(d)

(e)

(f)

(g)

(h)

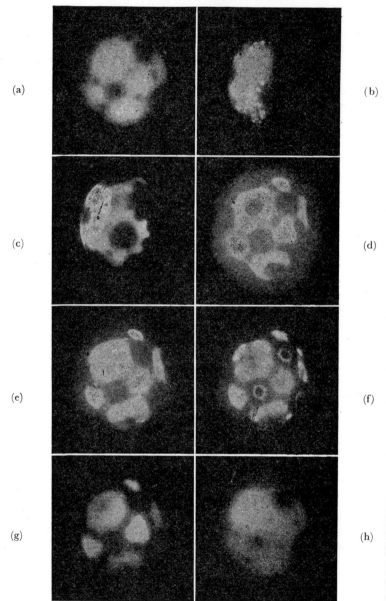

*Figure 94. Field emission microscope patterns for thorium on tungsten*
By courtesy of Benjamin, M. and Jenkins, R. O. *Proc. Roy. Soc.* **A180,** 225, 1942.

half of the tungsten point by evaporation from a nearby thorium bead. The work function of a thorium covered surface is much lower than that of a clean surface, and the higher emission on the left hand half of the picture indicates that the thorium is concentrated in this area. In other words the thorium has not spread over the surface—it is immobile at room temperatures. The uncovered tungsten occupying the right-hand half of the tip gives no emission in this picture because of the lower applied potential.

In (c) is shown the pattern obtained after heating the half covered tip to 600 °C for one minute, the applied potential again being 5,000 V. The thorium has clearly spread appreciably over the surface, especially in the regions around the central (011) face. This suggests that thorium spreads relatively easily over this plane and is deposited around its edge.

In (d) the tip has been heated to 600 °C for a further 9 minutes, and further spreading has taken place. In (e) the heating has been continued at 1,000 °C for 5 minutes, and in (f) at 1,100 °C for five minutes, the applied potentials being 4,800 and 4,450 V respectively.

In (f) spreading is probably complete, for further heating at temperatures up to 1,500 °C gave little or no change in the emission pattern. The (110) group of planes are finally covered as evidenced by the bright rings in (f). Presumably the thorium atoms are less tightly bound here than on most of the surface, and this is in accordance with their high mobility on these planes.

In (g) is shown the pattern obtained after heating the point to 1,800 °C for some time, the applied potential being 5,400V. The rise in potential between (f) and (g) in order to obtain the same emission intensity indicates that the work function of the surface is rising. In other words, some thorium has evaporated from the surface. In (h) heating has been continued at 2,000 °C, and the applied potential is 7,300V, the same as in (a). The similarity of (h) and (a), and the identity of the potentials, indicates that in (h) the surface is again clean.

Precisely similar experiments have been carried out with other adsorbed layers[3, 4] and these are summarized in Table 48 in terms of the temperatures $T_1$ and $T_2$ at which mobility and evaporation are first detectable after equal periods of heating. At these temperatures we may assume that the two processes proceed at approximately equal rates.

The Table shows that in each case mobility commences at roughly 40 to 50 per cent of the absolute temperature at which evaporation commences. If the assumption is then made that the differences in

TABLE 48

The Mobility of Some Adsorbed Layers

| System | $T_1(°K)$ | $T_2(°K)$ | $T_1/T_2$ |
|--------|-----------|-----------|-----------|
| Th on W | 870 | 2,100 | 0·41 |
| Th on Mo | 870 | 2,100 | 0·41 |
| Ba on W | 400 | 900 | 0·44 |
| Ba on Mo | ?400 | 900 | 0·44 |
| Na on W | 300 | 600 | 0.50 |
| Na on Mo | 300 | 600 | 0.50 |

velocities of the two processes are due primarily to differences in activation energy, the frequency factors being approximately the same, the activation energy of diffusion, $E_d$, is roughly 40–50 per cent of the activation energy of desorption $E'$. Since these adsorptions are non-activated, $E'$ is equal to $q$, the heat of adsorption, and therefore

$$E_d \simeq \tfrac{1}{2}q \qquad (9.1)$$

*The migration of adsorbed gases over metals*

The technique used to cover one side of a field emission tip with adsorbed gas has been described in Chapter II. A field emission tube is cooled to liquid helium or liquid hydrogen temperature, the tip cleaned by flashing, and gas introduced from a source situated on one side of the tip. Only those portions of the tip surface 'visible' from the source receive a deposit, the rest of the gas condensing on the walls of the field emission tube. The tip may be kept at any desired temperature during the deposition.

Results have been obtained in this way for $H_2$[5], $O_2$[6], $N_2$[7], CO[8, 9] and $CO_2$[10] on tungsten, and for $H_2$[11] on nickel. Diffusion is found to be a complex phenomenon, varying in rate with crystallographic plane, and with the quantity of gas initially deposited. However, the results with the various gases are often qualitatively similar, although the temperature ranges in which they occur may be quite different, and at least three general types of diffusion are known[12].

(*1*) If a large quantity of adsorbate is deposited on one side of the tip at a sufficiently low temperature and the tip is then warmed, diffusion occurs with a sharp boundary that moves almost uniformly over the whole tip. If the original deposit was insufficient to form a complete monolayer, the boundary ceases to move after a certain fraction of the tip is covered and no more diffusion is observed unless the tip is taken to much higher temperatures, or more gas is deposited.

This type of diffusion is quite general and is found with all the gases studied; using a tungsten tip it is observed at $\sim 27\,°K$ for oxygen[6], $40$–$50\,°K$ for nitrogen[7] and $\ll 20\,°K$ for hydrogen[5]. It is due to gas, physically adsorbed on top of the chemisorbed layer, diffusing to the edge of the deposit and becoming chemisorbed there, the chemisorbed layer itself being immobile.

The distance $x$ travelled by the boundary in time $t$ is found to obey the conventional diffusion equation

$$x = (Dt)^{\frac{1}{2}} \qquad (9.2)$$

where $D$ is the diffusion coefficient and may be expressed in the form

$$D = a^2 \nu \exp\left(-E_d/RT\right) \qquad (9.3)$$

In this equation $\nu$ is the jump frequency ($\sim 10^{12}\,\text{sec}^{-1}$), $a$ is the jump length ($\sim 3\text{Å}$), and $E_d$ is the activation energy for diffusion. If the frequencies of the modes leading to desorption and migration are equal it can be shown that

$$E' = E_d + 4\cdot6RT \log_{10}\left(\bar{x}/a\right) \qquad (9.4)$$

where $\bar{x}$ is the mean distance traversed by a diffusing molecule before evaporation and $E'$ is the heat of desorption from the second layer. When spreading occurs at temperatures much in excess of that at which the second layer is first mobile, the boundary is found to advance a certain distance and no further no matter how many molecules are deposited on the tip. This distance is identified with $\bar{x}$. In the case of oxygen[6] on tungsten values of $0\cdot9$ kcal/mole and $2\cdot8$ kcal/mole have been calculated for $E_d$ and $E'$ respectively using the equations given above. Similar results have been obtained for CO[8] and $CO_2$[10].

(2) For initial deposits where there is no physically adsorbed layer on top of the chemisorbed layer, a moving boundary diffusion is often observed at higher temperatures. It normally spreads radially from the central (011) face of the tungsten tip and moves most rapidly along the [110]–[211] directions. This is illustrated for hydrogen in *Figure 95*. The initial deposit appears as a dark region on the field emission pattern because the adsorption of hydrogen, and that of most other gases, raises the work function of tungsten (thorium on tungsten, however, lowers the work function). From an

Arrhenius plot the activation energy for the diffusion $E_d$ can be estimated as 5·9 kcal/mole. Similarly, oxgyen[6] is found to show this type of diffusion around 500°K with $E_d \sim 25$ kcal/mole, and carbon monoxide[8] at temperatures below 700°K with $E_d \sim 21$ kcal/mole.

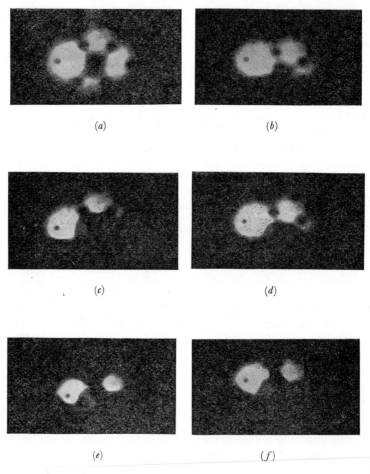

Figure 95.
with hydroge
longer perioa
and (101) j

By co

**ERRATUM**

The illustrations labelled (c) (d) (e) (f) in *Figure 95* should be read in the order (d) (c) (f) (e).

*Chemisorption*

The (110) faces of the body-centred cubic lattice are the closest packed but are surrounded by atomically rough regions except in the [110]–[211] directions. Here the surface consists of terraced (110) 'plateaux'[5] (see *Figure 96*). Adsorbed atoms and molecules will therefore spread rapidly over the central (011) face and be trapped

*Figure 96. Marble model of a portion of a spherical surface cut from a* bcc *crystal; the colour of the marbles corresponds to the number of nearest neighbours; (a) overall view*
By courtesy of Gomer, R., Wortman, R. and Lundy, R. *J. Chem. Phys.* **26**, 1147, 1957

on the rough regions of the surface. Since there are fewer trap sites along the [110]–[211] directions it follows that diffusion will be most rapid in these directions, in agreement with experiment. The fact that a sharp boundary is observed with this type of diffusion shows that the distance between trap sites is less than the resolution of the microscope ($\sim$20 Å). With nickel[11], however, no boundary diffusion is observed. This indicates a much lower density of trap sites, the surface of the face-centred cubic crystal being smoother and more homogeneous than that of the more open body-centred cubic structure.

Further boundary diffusion is found with some layers adsorbed on tungsten in the vicinity of the (100) planes.

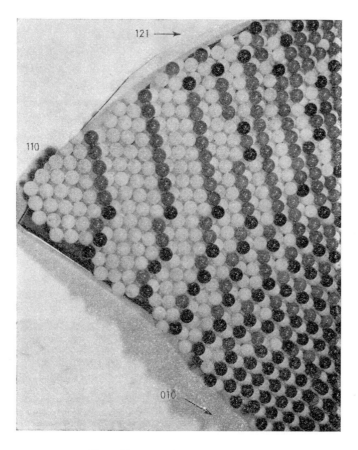

*Figure 96 (cont.)* (b) 110 *face and vicinals*

(*3*) If the initial deposit is insufficient to saturate the trap sites on the surface, a boundary-free diffusion is observed which is believed to involve migration from one trap site to another. Presumably the mean trapping distance is greater than the resolution of the microscope since there is no boundary. Activation energies for this process are 9·5 kcal/mole for hydrogen[5], 30 kcal/mole for oxygen[6] and 20 kcal/mole for nitrogen[7].

Table 49 lists some of the activation energies found for diffusion using the field emission microscope, together with the average energies of the surface bonds $E_{ads}$ as derived from measurements of heats of adsorption on evaporated metal films. It is interesting to

TABLE 49

The Variation of Mobility with Binding Energy

| System | $E_d{}^*$ | $E_{ads}{}^*$ | $E_d/E_{ads}$ |
|--------|-----------|---------------|---------------|
| H on W | 5·9 | 68 | 0·09 |
|        | 9·5 | 68 | 0·14 |
| H on Ni | 7·0 | 63 | 0·11 |
| N on W | 20 | 160 | 0·12 |
|        | 35 | 160 | 0·22 |
| O on W | 25 | 154 | 0·16 |
|        | 30 | 154 | 0·19 |
| CO on W | 21 | 80 | 0·26 |
|         | 36 | 80 | 0·45 |

\* $E_d$ and $E_{ads}$ are given in kcal/g. atom or per mole.

note the variation in the ratio $E_d/E_{ads}$ with the nature of the adsorbate. Strictly, $E_{ads}$ should be the value for the adsorption sites involved, but since these values are not known an average for the whole surface must be used. Even so a trend may be seen, the ratio increasing with the size of the adsorbed atom or molecule. Presumably the small size of the hydrogen atom enables it to diffuse, as it were, through the surface rather than over it and consequently the activation energy for migration is only a very small fraction of the adsorption bond energy. This is true to a lesser degree with nitrogen and oxygen. With CO, and also with the metals discussed earlier, quite a large proportion of the 'surface bonds' must be broken during diffusion.

The migration of carbon dioxide on tungsten[10] is of some interest since the results suggest that the $CO_2$ is dissociated into CO and O. Thus two diffusions at 400°K and 500°K indicate migration of oxygen, having the correct appearances and activation energies. Further diffusion occurs at about 750°K and this resembles that found for carbon monoxide. On raising the temperature further the emission patterns become typical of oxide formation. These findings demonstrate the possible use of the field emission microscope in identifying simple surface radicals.

### OTHER DIRECT INVESTIGATIONS

*Thorium on tungsten*

The activation energy of migration of thorium on tungsten has been measured by depositing thorium on the front face of a tungsten ribbon, and observing the velocity of migration to the back face in terms of changes in the electron emission from the two faces. The method depends on the surface concentration of thorium varying linearly with the work function, so that rates of migration can be equated to rates of change of work function. For the dilute thorium layers which were used, the assumption is probably justified.

Idealized curves, showing the way in which the emission currents from points on the two faces of the ribbon change during deposition and migration of thorium, are given in *Figure 97*. During deposition,

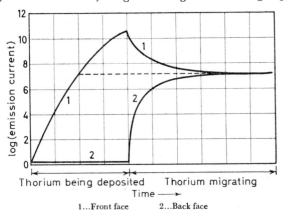

*Figure 97. Emission currents during deposition and migration of thorium on tungsten ribbon*

By courtesy of Brattain, W. H. and Becker, J. A. *Phys. Rev.* **43**, 428, 1933

the current from the front face rises while that from the back face remains constant: during migration the current from the front face falls, and that from the back face rises, until the concentration over the whole surface is uniform and the two currents are equal.

Experiments of this kind have been carried out by BRATTAIN and BECKER[13], who measured rates of migration at 1,535 °K and 1,655 °K. The temperature coefficient of these rates gave for the activation energy of migration 110 kcal/g. atom.

The mean of two values for the activation energy of desorption of thorium from dilute layers on tungsten was 191 kcal/g. atom. The activation energy of migration is therefore 0·57 times the activation energy of desorption, compared with the figure 0·41 obtained with the field emission microscope.

*Caesium on tungsten*

The mobility of caesium on a tungsten filament has been studied by TAYLOR and LANGMUIR.[14]

The method of obtaining the necessary non-uniform distribution of caesium depended on the fact that desorption of caesium from dilute layers on tungsten takes place almost entirely as positive ions. This means that desorption from one portion of a sparsely covered filament may be prohibited by surrounding it with a cylindrical electrode held at a positive potential, and simultaneously assisted from another portion by surrounding it with a second electrode at a negative potential. Covered and clean areas of surface may in this way be obtained, with a sharp boundary between them.

In an actual experiment, a filament was surrounded by three cylindrical electrodes placed end to end. The filament was covered with caesium, and then heated with the two outer electrodes held at +22 volts, and the centre electrode at −22 volts relative to the filament. This resulted in the centre portion of the filament being bare, and the two outer portions being covered with a uniform low concentration of caesium.

The filament was then heated to various temperatures for various lengths of time, with all three electrodes at +22 volts to inhibit desorption. Migration of caesium took place, and the total number of atoms which had migrated to the centre portion was measured by flashing the filament with all three electrodes at −22 volts to assist desorption, and measuring the positive ion current to the central electrode.

From the results it was possible to evaluate a surface diffusion coefficient, $D$. The values of $D$ obtained at various temperatures obeyed the equation

$$\ln D = -1·61 - 16,300/RT \qquad (9.5)$$

In other words, the activation energy of migration is 16·3 kcal/g. atom. The experiments were conducted at fractional surface coverages of about 0·03, when Table 18 shows the activation energy of desorption to be 63 kcal/g. atom. In this case the activa-

293

U

tion energy of migration is only about one quarter of the activation energy of desorption.

*Sodium and potassium on tungsten*

The mobility of sodium and of potassium on a tungsten ribbon has been studied by BOSWORTH.[15, 16] A small patch of adsorbed material was formed by heating a Kunsman source, separated from the ribbon by a system of slits, and spreading was then followed in terms of the change in photoelectric response to a fine beam of ultraviolet light, directed on the ribbon at various points along its length.

The ribbon could only be heated to temperatures of 1,900 °C, and these were shown to be insufficient to clean the surface. The experiments consequently refer to migration over a surface already covered by an adsorbed layer, probably oxygen.

Kunsman sources when heated give off ions rather than atoms of sodium and potassium, and consequently the amount of material which was deposited could be obtained by measuring the current between source and ribbon. By measuring photoelectric currents after a series of depositions it was possible to obtain a calibration curve relating concentration of adsorbed material and photo-response.

Spreading was then allowed to take place, and a series of curves was obtained showing concentrations of adsorbed material in the neighbourhood of the deposited patch. Typical curves for sodium[15] at 0 °C after 0, 33 and 60 minutes are shown in *Figure 98*.

With the temperature constant the concentration, $c$, of adsorbed sodium at any given point decayed according to the equation

$$\frac{1}{c^2} = K(t + t_0) \tag{9.6}$$

where $K$ and $t_0$ are constants. This equation was shown to be a solution of the diffusion equation, with $K$ proportional to the surface diffusion coefficient. The temperature coefficient of $K$ then gave the activation energy of migration:

$$E_d = R \frac{d \ln K}{d (1/T)} \tag{9.7}$$

For dilute sodium layers, at about room temperature, values of $E_d$ varying between 5·8 and 6·9 kcal/g. atom were obtained.

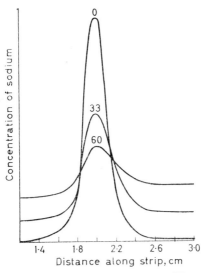

*Figure 98. The spreading of* Na *on a tungsten ribbon at* $0\,^{\circ}C$
By courtesy of Bosworth, R. C. L. *Proc. Roy. Soc.* **A150**, 58, 1935

With potassium layers[16], $E_d$ was obtained as a function of surface concentration, as shown in Table 50. The Table shows how markedly $E_d$ may decrease with increasing surface coverage, that is with decreasing heat of adsorption.

TABLE 50

Mobility of Potassium on Tungsten

| Surface concentration (atoms/cm² × 10⁻¹⁴) | $E_d$ (kcal/g atom) | Surface concentration (atoms/cm² × 10⁻¹⁴) | $E_d$ (kcal/g atom) |
|---|---|---|---|
| 0·06 | 15·9 | 1·2 | 12·0 |
| 0·12 | 15·5 | 1·5 | 10·8 |
| 0·24 | 14·5 | 2·4 | 8·1 |
| 0·48 | 13·6 | 3·0 | 7·6 |
| 0·60 | 13·1 | 4·8 | 6·7 |

INDIRECT INVESTIGATIONS OF MOBILITY

The mobility of gas layers on low melting point metals cannot readily be followed by the techniques just described. Field emission microscopy is suitable only for metals that can be cleaned by flashing, and at present nickel is the only low melting point metal for which results have been obtained[11]. The other techniques employ filaments and ribbons which must again be cleaned by flashing. A further objection in the case of the thermionic and photo-electric methods is that with most gas layers the work functions concerned are too high to be measured easily.

Certain indirect methods are available for such layers. They are the calculation of the entropy of the adsorbed layer and the determination of the variation either of the heat of adsorption or of the surface potential with the amount of gas adsorbed. With the latter methods a porous adsorbent such as a film must be used.

### ENTROPIES OF ADSORBED LAYERS

Comparison of the entropy of the adsorbed layer, derived from experimental measurements, with the values calculated for mobile and immobile layers using statistical mechanics may decide whether the layer is mobile or not.

Three different entropies associated with an adsorbed layer at coverage $\theta$ must, however, be distinguished, namely:

|  |  |
|---|---|
| the total entropy of the adsorbed layer | $S_\theta$ |
| the integral molar entropy | $s_\theta$ |

and

|  |  |
|---|---|
| the differential molar entropy | $\bar{s}_\theta$ |

These are related as follows:

$$S_\theta = n\theta s_\theta \tag{9.8}$$

$$\bar{s}_\theta = \left(\frac{\partial S_\theta}{\partial(n\theta)}\right)_T = \theta\left(\frac{\partial s_\theta}{\partial\theta}\right)_T + s_\theta \tag{9.9}$$

where $n\theta$ is the number of moles adsorbed at coverage $\theta$.

Statistical mechanical calculations of entropies normally give $s_\theta$, whereas the quantity most readily measured is $\bar{s}_\theta$. As can be seen from equation (9.9) $\bar{s}_\theta$ is equal to $s_\theta$ only when the latter does not vary with coverage, and this is rarely, if ever, the case with chemisorption. Much confusion has arisen in the past from comparisons of experimental differential molar entropies with theoretical integral molar entropies[17]. To obtain information about mobilities there are two possible methods; one is to find integral molar entropies experimentally and to compare them with the calculated entropies, the other is to differentiate the latter to give values of $\bar{s}_\theta$ and then to compare these with the experimental differential entropies. The last method gives only limited information about mobility.

*Method of obtaining experimental entropies*

The molar free energy change $\Delta G$ which occurs when an infinitesimal quantity of gas is transferred isothermally at $T°K$ from a reservoir at 1 atm. pressure to the adsorbed layer is given by

$$\Delta G = -(H_g - \bar{H}_\theta) + T(s_g - \bar{s}_\theta) \tag{9.10}$$

where $H_g$ and $s_g$ are, respectively, the integral molar enthalpy and entropy of the gas at 1 atm. pressure and $\bar{H}_\theta$ is the differential molar enthalpy of the adsorbed layer. $(H_g - \bar{H}_\theta) = q_{st}$, the isosteric heat of adsorption.

If the adsorbed layer is in equilibrium with a pressure $p$ atm.

$$\Delta G = RT \ln p \tag{9.11}$$

assuming ideal behaviour, and hence

$$\bar{s}_\theta = s_g - R \ln p - q_{st}/T \tag{9.12}$$

It follows that if $p$ and the isosteric heat of adsorption are measured $\bar{s}_\theta$ can be calculated. $q_{st}$ may be obtained from isosteres using the Clausius-Clapeyron equation.

If $s_\theta$ is required it can be obtained only by an integration over all coverages from zero to $\theta$.

From equation (9.9)

$$s_\theta = \frac{1}{\theta} \int_0^\theta \bar{s}_\theta \mathrm{d}\theta \tag{9.13}$$

and substituting in equation (9.12)

$$s_\theta = s_g - \frac{R}{\theta} \int_0^\theta \ln p \; \mathrm{d}\theta - (H_g - H_\theta)/T \tag{9.14}$$

where $(H_g - H_\theta)$ is the integral heat of adsorption up to coverage $\theta$. From this equation $s_\theta$ can be found, the integral being evaluated by the method of areas using a plot of $\ln p$ versus $\theta$. Experimentally it is very difficult to do this since integration must be carried out to zero coverage. The equilibrium pressure is normally extremely small near $\theta = 0$ and measurable only by using an ionization gauge.

$(H_g - H_\theta)$ is obtained by integrating the isosteric heats of adsorption to the given coverage. It is essential that the latter be accurately known, otherwise comparison of experimental and theoretical entropies becomes impossible.

*Calculation of entropies*

Integral molar entropies may be calculated from the equation

$$s_\theta = R \ln \Omega \qquad (9.15)$$

where $\Omega$ is the total number of equally probable micro-molecular states in which one mole of adsorbate may exist under given conditions.

The following expressions for integral entropies associated with various states are important.

(*1*) The translational molar entropy of a perfect gas of molecular weight $M$ at 1 atm. pressure is

$$s_g = R \ln M^{3/2} \, T^{5/2} - 2 \cdot 30 \text{ cal. deg.}^{-1}. \text{ mole}^{-1} \qquad (9.16)$$

Similarly the translational molar entropy of a two dimensional perfect gas has been shown by KEMBALL[18] to be

$$_2s_{\text{trans}} = R \ln MTA + 65 \cdot 8 \text{ cal. deg.}^{-1}. \text{ mole}^{-1} \qquad (9.17)$$

where $M$ is the molecular weight of the adsorbed species and $A$ is the area in cm$^2$ available for it on the surface.

This expression ignores the area occupied by the molecules themselves and will consequently be inaccurate near full coverage. KISLIUK[19] has carried out calculations of the translational molar entropy for a 'Volmer' gas i.e. a free two dimensional gas in which each atom occupies a finite area such that the surface is completely covered at $\theta = 1$.

(*2*) Immobile layers possess a configurational entropy which arises because the molecules or atoms may be distributed over the surface in a number of different ways.

For non-dissociative single site adsorption on a homogeneous surface this entropy[20] is

$$s_{\text{config}} = -R \left[ \ln \theta + \frac{(1 - \theta)}{\theta} \ln (1 - \theta) \right] \text{ cal. deg.}^{-1} \text{mole}^{-1}. \quad (9.18)$$

If adsorption is accompanied by dissociation into two equal parts, the configurational entropy is twice that calculated above provided the parts are randomly distributed over the surface. If the adsorbed particles are not randomly distributed but occur in pairs, more complicated expressions for the configurational entropy must be used[18].

(*3*) The degree of translational freedom perpendicular to the surface which is lost on adsorption is replaced by a vibration. For a vibration of frequency $\nu$ the entropy is

$$s_{\text{vib}} = R\left[\frac{h\nu}{kT}\cdot(e^{h\nu/kT}-1)^{-1} - \ln(1-e^{-h\nu/kT})\right] \quad (9.19)$$

In chemisorption $\nu$ will be high, and in this case the vibrational entropy at ordinary temperatures is small and less than about 3 cal. deg.$^{-1}$. mole$^{-1}$.

(*4*) During adsorption, rotational freedom may be lost. The entropy change due to this may be calculated from the expression for a molecule rotating in $n$ different ways

$$s_{\text{rot}} = R\left[\ln\frac{1}{\pi\Sigma}\left\{\frac{8\pi^3(I^a_A\,I^b_B\,..\,I^g_G)^{1/n}\,kT}{h^2}\right\}^{n/2} + \frac{n}{2}\right] \quad (9.20)$$

where $a+b+..+g=n$, $I_A$ *etc* are the moments of inertia and $\Sigma$ is the symmetry number.

*Comparison of theoretical and experimental entropies*

We now compare experimental entropies of adsorbed layers with values calculated for various degrees of freedom using the expressions of the previous section. In doing so, however, we are assuming that the adsorbed layer does not alter the thermodynamic properties of the adsorbent. This may not always be a sound assumption and the method should therefore be used with caution.

RIDEAL and SWEETT[21] have measured the pressure of hydrogen gas in equilibrium with adsorbed hydrogen on evaporated nickel films by means of an ionization gauge. Observations were made at temperatures up to 200 °C and down to coverages as low as $\theta = 0.005$. From the results the integral molar entropies of adsorbed hydrogen were calculated, and are shown in *Figure 99*, together with the calculated theoretical values for mobile and immobile layers.

In the range $\theta = 0$ to $\theta = 0.4$ there is close agreement between the experimental entropy and $s_{\text{config}}$, suggesting an immobile layer. At very small coverages the experimental entropy falls considerably below $s_{\text{config}}$ and this is attributed to adsorption on a few trap sites with very high adsorption potential. As $\theta$ increases from 0.4 to 1.0 the experimental entropy increases until at $\theta = 1$ it is equal to the entropy of a two dimensional gas. This is thought to indicate a progressive increase in the proportion of mobile hydrogen.

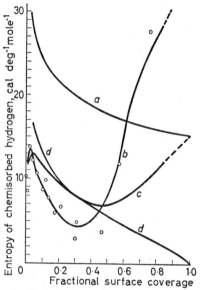

*Figure 99. Experimental and calculated entropies of hydrogen adsorbed on nickel.* o—$\bar{s}_{exp}$, *found directly from isosteres;* (a) $_2s_{trans}$, *calculated for hydrogen atoms;* (b) $\bar{s}_{exp}$, *obtained by differentiating* $s_{exp}$; (c) $s_{exp}$; (d) $s_{config}$, *calculated for hydrogen atoms*

By courtesy of RIDEAL, E. K. and SWEETT, F. *Proc. Roy. Soc.* **A257**, 291, 1960

If we assume that the mobile and immobile parts of the adsorbate each make their own contribution to the total entropy the fraction of molecules, $x$, which is mobile at any given instant is given by

$$x \cdot {}_2s_{trans} + (1 - x)\, s_{config} = s_{exp} \qquad (9.21)$$

the values of $_2s_{trans}$ and $s_{config}$ being taken at the appropriate coverages, and $s_{exp}$ being the experimental entropy. Since the mobile and immobile fractions of the adsorbate are in equilibrium

$$\Delta H = T \left({}_2s_{trans} - s_{config}\right) \qquad (9.22)$$

where $\Delta H$ is the molar change in enthalpy in going from the immobile to the mobile layer. It is equal to *twice* the activation energy for diffusion, being given in terms of hydrogen molecules rather than atoms. Activation energies calculated in this way from RIDEAL and SWEETT's data are given in Table 51.

In general it is wrong to assume that a layer is immobile just because $s_{config}$ and $s_{exp}$ are of approximately the same value — this merely means that an adsorbed particle spends more time in vibration at surface sites than it does in migration.

TABLE 51
Data on Surface Diffusions of $H_2$ on Nickel

| Fractional surface coverage | Fraction of mobile hydrogen at 25 °C | Activation energy for diffusion (kcal/mole) | Isosteric heat of adsorption (kcal/mole$^{-1}$) |
|:---:|:---:|:---:|:---:|
| 0·4 | 0·015 | 3·5 | 20·6 |
| 0·5 | 0·064 | 3·3 | 17·4 |
| 0·6 | 0·17 | 2·8 | 13·4 |
| 0·7 | 0·34 | 2·2 | 9·6 |
| 0·8 | 0·56 | 1·6 | 6·0 |
| 0·9 | (0·88) | (0·45) | (3.9) |

Apart from the work of RIDEAL and SWEETT[21] one other system has been investigated in detail. KISLIUK[19] has carried out measurements at elevated temperatures (about 1500 °K) and down to low coverages for nitrogen adsorbed on tungsten. The differential entropy of adsorption was found to be of the order expected for localized adsorption with a moderate contribution from vibrational degrees of freedom. However, the results obtained are somewhat ambiguous.

With many systems equilibrium pressure data are available only near full coverage and it is not possible to calculate integral molar entropies. The question arises as to whether it is possible to deduce anything from differential molar entropies.

It is true that the differential molar entropies, $\bar{s}_{config}$ and $_2\bar{s}_{trans}$, obtained by differentiation of the integral molar values, can be compared directly with the differential entropy derived from experimental measurements. However, the contributions of the mobile and immobile fractions of the adsorbate to the overall differential entropy are not simply additive as in the case of integral entropies. *Figure* 99 shows that, if there is a transition from immobility to mobility, the overall differential entropy may become very large, larger in fact than either $\bar{s}_{config}$ or $_2\bar{s}_{trans}$. However, if such a transition is not possible, $\bar{s}_{exp}$ should never fall below $\bar{s}_{config}$ even though both of these quantities may become negative.

Table 52 lists a few systems for which a differential molar entropy can be calculated.

With $C_2H_4$ adsorbed on Cu and Au, and with $N_2$ adsorbed on Fe, the experimental entropy is less than the configurational value. The difference between the two may not be significant since the values are subject to rather large errors, but it seems reasonable to assume that these layers are immobile whereas all the others are mobile. In the case of CO on W this conclusion is at variance with

TABLE 52

Differential Entropies of Adsorbed Layers

| System | Coverage | Temp. (°K) | $\bar{s}_{exp}$ (e.u.) | $\bar{s}_{config}$ (e.u.) | $\bar{s}_{trans}$ (e.u.) | Reference |
|---|---|---|---|---|---|---|
| CO on Cu | $\theta = 0.5$ | 195–210 | 19 | 0 | 12·8 | 22 |
| CO on Au | $\theta = 0.25$ | 195–210 | 22 | 2.2 | 14.1 | 22 |
| CO on W | $\theta = 0.7$ | 273–293 | 10 | −1·9 | 12·8 | 23 |
| $C_2H_4$ on Cu | $\theta = 0.1$ | 273–288 | 3 | 4·4 | 15·3 | 22 |
| $C_2H_4$ on Au | $\theta = 0.1$ | 273–288 | −6 | 4·4 | 15·3 | 22 |
| $N_2$ on Fe | $\theta \simeq 0.5$ | 660–720 | −6 | 0 | 15·3 | 24 |
| $H_2$ on W | $\theta = 0.8$ | 273–293 | 5 | −5·4 | 9·1 | 25 |

results obtained using the field emission microscope[8,9] although the coverages in the two cases may be different.

THE FORM OF $q-\theta$ CURVES IN ADSORPTION ON METALS

Usually, differential heats of chemisorption on metals decrease with increasing surface coverage. In some cases, however, notably in adsorption on metal films, $q$ appears to remain constant as $\theta$ increases. This constancy is in general found only when the heat of adsorption is very high, or when the temperature is very low, and these are conditions under which adsorbed layers may be expected to be immobile.

In hydrogen adsorption on iron films, the $q-\theta$ relation depends on the temperature at which the measurements are made[26]. At 23 °C, the heat falls progressively throughout the entire $\theta$ range from an initial value of 32 kcal/mole: at −183 °C, the heat remains constant at 27 kcal/mole until the layer is almost full, and then falls abruptly to very low values. Results are shown in *Figure 100*.

*The Beeck criterion of mobility*

The different behaviour of the two $q-\theta$ curves has been interpreted by BEECK in the following manner[26]. First, since films possess considerable internal surfaces apparently reached only by a relatively slow diffusion of gas, admission of a small charge of a gas which is rapidly adsorbed will tend to result in complete coverage of the small part of the surface with which the gas happens to collide first. If the adsorbed layer is immobile, the adsorbed molecules will not spread out, and there will not take place uniform distribution of gas throughout the film. The heat of adsorption is not a true differential heat, but an integral heat, an average for all coverages between $\theta = 0$ and $\theta = 1$. When further charges are admitted, the next

302

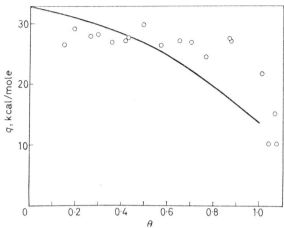

*Figure 100. q–θ curves for hydrogen adsorption on iron films at*
*— 183°C (points) and 23°C (curve)*
By courtesy of Beeck, O. *Adv. in Catalysis* **2**, 151, 1950

most accessible parts of the surface are completely covered, and again
the integral heat of adsorption is observed. Therefore with immobile
layers $q$ will appear to be independent of $\theta$.

If on the other hand the layer is mobile, the adsorbed molecules,
although initially forming a dense local layer, will spread rapidly
through the film and give a uniform distribution. In this case a true
differential heat is recorded, and admission of a sequence of charges
gives normal decreasing heats of adsorption corresponding to higher
and higher $\theta$ values.

These considerations suggest that hydrogen on iron is mobile at
room temperatures but immobile at $-183°C$. On this basis mobile
and immobile adsorptions may be distinguished according as $q$ falls
with $\theta$ or is constant.

Beeck considered that molecules reached the internal surfaces of
films by gas phase diffusion. Recent results[27], however, suggest
that this may not be so, at least in certain cases. It has been found
that, after the initial stages, carbon monoxide and nitrogen are
adsorbed at constant rates on films of molybdenum, even though
adsorption must be occurring on progressively less and less accessible
parts of the surface since the adsorbed layers in these cases are almost
certainly immobile. It follows that gas phase diffusion cannot be rate
determining, otherwise the rate of adsorption would decrease as the
adsorbed layer built up.

However, these results can be explained if, after the outer surface is covered, further adsorption proceeds via a mobile second layer, with consequent surface migration to the bare parts of the surface, and adsorption into the primary layer there. Provided the concentration in this second layer is always very small, the rate of adsorption will be constant.

This mechanism for penetration of the film differs considerably from that assumed by Beeck, but it does not invalidate the Beeck criterion of mobility since the adsorbed layer is built up in the same way in both cases.

However, there are two cases where the Beeck criterion of mobility does not hold.

(a) The adsorption of nitrogen on a tungsten film[26] gives a heat that is independent of $\theta$ but, since the same result is obtained if the adsorbent is a ribbon[28] with little or no internal surface, the Beeck criterion obviously cannot be applied. For this system EHRLICH[29] considers the heat of chemisorption to be genuinely independent of $\theta$, the binding energy being the same for all surface sites. Thus, although field emission experiments[7] show that nitrogen is immobile on tungsten at room temperature, this result cannot be inferred from the constant heat of adsorption found on films.

To date this is the only system for which there is experimental evidence of a genuinely constant differential heat, but it seems likely that some other nitrogen adsorptions may show similar behaviour.

It is worth noting that, if the true differential heat of adsorption is known to fall with coverage, a constant heat measured with an evaporated metal film can be taken as a definite indication of immobility.

(b) For the Beeck criterion to hold, an immobile layer must be built up in such a way that, at any intermediate stage in the adsorption, the more accessible parts of the surface are completely covered and the less accessible parts completely bare. However, this will be so only if the sticking probability of the gas molecules is fairly high on all regions of the surface. If it is uniformly low, gas molecules may be able to penetrate to the inner recesses of a clean film before being adsorbed. This will result in a uniform distribution of gas throughout the film and, hence, a falling heat even though the adsorbed layer may be immobile. Alternatively, if the rate of adsorption, controlled either by gas phase or surface diffusion, is high on certain regions of the surface and very low on others, the former regions will be covered preferentially. Subsequent doses of gas will therefore occupy larger fractions of the unreactive regions, and provided these correspond with the sites of lowest binding energy, the heat of adsorption will fall as adsorption proceeds. Similarly, formation of a more weakly bound second layer with a lower sticking probability than the first layer will give the same results.

It follows therefore that a falling heat is not necessarily indicative of mobility. For example, the heat of adsorption of carbon monoxide on tungsten films at 23 °C is found to decrease with increasing coverage[30] although it is known from field emission experiments[8, 9] that carbon monoxide is immobile on tungsten at this temperature.

*Experimental heats on films*

In Tables 53 and 54, fast, non-activated chemisorptions on metal films are classified according as $q$ falls with increasing $\theta$ or is constant.

TABLE 53

Adsorptions with Constant Heats

| System | Temp. (°C) | Heat of adsorption (kcal. mole$^{-1}$) | Reference |
|---|---|---|---|
| $O_2$ on W, Mo | 23 | 190, 170 | 31 |
| CO on Ti, Co, Ni, Pd | 0 | 150–40 | 30 |
| $H_2$ on Fe | −183 | 32 | 26 |
| $H_2$ on Ni | −183 | 22 | 30 |
| $H_2$ on W | −183 | 35 | 30 |
| $N_2$ on W | 23 | 95 | 26 |

TABLE 54

Adsorptions with Falling Heats

| System | Temp. (°C) | Initial heat (kcal. mole$^{-1}$) | Reference |
|---|---|---|---|
| $H_2$ on Ta, Fe, Ni, Pd | 23 | 40–27 | 32 |
| $H_2$ on W | 0,−78 | 45 | 30 |
| CO on W, Mo, Fe | 0 | 82–46 | 30 |
| $O_2$ on Rh | 23 | 120 | 31 |
| $C_2H_4$ on W, Ta, Fe, Ni, Rh | 23 | 137–50 | 32 |
| $NH_3$ on W, Fe, Ni | 23 | 72–36 | 33 |

In terms of Beeck's interpretation many of these results are not unexpected. Oxygen layers on tungsten and molybdenum are immobile at room temperature because of the high heats of adsorption. On the other hand, hydrogen adsorptions give lower heats and

305

the layers are mobile, but become immobile at lower temperatures.

However, because of the high heat of adsorption, it is doubtful whether oxygen is mobile on rhodium at room temperature as required by the Beeck criterion, and the same consideration may apply in the case of ethylene layers.

Carbon monoxide and nitrogen on tungsten have been discussed previously.

### THE VARIATION OF SURFACE POTENTIAL WITH COVERAGE

Measurements of surface potential changes during adsorption on evaporated metal films give values for the exposed surface of the film only, adsorption on the internal surfaces having little or no

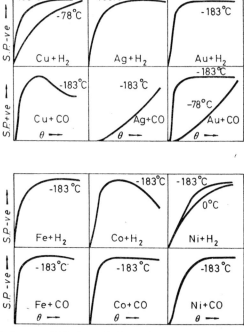

*Figure 101. Surface potential isotherms for* H₂ *and* CO *on* Cu, Ag, Au, Fe, Co *and* Ni
By courtesy of Culver, R. V., Pritchard, J. and Tompkins, F. C. *Proc. 2nd Intern. Congr. of Surface Activity, Vol.* 2 London; Butterworths, p. 243, 1957.

effect. In a rapid adsorption forming an immobile layer, the outermost areas of the film are covered first and the surface potential reaches its maximum value for only small adsorbed amounts, further adsorption proceeding with little or no change in surface potential. With mobile layers the adsorbate distributes itself uniformly throughout the film and the surface potential rises steadily, reaching its maximum value only when adsorption is practically complete.

CULVER, PRITCHARD and TOMPKINS[34] have made surface potential measurements for a number of adsorptions on evaporated metal films and their results are shown in *Figure 101*. Molecular hydrogen is not adsorbed by copper, silver or gold and adsorption in these cases was brought about by employing a hot filament to produce hydrogen atoms, which were then adsorbed.

For carbon monoxide layers on silver at $-183\,^{\circ}C$ and on gold at $-78\,^{\circ}C$ the shapes of the surface potential against coverage curves suggest complete mobility, whereas carbon monoxide layers on iron and cobalt at $-183\,^{\circ}C$ would appear to be examples of complete immobility. Some systems such as $Ni/H_2$ at $-183\,^{\circ}C$ show intermediate behaviour, probably due to restricted spreading of the adsorbed layer.

The decrease in surface potential at high coverages observed with CO on Cu and with $H_2$ on Co is due to second layer formation and is not connected with mobility.

The adsorption of $H_2$ on Ag and Au is peculiar in that, although the surface potential isotherms show the adsorbed layers to be immobile at $-183\,^{\circ}C$, desorption is complete at $-78\,^{\circ}C$ as evidenced by the return of the surface potential to its initial value. With these metals the adsorbed layer of hydrogen is thermodynamically unstable with respect to gas phase hydrogen molecules and desorption commences as soon as mobility occurs[34, 35].

## REFERENCES

[1] Kemball, C. *Adv. in Catalysis*, **2**, 233, 1950
[2] Good, R. H. and Müller, E. W. *Handbuch der Physik* **21**, 176, 1956
[3] Benjamin, M. and Jenkins, R. O. *Proc. Roy. Soc.* A**180**, 225, 1942
[4] Becker, J. A. and Hartman, C. D. *J. Phys. Chem.* **57**, 153, 1953
[5] Gomer, R., Wortman, R. and Lundy, R. *J. Chem. Phys.* **26**, 1147, 1957
[6] Gomer, R. and Hulm, J. K. *J. Chem. Phys.* **27**, 1363, 1957
[7] Ehrlich, G. and Hudda, F. G. *J. Chem. Phys.* **35**, 1421, 1961
[8] Gomer, R. *Disc. Faraday Soc.* **28**, 23, 1959
[9] Klein, R. *J. Chem. Phys.* **31**, 1306, 1959
[10] Hayward, D. O. and Gomer, R. *J. Chem. Phys.* **30**, 1617, 1959
[11] Wortman, R., Gomer, R. and Lundy, R. *J. Chem. Phys.* **27**, 1099, 1957
[12] Gomer, R., *Field Emission and Field Ionization*. Cambridge, U.S.A.; Harvard University Press, 1961, Chapter IV
[13] Brattain, W. H. and Becker, J. A. *Phys. Rev.* **43**, 428, 1933

[14] Taylor, J. B. and Langmiur, I. *Phys. Rev.* **44**, 423, 1933

[15] Bosworth, R. C. L. *Proc. Roy. Soc.* A**150**, 58, 1935

[16] Bosworth, R. C. L. *Proc. Roy. Soc.* A**154**, 112, 1936

[17] Hill, T. L. *Adv. in Catalysis* **4**, 211, 1952

[18] Kemball, C. *Proc. Roy. Soc.* A**187**, 73, 1946

[19] Kisliuk, P. *J. Chem. Phys.* **30**, 174, 1959

[20] Everett, D. H. *Proc. Chem. Soc.* p. 38, 1957

[21] Rideal, E. K. and Sweett, F. *Proc. Roy. Soc.* A**257**, 291, 1960

[22] Trapnell, B. M. W. *Proc. Roy. Soc.* A**218**, 566, 1953

[23] Rideal, E. K. and Trapnell, B. M. W. *Proc. Roy. Soc.* A**205**, 409, 1951

[24] Emmett, P. H. and Brunauer, S. *J. Amer. Chem. Soc.* **56**, 35, 1934

[25] Trapnell, B. M. W. *Proc. Roy. Soc.* A**206**, 39, 1951

[26] Beeck, O. *Adv. in Catalysis*, **2**, 151, 1950

[27] Roberts, M. W. *Trans. Faraday Soc.* **59**, 698, 1963

[28] Kisliuk, P. *J. Chem. Phys.* **31**, 1605, 1959

[29] Ehrlich, G. *J. Chem. Phys.* **36**, 1171, 1962

[30] Hayes, F. *Ph.D. Thesis* Liverpool University, 1962

[31] Brennan, D., Hayward, D. O. and Trapnell, B. M. W. *Proc. Roy. Soc.* A**256**, 81, 1960

[32] Beeck, O. *Disc. Faraday Soc.* **8**, 118, 1950

[33] Wahba, M. and Kemball, C. *Trans. Faraday Soc.* **49**, 1351, 1953

[34] Culver, R. V., Pritchard, J. and Tompkins, F. C. *Proc. 2nd Intern. Congr. of Surface Activity, Volume 2.* London; Butterworths, 1957, p. 243

[35] Pritchard, J. and Tompkins, F. C. *Trans. Faraday Soc.* **56**, 540, 1960

# INDEX OF ADSORPTION SYSTEMS

Adsorbates are listed alphabetically. The adsorbents are arranged under each adsorbate according to group number in the Periodic Table, in the order metals, carbon, oxides.

x

315

# SUBJECT INDEX